JUNIOR COLLEGE DISTRICT
of St. Louis - St. Louis County
LIBRARY

5545 West Park
St. Louis, Missouri 63105

PRINTED IN U.S.A.

FUNDAMENTALS OF ELECTRONICS
(VOLUME I)

HARPER'S
PHYSICS SERIES

Frederick Seitz, EDITOR

FUNDAMENTALS
OF ELECTRONICS

VOLUME I

George E. Owen

PROFESSOR OF PHYSICS
THE JOHNS HOPKINS UNIVERSITY

P. W. Keaton

OF THE LOS ALAMOS LABORATORY
LOS ALAMOS, NEW MEXICO

HARPER & ROW,
PUBLISHERS
NEW YORK, EVANSTON, AND LONDON

CONTENTS

CONTENTS
FOR VOLUME II

CONTENTS
FOR VOLUME III

PREFACE

Each field of science must in some manner pay tribute to electronics. Because of the wealth of material and the number of contributors to this technology it becomes a formidable task for the individual scientist to keep abreast of the advances in this area. To compensate somewhat for this problem the Department of Physics at the Johns Hopkins University has, for a number of years, offered a single course in electronics at an advanced level to students in physics, chemistry, biophysics, biology, and engineering. The emphasis in this course has been placed on fundamentals; the assumption has been that an understanding of the fundamental concepts would prepare the student for the many special applications which he might encounter in his future research work.

In order to provide adequate coverage of passive circuits, physical electronics, and electronic circuits, fairly sophisticated mathematical methods were essential. Over a period of years a presentation has evolved which entails a concentrated study of operational methods as applied to passive networks. Many concepts such as the asymptotic behavior of frequency responses, pulse response, and the application of matrix analysis are fully developed in conjunction with the study of the passive circuits. Such concentration in rather obvious areas seems to lighten the load later in the study of active circuits.

The three volumes presented under the title *Fundamentals of Electronics* represent the content of this course. In fact the material presented here has been partially expanded over that which could be conveniently presented in a two-semester course. This was done to achieve completeness and to account for the fact that the course has not had a static content. In some years the material concerning physical electronics has been emphasized at the expense of circuits, while in other periods the reverse was true.

The lectures are normally presented in conjunction with a laboratory. In order to maintain some correlation between the laboratory and the lectures, the subject is ordinarily introduced with an initial six-week discussion of basic active circuits. The material for this introduction is found at the beginning of Volume III under the heading of Ideal Diodes, Triodes, and the Ideal Transistor Circuits. In other words, the students begin their studies with rough calculations employing ideal elements. Concepts of self-biasing, cutoff, and saturation are available in this limit in the most convenient form. The introductory material in Volume I concerning Kirchhoff's Laws and the elements of the operational calculus are not essential to the course. These sections were added to provide a rationale for the main body of the text.

A major aim of these volumes has been to provide the main topics of electronics in a unified manner. As a result the techniques employed in Volume I concerned with passive circuits are identical in form and notation with those used in the succeeding volumes which present physical electronics and active circuits. Although most of the material is available in the literature in one form or another, we have made a serious attempt to rework each problem as completely as possible in terms of the methods and notations which are consistently employed throughout the three books. We feel that some of the viewpoints are original and will add to the student's understanding of the material.

These volumes represent many years of work and we are indebted to a number of our associates for their interest and contributions. Initially, we thank Professors Donald E. Kerr, Leon Madansky, Thomas Fulton, and Gordon Feldman, each of whom read a portion of the manuscript and contributed suggestions.

Mr. J. Oleson, Mr. W. Wiggins, and Mr. Ralph Stevens aided us by setting up and testing several of the circuit concepts presented in the books. For example, the statements concerning the dependence of the rise time of the blocking oscillator on the shape of the trigger pulse were studied in the laboratory.

We relied a great deal on the experience of Mr. Ronald Wagner and Mr. L. Foble, both of whom gave time to discussions of many practical problems. We are indebted to Mrs. Dencie Kent who typed and maintained the organization of the manuscripts. To all of these persons we extend our gratitude.

In closing, we should like to express our appreciation to our University. The Johns Hopkins University extends to its faculty a tradition of scholarship and a stimulating environment which has been of particular benefit to us in this endeavor. This project has given pleasure to both of us.

May, 1966
Baltimore, Maryland

GEORGE E. OWEN
P. W. KEATON

FUNDAMENTALS OF ELECTRONICS
(VOLUME I)

CHAPTER 1

CIRCUIT ANALYSIS: KIRCHHOFF'S LAWS

One can choose various approaches to linear circuit analysis. However, by and large, the most convenient introduction consists of a straightforward postulate of Kirchhoff's laws, with appropriate definitions of the voltage drops across passive circuit elements. This method becomes rather arbitrary in the case of time-dependent currents where problems of inductive coupling and radiation are necessary interests. Neglect of radiative effects in circuit analysis is appropriate in most cases in which such an assumption is made. On the other hand, it is certainly instructive for the student to observe the general problem and to understand at which step of the approximation the various quantities are lumped or, as in the case of radiation, neglected.

We employ the word "neglect" loosely, since quite often bounded radiation will be assumed in a problem of lumped circuit elements. For instance, the launching of signals onto transmission lines always implies an incorporation of bounded radiation. The use of shorted stubs for the purpose of pulse shaping again implies a transmission line and a radiation problem. Antennas and wave guides also necessitate such considerations. We shall follow a procedure by which Kirchhoff's laws are derived as a consequence of the Maxwell equations, Ohm's law, and the equation of continuity. Because of limitations of space and time, the student is referred to texts concerned with electromagnetic theory for detailed developments of the Maxwell equations. Our aim will be to block out the transition from Maxwell's equations to Kirchhoff's laws. In principle, the reader can omit the introductory sections and commence with the rules of circuitry.

Regarding:

$\mathscr{E}$ = the electric field intensity in volts per meter. This is the electric force per unit charge exerted upon a test charge of vanishingly small magnitude.

$\mathbf{p}_v$ = the dipole moment per unit volume.

$\mathbf{D} = \varepsilon_0 \mathscr{E} + \mathbf{p}_v = \varepsilon \varepsilon_0 \mathscr{E}$ (in homogeneous isotropic media).

$\mathbf{D}$ = the electric displacement vector in coulombs per square meter. Here ε is the dielectric constant.

$\mathbf{B}$ = the magnetic induction vector. This is the field vector that gives rise to the transverse force on a moving charge, and is a portion of the Lorenz force, $(q\mathbf{v} \times \mathbf{B})$.

$\mathbf{m}_v$ = the magnetic moment per unit volume.

$\mathbf{H}$ = the magnetic intensity = $\dfrac{\mathbf{B}}{\mu_0} - \mathbf{m}_v$

$= \mathbf{B}/\mu\mu_0$ (in homogeneous isotropic magnetic media).
Here μ is the relative magnetic permeability.

The four Maxwell equations are

$\text{div } \mathbf{D} = \rho$ a statement of the inverse square law. ρ equals the free-charge density and represents the sources of $\mathbf{D}$.

$\text{div } \mathbf{B} = 0$ a statement of the solenoidal nature of $\mathbf{B}$.

$\text{curl } \mathbf{H} = \mathbf{J} + \dfrac{\partial \mathbf{D}}{\partial t}$ indicating that the circulation of $\mathbf{H}$ is a measure of $\mathbf{J}$ and $\partial \mathbf{D}/\partial t$. $\mathbf{J}$ is the current-density vector in amperes per square meter.

$\text{curl } \mathscr{E} = -\dfrac{\partial \mathbf{B}}{\partial t}$ Faraday's law, indicating that a time-varying magnetic field induces a circulating electric field.

We include with these four equations:

$$\mathbf{J} = \sigma \mathscr{E} \qquad \text{Ohm's law } (\sigma = \text{the conductivity}),$$

and

$$\text{div } \mathbf{J} + \frac{\partial \rho}{\partial t} = 0 \qquad \text{the continuity equation, a statement of the conservation of charge.}$$

Initially, let us regard Ohm's law and also the definition of a seat of emf or the presence of an active source of potential. In a portion of a conductor, say between points a and b (Fig. 1), current will flow according to Ohm's law as

$$\mathbf{J} = \sigma(\mathscr{E} + \mathscr{E}'),$$

where $\mathscr{E}$ = the conservative field component in the volume τ, and
$\mathscr{E}'$ = the nonconservative fields associated with seats of emf or induced emfs.

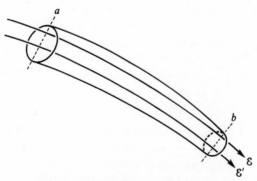

Fig. 1. Electric fields in a conductor.

For simplicity, we take the cross-sectional area of the conductor as a constant, $\mathscr{A}$, and perform a line integration of Ohm's law between a and b:

$$\int_a^b \sigma(\mathscr{E} + \mathscr{E}') \cdot d\mathbf{l} = \int_a^b \mathbf{J} \cdot d\mathbf{l}.$$

The emf between a and b is defined as the line integral of the nonconservative electric field vector $\mathscr{E}'$,

$$E_{ab} = \int_a^b \mathscr{E}' \cdot d\mathbf{l}.$$

The conservative term gives rise to a potential difference

$$-V_b + V_a = \int_a^b \mathscr{E} \cdot d\mathbf{l}.$$

Then

$$-V_b + V_a + E_{ab} = \frac{1}{\sigma \mathscr{A}} \int_a^b \mathscr{A} \mathbf{J} \cdot d\mathbf{l},$$

where $\mathscr{A}$ is the cross-sectional area.

In the case of lumped circuits, $\mathbf{J}$ and $d\mathbf{l}$ are parallel; and $\mathscr{A}\mathbf{J} \cdot d\mathbf{l} = l_{ab}i$, where i is the total current in amperes. The resistance R_{ab} between a and b can be defined by

$$R_{ab}i = \frac{1}{\sigma} \int_a^b \mathbf{J} \cdot d\mathbf{l} = \frac{l_{ab}}{\sigma \mathscr{A}} i.$$

From the preceding equation we observe that when there are no active seats of emf in the interval $a \to b$ ($E_{ab} = 0$), the potential drop is equal to Ri, the point a being at a potential higher than that at b. The reader should also notice that for a closed loop,

$$E = \oint \mathscr{E}' \cdot d\mathbf{l} = Ri.$$

The power dissipated in the form of heat in the conductor volume between a and b, again assuming $E_{ab} = 0$ (no emfs), is given by

$$P_{ab} = \underset{\substack{\text{conductor} \\ \text{vol between} \\ a \text{ and } b}}{\int \left| \int \right. } \mathscr{E} \cdot \mathbf{J} \, d\tau = \frac{1}{\sigma} \int_{\tau_{ab}} \left| \int \right. \mathbf{J} \cdot \mathbf{J} \, d\tau.$$

With a constant cross section $\mathscr{A}$ and $\mathbf{J}$ parallel to $d\mathbf{l}$ and uniform across $\mathscr{A}$,

$$P_{ab} = -\{V_b - V_a\}i = \frac{l_{ab}}{\sigma \mathscr{A}} i^2 = Ri^2.$$

The negative sign indicates a loss of electric-energy from the system. To obtain the circuit relations, we assume that the dielectric media and magnetic media are homogeneous and isotropic, so that $\mathbf{D} = \varepsilon\varepsilon_0\mathscr{E}$, and $\mathbf{B} = \mu\mu_0\mathbf{H}$. To begin, we merely regard the loops and meshes of the circuit as a distribution of ρ, $\mathbf{J}$, $\mathscr{E}$, and $\mathbf{H}$ in space. Once the power relations are derived, we shall restrict the currents and charges to specific circuit loops. The power relation is developed by multiplying the third Maxwell equation by $-\mathscr{E}$ and the fourth equation by $\mathbf{H}$. These are then added, giving

$$\text{div}(\mathscr{E} \times \mathbf{H}) = \mathbf{H} \cdot \text{curl } \mathscr{E} - \mathscr{E} \cdot \text{curl } \mathbf{H} = -\mathscr{E} \cdot \mathbf{J} - \frac{\partial u}{\partial t}.$$

u is the energy density: $u = \frac{1}{2}\{\mathscr{E} \cdot \mathbf{D} + \mathbf{B} \cdot \mathbf{H}\}$. One ordinarily interprets $(\mathscr{E} \times \mathbf{H})$

as the Poynting vector $\mathbf{N}$. The integral of the normal component of $\mathbf{N}$ across a closed surface gives the electromagnetic radiation power escaping across the surface. If the electric fields of condensers and magnetic fields of coils are relatively well confined within a circuit volume τ_c that is surrounded by a close surface S_c, we can write

$$-\iiint_{\tau_c} \mathscr{E} \cdot \mathbf{J} \, d\tau = \iiint_{\tau_c} \operatorname{div} \mathbf{N} \, d\tau + \iiint_{\tau_c} \frac{\partial u}{\partial t} \, d\tau.$$

$$= \iint_{S_c} \mathbf{N} \cdot \mathbf{n} \, dS + \iiint_{\tau_c} \frac{\partial u}{\partial t} \, d\tau.$$

The field term on the left represents the nonbattery fields. On the other hand, the current $\mathbf{J}$ is related to the total electric field by Ohm's law, $\mathscr{E}$ plus the fields of active elements $\mathscr{E}_B$:

$$\mathbf{J} = \sigma(\mathscr{E}_B + \mathscr{E})$$

and

$$-\mathscr{E} \cdot \mathbf{J} = -\frac{1}{\sigma} \mathbf{J}^2 + \mathbf{J} \cdot \mathscr{E}_B.$$

Substituting into the left-hand volume integral in the power balance, we obtain

$$\iiint_{\tau_c} \mathscr{E}_B \cdot \mathbf{J} \, d\tau = \frac{1}{\sigma} \iiint_{\tau_c} J^2 \, d\tau + \iiint_{\tau_c} \frac{\partial u}{\partial t} \, d\tau + \iint_{S_c} \mathbf{N} \cdot \mathbf{n} \, dS.$$

It is at this stage that the concept of lumped parameters and radiationless circuits becomes meaningful. If the dimensions of the circuit are much less than the wave length of the radiation field, the total power radiated is negligible, and the surface integral over N can be taken as zero. Then the power supplied from seats of emf equals

$$\iiint_{\tau_c} \mathscr{E}_B \cdot \mathbf{J} \, d\tau = \iiint_{\tau_c} \left\{ \frac{J^2}{\sigma} + \frac{\partial u}{\partial t} \right\} d\tau.$$

To transform this expression to circuit relations, we first conceive of N separate loops, each carrying a current i_j. If the emfs of each loop are E_j, then our integral reduces to a sum:

$$\text{Total power supplied} = \sum_{j=1}^{N} E_j i_j$$

$$= \sum_{j=1}^{N} \left\{ i_j \sum_{k=1}^{N} L_{jk} \frac{\partial i_k}{\partial t} + i_j^2 R_j + \frac{i_j q_j}{C_j} \right\}.$$

In this expression,

$$\sum_{j=1}^{N} i_j \sum_{k=1}^{N} L_{jk} \frac{\partial i_k}{\partial t} = \frac{1}{2} \iiint_{\tau_c} \frac{\partial}{\partial t} \{\mathbf{B} \cdot \mathbf{H}\} \, d\tau,$$

where L_{jk} is the mutual inductance between loops j and k, and L_{jj} is the self-inductance of the jth loop, and

$$\sum_{j=1}^{N} i_j^2 R_j = \iint_{\tau_c}\int \frac{J^2}{\sigma}\, d\tau,$$

where R_j is the resistance of the jth loop; finally,

$$\sum_{j=1}^{N} \frac{i_j q_j}{C_j} = \frac{1}{2} \frac{\partial}{\partial t} \iint_{\tau_c}\int \{\mathscr{E} \cdot \mathbf{D}\}\, d\tau,$$

where C_j is the jth condenser, and q_j is the magnitude of the charge on it. Thus, for the N separate loops, it is sufficient to write

$$E_j = \sum_{k=1}^{N} L_{jk} \frac{\partial i_k}{\partial t} + i_j R_j + \frac{q_j}{C_j}.$$

One should also keep in mind that the charge q_j is, by definition,

$$q_j(t) = \int_0^t i_j(t')\, dt' + q_j(0).$$

In the expression for E_j, we find that E_j is equal to the sum of the voltage drops about the loop.

This expression can be extended to a circuit mesh of M branches. Each branch contains a separate branch current $\mathscr{I}_l$ and a separate emf E_l (which may in some cases be zero). The power relation is still written as

$$\sum_{l=1}^{M} \mathscr{I}_l E_l = \sum_{l=1}^{M} \left\{ \mathscr{I}_l \sum_{k=1}^{M} L_{lk} \frac{\partial \mathscr{I}_k}{\partial t} + \mathscr{I}_l^2 R_l + \mathscr{I}_l \frac{q_l}{C_l} \right\}.$$

There is no longer a one-to-one correspondence between the battery currents and all the branch currents. If, on the other hand, we double-subscript the impedance term R_l and C_l and number the loops instead of the branches, the problem becomes quite simple. Take the branch current $\mathscr{I}_{mn}$ adjoining loop m and loop n to be $(i_m - i_n)$, where i_k is the current associated with the kth loop. This is an expression of the conservation of charge, as shown in Fig. 2.

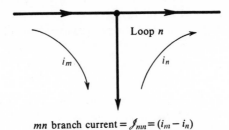

mn branch current $= \mathscr{I}_{mn} = (i_m - i_n)$

Fig. 2. Loop currents and the resultant branch current.

The branch equations can then be written as a sum over the N loops. To obtain Kirchhoff's laws, we split the branch-current term on the left into loop currents and leave the branch current or branch charge on the right as it was. For instance, in a three-branch, two-loop system, as shown in Fig. 3, the splitting would be done in the following fashion. Starting with

$$P = \mathscr{I}_{11}E_{11} + \mathscr{I}_{12}E_{12} + \mathscr{I}_{22}E_{22},$$

and

$$P = \mathscr{I}_{11}Z_{11}\mathscr{I}_{11} + \mathscr{I}_{12}Z_{12}\mathscr{I}_{12} + \mathscr{I}_{22}E_{22}\mathscr{I}_{22}.$$

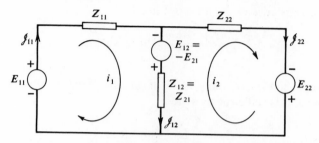

FIG. 3.   A circuit composed of three branches and two loops. An illustration of the index notation for the circuit elements and the currents.

Now, for currents on the left, let $\mathscr{I}_{lm} = (i_l - i_m)$. We must exercise care to maintain the proper sign. If $\mathscr{I}_{lm}$ is opposite in sign to E_{lm} then the sign of E_{lm} should be negative in the original branch equation. Another way of stating this is to assume that the sign is positive if i_l flows from minus to plus through E_{lm}, where $l < m$. In addition, the loop currents are all taken clockwise. In our example, then,

$$(i_1 - 0)E_{11} + (i_1 - i_2)E_{12} + (i_2 - 0)E_{22}$$

$$= (i_1 - 0)Z_{11}\mathscr{I}_{11} + (i_1 - i_2)Z_{12}\mathscr{I}_{12} + (i_2 - 0)Z_{22}\mathscr{I}_{22}.$$

This equation can then be written as two by setting the coefficients of i_k equal to zero:

$$E_{11} + E_{12} = Z_{11}\mathscr{I}_{11} + Z_{12}\mathscr{I}_{12},$$

$$-E_{12} + E_{22} = -Z_{12}\mathscr{I}_{12} + Z_{22}\mathscr{I}_{22}.$$

This leads to a general expression for the branches, which states that *the sum of the instantaneous emfs about any loop is equal to the sum of the voltage drops*. Again we pass about a loop in a clockwise direction. If the polarity of a seat of emf is minus to plus in this passage, the sign is positive.

The term *voltage drops* refers to the three passive terms of a branch,[†] i.e.,

$$v_l(t) = \sum_{k=1}^{M} L_{lk}\frac{\partial \mathscr{I}_k}{\partial t} + R_l\mathscr{I}_l + \frac{q_l}{C_l}.$$

When the branch current $\mathscr{I}_l$ is taken in the direction of the loop, the sign is positive. When the direction is reversed, the sign is negative.

This rule concerning the sum of the emfs and voltage drops about a loop is known as Kirchhoff's first law. The second law is merely the conservation of charge at any nodal point in the circuit. This states that the vector sum of the currents at any nodal point is zero. Here the word "vector" means the algebraic sign. If the current flows into a point, the sign is negative. When the current flows away from the nodal point,

---

† Single subscripts are employed here because it is sufficient in this case to take all the branch currents into account.

the sign is positive. Consider the node P and the five currents $\mathscr{J}_j$ shown in the diagram, Fig. 4:

$$-\mathscr{J}_1 + \mathscr{J}_2 + \mathscr{J}_3 + \mathscr{J}_4 - \mathscr{J}_5 = 0.$$

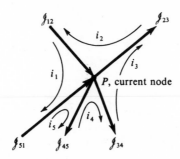

FIG. 4.   A current node and five branch currents.

By inserting current conservation into the first law, the equations are exhibited in terms of the Maxwell loop currents used before. We regard the (mn) branch adjoining the mth loop and the nth loop.

In this case, $\mathscr{J}_{mn} = +(i_m - i_n)$, and the drop across the passive elements is (excluding mutual inductance for the moment)

$$v_{mn}(t) = L_{mn}\frac{d}{dt}(i_m - i_n) + R_{mn}(i_m - i_n) + \frac{1}{C_{mn}}\int(i_m - i_n)\,dt.$$

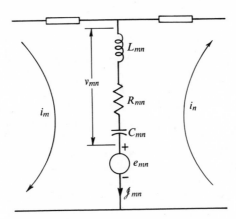

FIG. 5.   A typical branch with passive elements and a source of emf.

Later, L_{mn} can be extended in order to include coupled currents i_n.

We should also notice that as we move across this branch, the instantaneous value of $e_{mn}(t)$ is negative according to the polarity shown. Kirchhoff's first law when applied to a loop (say the mth) is

$$\sum_{j=1}^{N} e_{mj}(t) = \sum_{j=1}^{N}\left[L_{mj}\left(\frac{di_m}{dt} - \frac{di_j}{dt}\right) + R_{mj}(i_m - i_j) + \frac{1}{C_{mj}}\int i_m\,dt - \frac{1}{C_{mj}}\int i_j\,dt\right].$$

If we define the time-dependent operators

$$Z_{kk}(t) = \sum_{\substack{\text{all loops } n \\ \text{adjoining loop } k}} \left\{ L_{kn} \frac{\partial}{\partial t} + R_{kn} + \frac{1}{C_{kn}} \int dt \right\},$$

and

$$Z_{kj}(t) = -\left\{ L_{kj} \frac{\partial}{\partial t} + R_{kj} + \frac{1}{C_{kj}} \int dt \right\} \qquad (k \neq j).$$

Then

$$\sum_{n=1}^{N} e_{mn}(t) = \sum_{n=1}^{N} Z_{mn}(t) i_n(t).$$

For instance, a circuit of four loops would have the following formal relations in Fig. 6:

$$e_{11} + e_{12} + e_{13} + e_{14} = Z_{11}i_1 + Z_{12}i_2 + Z_{13}i_3 + Z_{14}i_4,$$

$$e_{21} + e_{22} + e_{23} + e_{24} = \sum_{j=1}^{4} Z_{2j}i_j,$$

$$\vdots$$

$$\sum_{j=1}^{4} e_{4j} = \sum_{j=1}^{4} Z_{4j}(t) i_j(t).$$

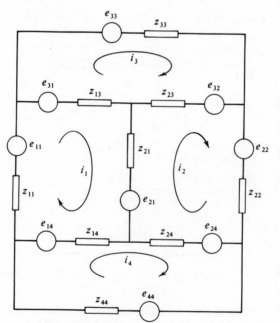

FIG. 6.   A circuit of four loops. Notice that the effective impedances are given by $Z_{jj} = \sum\limits_{\text{all } k} Z_{jk}$ and $Z_{lm} = Z_{ml}$, $(l \neq m)$.

The branches adjoining the exterior of the entire circuit are labeled e_{mm}. After these very formal thoughts, we should consider several elementary problems in the time domain, if for no other reason than to be able to appreciate better the operator calculus when it is introduced. The following one-loop and two-loop circuits illustrate a great deal. They are shown for arbitrary excitation. In Fig. 7,

$$e_{11} = v_R(t) + v_c(t) = Ri_1 + \frac{1}{C}\int_0^t i_1(t')\,dt' + \frac{q(0+)}{C}.$$

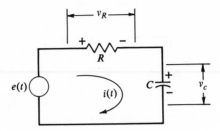

FIG. 7.   A one-loop RC circuit.

Suppose e_{11} is a switch which is closed at $t = 0$. Then

$$Ri_1 + \frac{1}{C}\int_0^t i_1(t')\,dt' = -\frac{q(0+)}{C}; \qquad 0 < t.$$

This is a first-degree integral equation.

By differentiating the equation or by assuming a trial solution e^{st}, or both, we find that

$$i_1(t) = -\frac{q(0+)}{RC}\,e^{-(t/RC)}U(t).$$

This solution has been multiplied by the unit-step function $U(t)$, where

$$U(t) = 0, \qquad \text{for}\quad t < 0;$$

and

$$U(t) = +1, \qquad \text{for}\quad 0 < t.$$

The use of $U(t)$ automatically describes the function for $t < 0$ as zero. See Fig. 8.

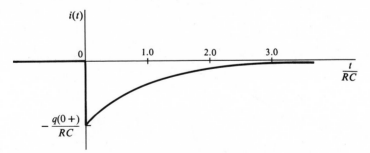

FIG. 8.   Current in the RC circuit as a function of t. At $t = 0$, the circuit is closed by means of a switch. $q(0+)$ is the initial charge on the condenser C.

As a second example, we take an elementary differential operator. This situation is characteristic of a circuit involving a series combination of an inductance and a resistance. As shown, a battery of terminal emf E_0 is switched in series with the L,R

circuit at $t = 0$. This operation can be described by an excitation

$$e(t) = E_0 U(t),$$

with

$$i(0+) = 0.$$

See Fig. 9.

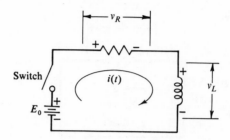

FIG. 9.   An LR circuit actuated by a switch and a battery.

The defining equation for the current is again obtained by equating the sum of the emfs about the loop (with appropriate signs) to the sum of the voltage drops across the passive elements:

$$e(t) = v_R(t) + v_L(t) = Ri(t) + L\frac{di(t)}{dt}.$$

At $t\,(0+)$, $e(0+) = E_0$, and $i(0+) = 0$. Thus,

$$E_0 = Ri + L\frac{di}{dt}; \quad \text{for} \quad 0 < t.$$

This equation has a complementary solution e^{st} of the homogeneous equation and a particular solution $(A + Bt)$ to the inhomogeneous equation. By including the initial condition on $i(t)$,

$$i(t) = \frac{E_0}{R}(1 - e^{-(t/RC)})U(t).$$

See Fig. 10.

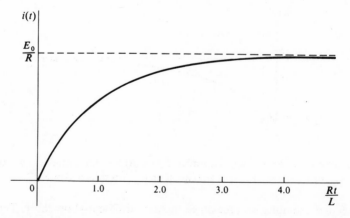

FIG. 10.   Current buildup in a series LR circuit actuated by a battery of terminal emf equal to E_0.

As a final example, we regard a two-loop circuit subject to a sinusoidal excitation:

$$e_{11} = E_0 \sin \omega_0 t U(t).$$

This circuit can be considered to be initially relaxed; that is, the currents and branch charges at $t = 0$ are zero. See Fig. 11.

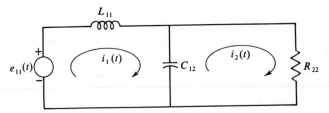

FIG. 11.   A two-loop LRC circuit.

The solution to this problem by standard techniques is quite involved. It serves our purpose, however, to set this problem up and map out the solution because the value of the double-subscripted loop notation becomes apparent rather quickly.

The first loop equation is

$$e_{11}(t) = L_{11} \frac{di_1}{dt} + \frac{1}{C_{12}} \int i_1 \, dt - \frac{1}{C_{12}} \int i_2 \, dt.$$

The second loop equation is

$$0 = -\frac{1}{C_{21}} \int i_1 \, dt + \frac{1}{C_{21}} \int i_2 \, dt + R_{22} i_2(t).$$

The reader will observe that $C_{12} = C_{21}$. The interchange of subscripts does not entail a change in sign. To solve this problem, we differentiate both equations with respect to t. The current $i_2(t)$ can be eliminated from the resulting set of simultaneous differential equations by differentiating the first equation again, multiplying by $C_{12} R_{22}$, and adding the result to the first equation after one differentiation. Adding this result to the second equation (differentiated once) gives

$$C_{12} R_{22} \frac{d^2 e_{11}}{dt^2} + \frac{de_{11}}{dt} = L_{11} C_{12} R_{22} \frac{d^3 i_1}{dt^3} + L_{11} \frac{d^2 i_1}{dt^2} + R_{22} \frac{di_1}{dt}.$$

This equation has a complementary solution and a particular solution subject to the initial conditions that $i_1(t) = 0$ and $q_1(0) = 0$. In general, then,

$$i_1(t) = \{Ae^{s_1 t} + Be^{s_2 t} + C\} + D \cos \omega_0 t + F \sin \omega_0 t.$$

The characteristic modes s_1, s_2 and 0 are roots of the characteristic equation

$$C_{12} R_{22} L_{11} s^3 + L_{11} s^2 + R_{22} s = 0.$$

If, for example,

$$R_{22}^2 \ll \frac{L_{11}}{C_{12}},$$

the roots are approximately

$$s_1 = -\frac{1}{R_{22} C_{12}},$$

and

$$s_2 = -\frac{R_{22}}{L_{11}}$$

$$s_3 = 0.$$

This also indicates that $s_2 \ll s_1$ for this solution. The constants D and F are obtained directly, in terms of L_{11}, C_{12}, R_{22}, ω_0, and E_0, by the method of undetermined coefficients. The initial conditions upon $i_1(t)$ and $i_2(t)$ serve to determine the transient coefficients A, B, and C. In the process of doing this, the solution shown for $i_1(t)$ must be substituted into the differential equation relating $i_2(t)$ and $i_1(t)$. Subsequently, a solution for $i_2(t)$ must be used.

From this seemingly simple problem, we can draw several conclusions. First, linear differential equations with constant coefficients are essentially algebraic because the complementary solutions in terms of the characteristic modes are linear combinations of complex exponential functions. Second, we observe that the application of direct methods of differentiation and integration become extremely tedious when the number of Maxwell loops is greater than one.

One final observation is called for, and that is the fact that systems of simultaneous linear differential equations can be handled much more systematically by matrix methods. These observations then serve as a rational for the sections that follow. The operational methods will be developed, and these will be employed subsequently in conjunction with the more powerful matrix notation.

The operational calculus reduces differentiation and integration to multiplication and division. To do this, we shall transform our problems from the real-positive time axis to the complex frequency plane.

Because the solutions to linear problems in the complex frequency plane are on the whole very simple, the reader will be encouraged to think of active and passive networks in terms of their poles and zeros in the complex frequency plane. This will be done by constantly referring these rather simple concepts to the traditional frequency response and the corresponding integro-differential equations in the time domain.

The order of events will consist of an elementary discussion of the operational method, followed by a discussion of Fourier series, Fourier integrals, and finally the Laplace transform. The ultimate transform methods will present the problems in the same form as the more direct operational method. Thus the reader will be able to view the technique at various levels of sophistication and thereby achieve some attitudes of comfort relative to the method.

CHAPTER 2

OPERATIONAL METHODS

THE DELTA FUNCTION OR IMPULSE FUNCTION

A physical excitation function is ordinarily a continuous function with a continuous derivative. Certainly, in the theory of lumped circuits, it is impossible to construct an element that consists of either a pure lumped inductance or a pure lumped capacitance. All real inductors and capacitors have a finite size and are subject to some resistive dissipation. Further, the physical nature and size of switches and active elements prevent the realization of operations that are discontinuous.

Mathematically, it is often tedious to initiate solutions of inhomogeneous equations with arbitrary but continuous excitations from first principles. Invariably, a solution entails an integration of the excitation and its derivatives. These integrations can be viewed as the sum of small rectangles of infinitesimal width Δt and a height governed by the value (see Fig. 12) of $e(t)$ at the position of the rectangle. Mathematically, this rectangle is a discontinuous function. In practice, it is not possible to

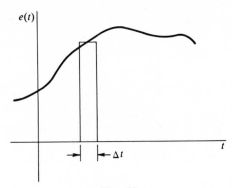

FIG. 12.

describe a function to all orders if the function is zero for times less than some t_0 and achieves a maximum nonzero value for some $t > t_0$.

The rectangular excitation is a very convenient device in idealized problems. In the most elementary of treatments, one can visualize solutions away from the discontinuities and regional connections at the discontinuities to give a piecewise linear solution. The rectangular excitation has the further convenient property that all its integrals exist for finite t.

Consider

$$\Delta(t) = 0, \qquad t < 0,$$

$$\Delta(t) = \frac{1}{T}, \qquad 0 < t < T,$$

and

$$\Delta(t) = 0, \qquad T < t.$$

Then

$$\int_{-\infty}^{t} \Delta(t') \, dt' = 0, \qquad t < 0$$

$$= \frac{t}{T}, \qquad 0 < t < T$$

$$= +1, \qquad T < t.$$

Many problems could be analyzed by employing this function $\Delta(t)$ directly, with the understanding that T is much smaller than the customary time response of the circuit. Further, unless additional definition is attached, we would be confined to the function $\Delta(t)$ and its integrals.

The first integral is in the nature of a step function of unit amplitude. The second integral behaves as $t + C$ for $T < t$. The nth integral would provide a function behaving as t^{n-1}.

One form of the delta function, or impulse function, is evolved if we consider $\Delta(t)$

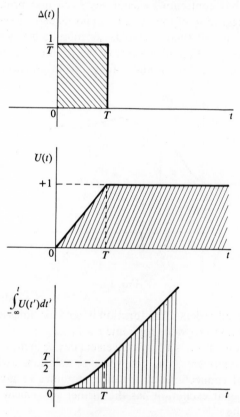

FIG. 13.   The function $\Delta(t)$ and the first two integrals.

in the limit as T approaches zero (see Fig. 13). A great deal of controversy concerning the use of the delta function arises from an effort on the part of a number of authors to separate the function and its use under an integral. If one assumes that the delta function is defined outside the integral, certain mathematical nonsense can take place. On the other hand, if the order of integration and of taking the limit are always maintained clearly in the mind's eye, the delta function is a consistent and extremely useful mathematical device.

The delta function in the form to be employed for the present is defined by

$$\lim_{T \to 0} \int_{-\infty}^{t} \Delta(t' - t_0)\, dt' = \int_{-\infty}^{t} \delta(t' - t_0)\, dt' = 0, \qquad \text{for} \quad t < t_0$$
$$= +1, \qquad \text{for} \quad t_0 < t.$$

This integral then defines the unit-step function $U(t - t_0)$, which is zero for $t < t_0$ and has the value $+1$ for $t_0 < t$:

$$\int_{-\infty}^{t} \delta(t' - t_0)\, dt' = U(t - t_0).$$

Some future notation can be anticipated by indicating that we could have defined $\Delta(t)$ more conveniently with $U(t - t_0)$:

$$\Delta(t) = \frac{1}{T}\{U(t) - U(t - T)\}.$$

Then, using the origin as a convenient t_0,

$$\lim_{T \to 0} \int_{-\infty}^{t} \frac{1}{T}\{U(t') - U(t' - T)\}\, dt' = \int_{-\infty}^{t} \delta(t')\, dt'.$$

Because $U(t)$ has a limited definition outside the integral sign, we can interchange the order of integration and of taking the limit in the first integral, and

$$\int_{-\infty}^{t} \frac{dU(t')}{dt'}\, dt' = \int_{-\infty}^{t} \delta(t')\, dt'.$$

It is in this context that the delta function may be regarded as the derivative of the step function.

Later in the discussion of the Fourier integral theorem, the delta function will appear in a modified form in the integral relation

$$f(t) = \int_{-\infty}^{\infty} f(t')\delta(t' - t)\, dt'.$$

We assume that $f(t)$ is well behaved and has an indefinite integral $g(t)$ such that $f(t) = [dg(t)]/dt$. The preceding integral can now be expanded according to our definition of $\delta(t' - t)$:

$$\int_{-\infty}^{\infty} f(t')\delta(t' - t)\, dt' = \lim_{T \to 0} \int_{-\infty}^{\infty} \frac{1}{T}f(t')\{U(t' - t) - U(t' - t - T)\}\, dt'$$
$$= \lim_{T \to 0} \int_{t}^{t+T} \frac{1}{T}f(t')\, dt' = \lim_{T \to 0}\left\{\frac{g(t + T) - g(t)}{T}\right\}$$
$$= \frac{dg}{dt} = f(t).$$

This expansion demonstrates the theorem.

In the examples with which we shall be concerned, all functions will be assumed to be zero for $t < 0$, and it will be further assumed that they are turned on at $t = 0$. Therefore, most of the integrals will have zero as the lower limit. To maintain a consistent approach, we should notice that

$$\int_0^t \delta(t' - t_0) \, dt' = 0, \qquad \text{for } t < t_0$$

$$= +1, \qquad \text{for } t_0 < t$$

$$= U(t - t_0), \qquad \text{positive time axis.}$$

Often in the solutions of differential equations, integrals will be taken from $(0+)$ to t. We must keep in mind that

$$\int_{(0+)}^t \delta(t' - 0) \, dt' \equiv 0.$$

In other words, $\{U(t) - U(0+) = 0\}$. The term $(0+)$ then implies $0 + \varepsilon$ in the limit as ε approaches zero from the right. Other relations that we might have a chance to use are

$$\underbrace{\int_0^t \cdots \int_0^t}_{n\text{-fold}} \delta(t'^{\cdots\,\prime} - t_0) \, dt^n = \frac{(t - t_0)^{n-1}}{(n - 1)!} \, U(t - t_0).$$

When n-fold integrals are involved, it is possible to use

$$\frac{d^{n-1}\delta(t)}{dt^{n-1}}$$

as a mathematical device.

The delta function is of basic mathematical importance in the study of differential operators. It can be employed as a point-source excitation. In this role, the solutions of an equation subject to a point source show characteristic modes or eigenvectors of the operator. In the next section, linear differential equations with constant coefficients will be analyzed in terms of their characteristic modes as extracted by delta function excitation.

DEFINITION OF A LINEAR SYSTEM AND THE STRUCTURE OF LINEAR DIFFERENTIAL EQUATIONS WITH CONSTANT COEFFICIENTS

The mathematical analysis that is available for the investigation of physical systems is for the most part quite limited. It is indeed fortunate that many physical systems behave in a linear manner to a high degree of approximation. As we have observed, the formalism of passive electric-circuit theory is linear.† Many electronic circuits that employ small signal excitations can be adequately represented by linear equations. Even problems of nonlinear elements can be approximated often by several linear regions. For example, a transistor operating between and in regions of saturation,

---

† Actually there are passive nonlinear circuit elements. Here we shall use the term passive to imply linearity unless stated otherwise.

linear characteristics, and cutoff can be described sometimes as a device operating in a linear saturation region joined at a convenient boundary to the customary linear region, which in turn is joined at a second boundary to a linear cutoff region. The problem can be solved in each of the three regions. The final solution would then be formed by joining the appropriate solutions at the boundaries forming cusps or discontinuities at worst. This will be referred to as *piecewise* linear analysis.

In the development of the passive networks, we found that our problems had some generalized properties. An excitation function $e(t)$ is applied to the circuit and produces a response $v(t)$. We have already discussed several elementary cases in which the excitation was produced by closing a switch to some source of emf (in the first example this was a short circuit) and in which the response was a charge function or a current. We could have also asked for the voltage across some passive element as a response.

In the case of the two-loop example, the final excitation function after uncoupling the two differential equations was a sum of derivatives of the emf of the active element. Each example, however, gave a defining equation consisting of a differential operator acting upon the response function, to give the generalized excitation which could, as we have seen, be formed from the active emf and time derivatives of the emf. Our discussion of a linear system will imply that the system operates completely upon the generalized response function to produce a response $v(t)$. Thus, the ordinary differential operator that acts upon $v(t)$ must be inverted. The inversion of this operator will be the center of discussion of the last portion of this section and will exhibit the algebraic nature of the differential operators with which we shall concern ourselves.

The linear properties that we now discuss will be directed to the inverted operator. All principles, however, must apply equally to the differential operator.

Our equations can be regarded as consisting of a generalized excitation function $g(t)$, which is applied to a system described by an operator $H(t)$ to produce a response $v(t)$. See Fig. 14.

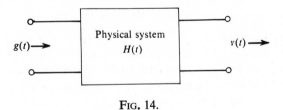

FIG. 14.

Symbolically, this can be written

$$v(t) = H(t)g(t).$$

As we have seen, our equations generally are formulated as†

$$H^{-1}(t)v(t) = g(t) = G(t)e(t).$$

Here, $H^{-1}(t)$ is a linear differential operator with constant coefficients, and $G(t)$ is another linear differential operator, also with constant coefficients. The function $e(t)$ shown above indicates the generator excitations that suffer transformation to $g(t)$ when a series of coupled differential equations are involved.

---

† Some care must be exercised in interpreting $H^{-1}(t)$. This is not 1 over $H(t)$, but may be an inverse operation. If $H(t)$ is an integration, $H^{-1}(t)$ may be a differentiation.

If $H(t)$ is a linear operator, it must satisfy three conditions†:

The Principle of Superposition

In the presence of more than one excitation, the response is the sum of the individual responses of the excitations, taken one at a time. Consider two functions $g_1(t)$ and $g_2(t)$. Corresponding to each there is a response $v_1(t)$ and $v_2(t)$, respectively:

$$v_j(t) = H(t)g_j(t).$$

The principle of superposition requires that

$$g(t) = \sum_{\text{all } n} g_n(t)$$

produce a total response

$$v(t) = \sum_{\text{all } n} v_n(t)$$

or

$$\sum_{\text{all } n} v_n(t) = H(t) \sum_{\text{all } n} g_n(t) = \sum_{\text{all } n} \{H(t)g_n(t)\}.$$

This is a statement that the responses are independent and that the excitations interact in $H(t)$ only linearly.

The Principle of Homogeneity

This condition could be called the "conservation of scale." In a limited sense, it represents the nonoverloading property of the operator $H(t)$. This principle is not independent of the principle of superposition in that an excitation could be applied n times in a sum to give a scale of n. On the other hand, the principle of superposition is not sufficient to assure the principle of homogeneity, which requires that

$$nv(t) = H(t)\{ng(t)\}.$$

The difference between the two principles can be seen by considering a device that splits two signals, $g_1(t) + g_2(t)$, of different frequency and subjects each to a nonlinear operation. The output in this special case could still be $\{v_1(t) + v_2(t)\}$. On the other hand, if a second experiment employs $g_1(t) = g_2(t)$, i.e., of the same frequency, the output would not necessarily be $2v_1(t)$.

This principle need not be stated separate from the principle of superposition if linear superposition is interpreted in the most general manner.

The Principle of Frequency Conservation

Simply stated, the operator $H(t)$ should not create frequency shifts. In other words, if

$$v(t) = H(t)g(t),$$

then

$$v(t - T) = H(t)g(t - T).$$

---

† In practice the three conditions are satisfied if $H \sum_j a_j g_j = \sum_j a_j v_j$ where $Hg_j = v_j$.

With these preliminaries out of the way, we can investigate the structure of our differential equations and examine some of the fundamental properties of their solutions.

The general type of differential equation that we encounter in circuit analysis is

$$H^{-1}(t)v(t) = \sum_{n=0}^{N} a_n \frac{d^n}{dt^n} v(t) = G(t)e(t),$$

where

$$G(t)g(t) = \sum_{m=0}^{M} b_m \frac{d^m}{dt^m} e(t).$$

In passive circuit analysis, the highest derivative on the right is less than or equal to the highest derivative on the left: $M \leqslant N$. This has an important interpretation; one can demonstrate that a term of order $M = N$ will give rise to a delta function in the solution. A term of $N < M$ will produce solutions that are derivatives of the delta function and thereby nonphysical.

In our introductory examples, the operator $H^{-1}(t)$ was observed to contain integrals of the response function. The operation of integration can be assumed to be a derivative of negative power. On the other hand, our expression can be assumed to be quite general if we consider the indefinite integrals removable by repeated differentiation. The following analysis is pertinent, therefore, if we regard

$$\int dt = \left(\frac{d^{-1}}{dt^{-1}} \right).$$

Linear differential equations are often solved by the expansion of the solution in a series that is expanded about appropriate singularities of the coefficients. When the coefficients are constants, an expansion can be performed about any point on the real axis. Therefore, we could certainly approach the problem at hand by expanding the solutions of the homogeneous equation

$$\sum_{n=0}^{N} a_n \frac{d^n}{dt^n} v_c(t) = 0$$

in an infinite series about $t = 0$. When this is done, one obtains a solution of the type

$$v_c(t) = \sum_{n=1}^{N} A_n \sum_{k=0}^{\infty} \frac{1}{k!} (-\gamma_n t)^k = \sum_{n=1}^{N} A_n e^{-\gamma_n t}.$$

The parameters γ_n of this solution are the eigenvalues or charactertistic roots of the factored form of the differential equation

$$\sum_{n=0}^{N} a_n \frac{d^n}{dt^n} = \left(\frac{d}{dt} + \gamma_N \right) \left(\frac{d}{dt} + \gamma_{N-1} \right) \cdots \left(\frac{d}{dt} + \gamma_1 \right)$$

$$= \prod_{n=1}^{N} \left(\frac{d}{dt} + \gamma_n \right).$$

This factorization is the first hint that the differential equations with constant coefficients are algebraic in nature. The roots γ_n, as we have said, are called the *eigenvalues* or *characteristic frequencies* of the differential equation. Thus, eigenvalues are generally complex and determine the eigenvectors or characteristic modes of the differential equation. In our previous solution, the exponential $e^{-\gamma_n t}$ in the interval $0 \leqslant t < \infty$ is the eigenvector of the nth mode.

In contrast with the Hermitean eigenvalue problems for which the eigenvalues are real and the eigenvectors are orthogonal, our problem involves complex eigenvalues with functions that are generally not orthogonal,† and are not even well behaved for large t in some instances. The solutions $e^{-\gamma_n t}$ do form a linearly independent set of functions from which the most general homogeneous solution to the differential equation can be constructed.

Before proceeding to a more concise treatment of this problem, we should notice a further indication of the algebraic nature of our equation. If we considered the individual factors of $H^{-1}(t)$, [i.e., $(d/dt + \gamma_n)$], we see immediately that the eigenvectors of $H^{-1}(t)$ are simply solutions of these first-order factors, taken one at a time. If

$$\left(\frac{d}{dt} + \gamma_n\right) v_c^{(n)}(t) = 0,$$

then

$$v_c^{(n)}(t) = \sum_{l=0}^{\infty} \frac{1}{l!} (-\gamma_n t)^l = e^{-\gamma_n t},$$

and

$$v_c(t) = \sum_{n=1}^{N} A_n v_c^{(n)}(t).$$

We shall consider an approach that exhibits the importance of the normal modes in both the complementary and particular (inhomogeneous equation) solutions to

$$H^{-1}(t)v(t) = G(t)e(t) = g(t).$$

Our method will depend upon the development of the individual source functions or Green's functions for each operator $[(d/dt) + \gamma_n]$ and for the complete operator $H^{-1}(t)$. Instead of using a technique which assumes an algebraic nature for $H^{-1}(t)$ and inverting, we shall attempt our solutions from simple indefinite integrals and some definite integrals when the initial conditions are inserted into the problem. This approach to the operational method is tedious; however, it does illustrate the fact that the algebraic properties of $H^{-1}(t)$ are quite general and do not specifically depend upon the Laplace integral. The Laplace transform is important because it is the most convenient technique for converting the differential equation to an algebraic equation.

As we have indicated, the differential operator $H^{-1}(t)$ can be factored to provide the characteristic roots or eigenvalues $-\gamma_n$. Assume for the time being that all the roots are different,†† $\gamma_n \neq \gamma_m$, if $n \neq m$. Then

$$H^{-1}(t) = \sum_{n=0}^{N} a_n \frac{d^n}{dt^n} = \prod_{n=1}^{N} \left(\frac{d}{dt} + \gamma_n\right),$$

where we have taken $a_N = 1$.

---

† Orthogonality of the inner product of two functions $g(t)$ and $f(t)$ assumes that $\int_{-\infty}^{\infty} g^*(t)f(t)\, dt$ is 1 if $g = f$, and is zero if $g \neq f$. In our problems, the interval would be $0 \rightarrow \infty$.

†† We shall take up the case of degenerate roots after the present example has been developed.

The Green's function, or source function, $h(t - t')$, for $H^{-1}(t)$ is defined as the solution when the system is excited by an impulse or delta function $\delta(t' - t)$:

$$H^{-1}(t)h(t - t') = \delta(t' - t).$$

The Green's function $h(t - t')$ allows us to obtain the particular solution to

$$H^{-1}(t)v(t) = g(t).$$

We can demonstrate this as follows: Assume a trial solution for the particular function $v_P(t)$ of the form

$$v_P(t) = \int_0^\infty h(t - t')g(t') \, dt', \qquad 0 \leqslant t.$$

By operating from the left with $H^{-1}(t)$, we obtain

$$H^{-1}(t)v_P(t) = \int_0^\infty H^{-1}(t)h(t - t')g(t') \, dt'$$

$$= \int_0^\infty \delta(t' - t)g(t') \, dt'$$

$$= g(t).$$

The last step represents the fundamental operation of the delta function under the integral sign. Notice that the lower limit of integration is (0), not (0+). When h involves a step function the upper limit can be placed at $(t+)$ to give the same result.

The importance of $h(t - t')$ is established. Because of the algebraic nature of $H^{-1}(t)$, we can demonstrate that $h(t - t')$ can be formed from a linear combination of the individual eigenvectors or characteristic modes $h_n(t - t')$, where h_n is defined by

$$\left(\frac{d}{dt} + \gamma_n\right)h_n(t - t') = \delta(t' - t).$$

Actually, this problem has been solved to some extent as $v_c^{(n)}(t)$. The presence of $\delta(t' - t)$ makes the solution less apparent, but it can be integrated in a relatively simple fashion. For ease, we let $t' = 0$ and use the symmetry relation $\delta(t) = +\delta(-t)$. Integrating once between 0 and t, we obtain

$$h_n(t) + \gamma_n \int_0^t h_n(t') \, dt' = \int_0^t \delta(t') \, dt' = U(t).$$

We have assumed that $h(0) = 0$, and $h(0+) = 1$. Rearranging, we write

$$h_n(t) = U(t) - \gamma_n \int_0^t h_n(t') \, dt'.$$

This integral equation can be expanded by iteration. In other words, we substitute the expression on the right into every integral over h_n, giving

$$h_n(t) = U(t) - \gamma_n \int_0^t U(t') \, dt' + \gamma_n^2 \int_0^t dt' \int_0^{t'} dt'' U(t'') - \cdots.$$

The mth integral of $U(t)$ is $(t^m/m!)U(t)$; therefore,

$$h_n(t) = \left\{\sum_{m=0}^\infty \frac{1}{m!}(-\gamma_n t)^m\right\}U(t) = e^{-\gamma_n t}U(t).$$

These are the characteristic modes of the system. The total source function for $H^{-1}(t)$ can be constructed from the $h_n(t)$ in linear combination:

$$h(t) = \sum_{n=1}^{N} K_n h_n(t).$$

We again assume that all roots are different.

The operator $H^{-1}(t)$ then acts upon each $h_n(t)$ independently. To facilitate a solution for the K_n, we cycle the products in

$$\prod_{n=1}^{N} \left(\frac{d}{dt} + \gamma_n\right)$$

to have $[(d/dt) + \gamma_j]$ as the leading operator for the term $h_j(t)$; then

$$H^{-1}(t) \sum_{n=1}^{N} K_n h_n(t) = \sum_{n=1}^{N} K_n \left\{\prod_{m \neq n}\left(\frac{d}{dt} + \gamma_m\right)\right\}\left(\frac{d}{dt} + \gamma_n\right) h_n(t)$$

$$= \sum_{n=1}^{N} K_n \left\{\prod_{m \neq n}\left(\frac{d}{dt} + \gamma_m\right)\right\}\delta(t)$$

$$= \delta(t).$$

The operator $\prod_{m \neq n}[(d/dt) + \gamma_m]$ is a differential operator whose highest degree is $N - 1$. To solve for the K_n, we set the coefficient of each term of the type $[(d^m/dt^m)\delta(t)]$ equal to zero. In other words, working with the relation

$$\sum_{n=1}^{N} K_n \prod_{m \neq n}\left(\frac{d}{dt} + \gamma_m\right)\delta(t) = \delta(t),$$

we obtain

$$\sum_{n=1}^{N} \left(\prod_{m \neq n} \gamma_m\right) K_n = 1$$

and

$$\sum_{n=1}^{N} \left\{\sum_{j=1}^{m+1} \prod_{\substack{m \neq n \\ m \neq j}} \gamma_m\right\} K_n = 0; \qquad m \neq 0.$$

Solving this set of N equations for the K_n, we obtain

$$K_n = \frac{1}{\prod_{m \neq n}(\gamma_m - \gamma_n)}.$$

This solution can be obtained much faster with an algebraic inversion of $H^{-1}(t)$. We shall perform this feat later with the "Heaviside expansion coefficients." On the other hand, it is well that we notice the appearance of the Heaviside expansion coefficients in this primitive treatment.

It will perhaps be instructive to solve this problem for first- and second-degree examples. First let us try an example of degree 1:

$$\left(\frac{d}{dt} + \gamma_1\right) h_1(t) = \delta(t).$$

In this case, $h_1(t) = h(t)$ and the solution is trivial, with $K_1 = 1$. A more complex form is

$$\left(\frac{d}{dt} + \gamma_2\right)\left(\frac{d}{dt} + \gamma_1\right)\{K_1 h_1(t) + K_2 h_2(t)\} = \delta(t).$$

Operating as described by using $[(d/dt) + \gamma_j]$ as the leading term for the function $h_j(t)$, we obtain

$$K_1\left(\frac{d}{dt} + \gamma_2\right)\delta(t) + K_2\left(\frac{d}{dt} + \gamma_1\right)\delta(t) = \delta(t).$$

Collecting terms and setting the coefficients of $(d/dt)\delta(t)$ and $\delta(t)$ equal to zero, we obtain

$$K_1 = \frac{1}{\gamma_2 - \gamma_1}$$

and

$$K_2 = \frac{1}{\gamma_1 - \gamma_2}.$$

If some of the roots are degenerate, our characteristic modes are no longer pure exponential functions. The presence of a degeneracy of order $P < N$ will give an exponential solution times a power series in t of degree $(P - 1)$. Regard the problem

$$\left(\frac{d}{dt} + \gamma\right)^2 h(t) = \delta(t).$$

The single solution $\exp(-\gamma t)U(t)$ will not satisfy this equation. The factor $[(d/dt) + \gamma]h(t)$ can be considered a single term $h_1(t)$, and then

$$\left(\frac{d}{dt} + \gamma\right)h_1(t) = \delta(t),$$

with

$$h_1(t) = e^{-\gamma t}U(t).$$

By definition, then, this gives an inhomogeneous equation for $h(t)$:

$$\left(\frac{d}{dt} + \gamma\right)h(t) = h_1(t).$$

Because $h_1(t)$ is the Green's function for the single factor†

$$h(t) = h_1(t) + \gamma\int_0^t h_1(t - t')h_1(t')\, dt'$$

and

$$h(t) = (1 + \gamma t)h_1(t).$$

---

† The integral can be taken from 0 to ∞ as shown previously. The step function $U(t - t')$ in $h_1(t - t')$ allows the limit to be taken at t.

In general, a degeneracy of order P can be removed by a solution of the form

$$\sum_{m=0}^{P-1} C_m t^m e^{-\gamma t}.$$

This problem is handled quite readily by algebraic technique; therefore, we shall leave the coefficients C_m until these methods are introduced. We can at this point indicate the algebraic nature of $H^{-1}(t)$. To accomplish this, we designate d/dt as a complex frequency operator s. The homogeneous differential operator can then be written as

$$\sum_{n=0}^{N} a_n \frac{d^n}{dt^n} \Rightarrow \sum_{n=0}^{N} a_n s^n.$$

The eigenvalues γ_n are obtained as the roots of the characteristic equation

$$\sum_{n=0}^{N} a_n s^n = \prod_{n=1}^{N} (s + \gamma_n) = 0; \qquad (a_N = 1).$$

The Green's function solution is obtained by the algebraic inversion of†

$$\prod_{n=1}^{N} (s + \gamma_n) H(s) = 1$$

or

$$H(s) = \frac{1}{\displaystyle\prod_{n=1}^{N} (s + \gamma_n)}.$$

This expression can be expanded by the method of partial fractions to give

$$H(s) = \sum_{n=1}^{N} \frac{K_n}{(s + \gamma_n)}.$$

Working now only with the nondegenerate case ($\gamma_m \neq \gamma_n$), we notice that

$$K_n = [(s + \gamma_n)H(s)]_{s = -\gamma_n} = \frac{1}{\displaystyle\prod_{m \neq n} (\gamma_m - \gamma_n)}.$$

From the first-degree equation we can solve for the components of $H(s)$,

$$(s + \gamma_j)H_j(s) = 1,$$

to give the solution

$$H_j(s) = \frac{1}{(s + \gamma_j)}.$$

In the time domain, as we have shown, $\{1/(s + \gamma_j)\}$ is associated with the characteristic mode or eigensolution $h_j(t) = \exp(-\gamma_j t)$.

Therefore, the series term

$$H(s) = \sum_{n=1}^{N} K_n H_n(s) = \sum_{n=1}^{N} \frac{K_n}{(s + \gamma_n)}$$

---

† The delta function $\delta(t)$ becomes 1 in the algebraic inversion. This will be demonstrated at the conclusion of this section and again in a more rigorous manner in the development of Laplace transforms.

is associated with the time-dependent Green's function,

$$h(t) = \sum_{n=1}^{N} K_n e^{-\gamma_n t}.$$

In the instance of degenerate roots, we can expand within the degeneracy to give the C_m. Suppose in an Nth-order equation there is a degeneracy of order P, with $P < N$. To simplify the expression, we assume that the first P terms are degenerate and that there is only one degeneracy. Thus,

$$\sum_{n=1}^{N} a_n s^n H(s) = (s + \gamma_1)^P \prod_{n=(P+1)}^{N} (s + \gamma_n) H(s) = 1.$$

Solving for $H(s)$, we obtain

$$H(s) = \frac{1}{(s + \gamma_1)^P \prod\limits_{n=(P+1)}^{N} (s + \gamma_n)}.$$

This algebraic function can be expanded in a series of partial fractions:

$$H(s) = \sum_{m=1}^{P} \frac{C_m}{(s+\gamma)^m} + \sum_{n=(P+1)}^{N} K_n \left\{ \frac{1}{s+\gamma} \right\}.$$

The K_n are evaluated as before:

$$K_n = [(s + \gamma_n) H(s)]_{s=-\gamma_n}.$$

The C_m must be handled in steps. To begin,

$$C_P = [(s + \gamma_1)^P H(s)]_{s=-\gamma_1}.$$

If the expression inside the brackets is differentiated a step at a time, we see that

$$C_{P-1} = \left[\frac{d}{ds} \{(s + \gamma_1)^P H(s)\} \right]_{s=-\gamma_1}$$

and

$$C_{P-k} = \left[\frac{d^k}{ds^k} \{(s + \gamma_1)^P H(s)\} \right]_{s=-\gamma_1}.$$

The reader will notice that the first P eigenvalues have been taken as $-\gamma_1$. From our previous discussion, we associate

$$\frac{1}{(s + \gamma_1)^m}$$

with the time-dependent solution

$$\frac{(-\gamma_1 t)^m}{m!} e^{-\gamma_1 t}.$$

As a result, the expansion

$$H(s) = \sum_{m=1}^{P} \frac{C_m}{(s + \gamma_1)^m} + \sum_{n=(P+1)}^{N} \frac{K_n}{(s + \gamma_n)}$$

converts to the time-dependent form

$$h(t) = \sum_{m=1}^{P} C_m \frac{(-\gamma_m t)^m}{m!} e^{-\gamma_1 t} + \sum_{n=(P+1)}^{N} K_n e^{-\gamma_n t}.$$

This rough description indicates the one-to-one correspondence between the algebraic description of the problem and the differential equation. When the Laplace transform is introduced, we shall obtain the same results plus some additional advantages.

One of the great disadvantages of the present laborious method lies in the difficulties we encounter with the initial conditions. It is quite apparent that the modes $h_j(t)$ are the solutions to the homogeneous equation. We can demonstrate this fact in some simple cases and indicate simultaneously how the initial conditions appear in the solution.

We shall integrate the homogeneous equation directly, using $(0+)$ as the lower limit. The introduction of $(0+)$ will eliminate integrations of $\delta(t)$.

Consider the equation

$$\left(\frac{d}{dt} + \gamma\right) v_c(t) = 0,$$

with $v_c(0+)$ given as an initial condition. For a trial solution, take

$$v_c(t) = A h_1(t),$$

where $h(t)$ is defined by

$$\left(\frac{d}{dt} + \gamma\right) h_1(t) = \delta(t),$$

with

$$h_1(t) = 1 - \gamma \int_{(0+)}^{t} h_1(t')\, dt'.$$

Notice that the 1 in the preceding equation is $h_1(0+)$.

If we integrate the differential equation for $v_c(t)$ from $(0+)$ to t, we obtain

$$v_c(t) - v_c(0+) + \gamma \int_{(0+)}^{t} v_c(t')\, dt' = 0.$$

Substituting for $v_c(t)$ the trial solution $A h_1(t)$, we obtain

$$A h_1(t) + \gamma \int_{(0+)}^{t} A h_1(t')\, dt' = v_c(0+),$$

giving

$$\left\{ A h_1(t) + \gamma A \left[\frac{1 - h_1(t)}{\gamma}\right] \right\} = v_c(0+),$$

or

$$A = v_c(0+).$$

Finally

$$v_c(t) = v_c(0+) h_1(t).$$

By treating a homogeneous second-order equation (nondegenerate), we can further indicate the manner in which the initial conditions appear with the normal modes of the system. Equations of higher order become successively complex; thus, we shall then turn to the formal transform techniques, which reduce the difficulties of initial conditions.

Take as an example the equation

$$\left\{\frac{d^2}{dt^2} + (\gamma_1 + \gamma_2)\frac{d}{dt} + \gamma_1\gamma_2\right\}v_c(t) = 0,$$

with

$$\left(\frac{d}{dt} + \gamma_n\right)h_n(t) = \delta(t).$$

The integrals of $h_n(t')$ between $(0+)$ and t are

$$\int_{(0+)}^{t} h_n(t')\,dt' = \frac{1}{\gamma_n}\{h_n(0+) - h_n(t)\} = \frac{1}{\gamma_n}\{1 - h_n(t)\}.$$

We expand the response $v_c(t)$ as

$$v_c(t) = \sum_{n=1}^{2} A_n h_n(t).$$

Substituting into the differential equation and integrating, we obtain

$$\frac{d}{dt}v_c(t) - \left[\frac{dv_c}{dt}\right]_{(0+)} + (\gamma_1 + \gamma_2)\sum_{n=1}^{2} A_n h_n(t) - (\gamma_1 + \gamma_2)v_c(0+)$$
$$+ \gamma_1\gamma_2\left\{\frac{A_1}{\gamma_1}(1 - h_1(t)) + \frac{A_2}{\gamma_2}(1 - h_2(t))\right\} = 0.$$

The term dv_c/dt and $[dv_c/dt]_{(0+)} = v_c'(0+)$ have been retained in this form only for convenience. Integrating once more between $(0+)$ and t,

$$-v_c(0+) + A_1 + A_2 = \{v_c'(0+) + (\gamma_1 + \gamma_2)v_c(0+) - \gamma_2 A_1 - \gamma_1 A_2\}t.$$

The $h_j(t)$ dependence has dropped out. The preceding equation can hold only if the coefficients of like powers of t vanish; thus,

$$A_1 = \frac{\gamma_2 v_c(0+) + v_c'(0+)}{(\gamma_2 - \gamma_1)}$$

and

$$A_2 = \frac{\gamma_1 v_c(0+) + v_c'(0+)}{(\gamma_1 - \gamma_2)}.$$

This is the result that we would have obtained if we had taken the trial solution $\sum_{n=1}^{2} A_n h_n(t)$ and equated it and the derivative evaluated at $(0+)$ to the respective initial conditions. The demonstration given above, however, indicates that the complementary solution $v_c(t)$ can be expanded in the characteristic modes $h_n(t)$.

We can now write down the general solution to an inhomogeneous equation. If

$$H^{-1}(t)v(t) = g(t),$$

and if

$$H^{-1}(t)h(t - t') = \delta(t' - t),$$

we employ the modes $h_n(t)$, where

$$\left(\frac{d}{dt} + \gamma_n\right)h_n(t - t') = \delta(t' - t),$$

to form $h(t - t')$, the Green's function, and to form the complementary solution.

Assume a solution of the form

$$v(t) = \sum_{n=1}^{N} A_n h_n(t) + \int_0^t h(t - t')g(t')\,dt',$$

where

$$H^{-1}(t)\sum_{n=1}^{N} A_n h_n(t) = 0.$$

Then

$$H^{-1}(t)\int_0^t h(t - t')g(t')\,dt' = \int_0^t \delta(t' - t)g(t')\,dt' = g(t),$$

with

$$h(t - t') = \sum_{n=1}^{N} K_n h_n(t - t').$$

The K_n are again the Heaviside expansion coefficients:

$$K_n = \frac{1}{\prod_{m \neq n}(\gamma_m - \gamma_n)}.$$

It is useful at this point to list some of the defining differential equations, their algebraic inverses, and the corresponding time-dependent Green's functions which are linear combinations of the characteristic modes. These are given in Table 1.

TABLE 1

$H^{-1}(t)$	$H(s)$	$h(t)$
$\left\{\dfrac{d}{dt} + \gamma\right\}$	$\dfrac{1}{s + \gamma}$	$e^{-\gamma t}U(t)$
$\left\{\dfrac{d^2}{dt^2} + (\gamma_1 + \gamma_2)\dfrac{d}{dt} + \gamma_1\gamma_2\right\}$	$\dfrac{1}{(s + \gamma_1)(s + \gamma_2)}$	$\dfrac{1}{(\gamma_2 - \gamma_1)}\left\{e^{-\gamma_1 t} - e^{-\gamma_2 t}\right\}U(t)$
$\left(\dfrac{d}{dt} + \gamma\right)^2$	$\dfrac{1}{(s + \gamma)^2}$	$(1 + \gamma t)e^{-\gamma t}U(t)$
$\left\{1 + \gamma\displaystyle\int dt\right\}$	$\dfrac{s}{(s + \gamma)} = 1 - \dfrac{\gamma}{(s + \gamma)}$	$\left\{\delta(t) - \gamma e^{-\gamma t}U(t)\right\}$
$\left\{\dfrac{d}{dt} + (\gamma_1 + \gamma_2) + \gamma_1\gamma_2\displaystyle\int dt\right\}$	$\dfrac{s}{(s + \gamma_1)(s + \gamma_2)}$	$\dfrac{\gamma_1\gamma_2}{(\gamma_2 - \gamma_1)}\left\{-\dfrac{e^{-\gamma_1 t}}{\gamma_2} + \dfrac{e^{-\gamma_2 t}}{\gamma_1}\right\}U(t)$

Table 1 illustrates a significant fact, namely, that many functions $f(t)$ have a corresponding $H(s)$ and therefore a defining differential equation $H^{-1}(t)$. For instance, consider

$$f(t) = \sin \omega t = \frac{1}{2i} \{e^{i\omega t} - e^{-i\omega t}\}.$$

This function can be resolved into two characteristic modes, $e^{i\omega t}$ and $e^{-i\omega t}$. Thus, $f(t)$ must have a corresponding $F(s)$, given by

$$F(s) = \frac{1}{2i} \left\{ \frac{1}{(s - i\omega)} - \frac{1}{(s + i\omega)} \right\}$$

or

$$F(s) = \frac{\omega}{(s^2 + \omega^2)}.$$

In turn, we can go back one step and assume that $f(t)$ is the Green's function for the differential equation $F^{-1}(t)$, where

$$F^{-1}(t) = \frac{1}{\omega} \left\{ \frac{d^2}{dt^2} + \omega^2 \right\}.$$

To test this, we reverse the procedure, starting with

$$\frac{1}{\omega} \left\{ \frac{d^2}{dt^2} + \omega^2 \right\} f(t) = \delta(t).$$

Integrating twice, we obtain

$$f(t) = \omega \int_0^t U(t') \, dt' - \omega^2 \int_0^t dt' \int_0^{t'} dt'' f(t'').$$

By iteration,

$$f(t) = \omega t - \omega^3 \int_0^t dt' \int_0^{t'} dt'' \int_0^{t''} dt''' U(t''') + \cdots - .$$

Then

$$f(t) = \sum_{n=0}^{\infty} \frac{(-1)^n (\omega t)^{(2n+1)}}{(2n+1)!} U(t) = \sin \omega t \, U(t).$$

It is interesting to observe that because $\sin \omega t$ is not a single exponential, it cannot be obtained as a single characteristic mode. On the other hand, it is a Green's function and can be expressed as a linear combination of the two characteristic modes arising from

$$\left\{ \frac{d^2}{dt^2} + \omega^2 \right\} = \left(\frac{d}{dt} + i\omega \right) \left(\frac{d}{dt} - i\omega \right).$$

The familiar relation between sine and cosine also holds in the algebraic form; for instance,

$$\frac{1}{\omega} \frac{d}{dt} (\sin \omega t) = \cos \omega t$$

is expressed in the algebraic notation as $s \cdot F(s)$ or

$$\frac{s}{\omega}\left\{\frac{\omega}{(s^2 + \omega^2)}\right\}.$$

Then $\cos \omega t$ must be the Green's function for the equation

$$\left(\frac{s}{s^2 + \omega^2}\right)^{-1} = \left\{s + \frac{\omega^2}{s}\right\} \rightarrow \left\{\frac{d}{dt} + \omega^2 \int_0^t dt'\right\}g(t) = \delta(t).$$

Integrating between (0) and t, and iterating the solution, gives

$$g(t) = U(t) - \omega^2 \int_0^t dt' \int_0^{t'} dt'' U(t'') + \text{higher terms},$$

$$g(t) = \cos \omega t U(t).$$

When the differential operator was converted to an algebraic operator and inverted to give $H(s)$, we took the algebraic form of $\delta(t)$ to be 1. This assumption can be demonstrated by the defining relation in the time domain,

$$\delta(t) \Rightarrow \frac{d}{dt} U(t).$$

We find the algebraic form of $U(t)$ by noting that

$$U(t) = \lim_{\alpha \to 0} e^{-\alpha t} U(t).$$

Thus,

$$U(s) = \lim_{\alpha \to 0} \frac{1}{(s + \alpha)} = \frac{1}{s}.$$

Differentiating algebraically is a multiplication by s; therefore,

$$\delta(t) \xrightarrow[\substack{\text{transformed to} \\ \text{algebraic form}}]{} s \cdot \frac{1}{s} = 1.$$

To complete this section, we should indicate in simple fashion how an inhomogeneous differential equation can be solved by using the algebraic form of the differential operator *and* the excitation function.

Consider the following differential equation, which is intitially relaxed; that is, the function and its first derivative (in this case) are zero at $(0+)$.

$$\left\{\frac{d^2}{dt^2} + (\gamma_1 + \gamma_2)\frac{d}{dt} + \gamma_1\gamma_2\right\}v(t) = g_0 \sin \omega_0 t U(t).$$

As we have seen, the inhomogeneity can be written in terms of the algebraic inverse of its defining operator. In other words, $\sin \omega t$ expressed in the s domain becomes $\{\omega_0/(s^2 + \omega_0^2)\}$. Transforming the differential operator and the inhomogeneity, we obtain $V(s)$, the s-plane algebraic form of $v(t)$:

$$V(s) = \frac{1}{(s + \gamma_1)(s + \gamma_2)} \cdot \frac{g_0\omega_0}{(s^2 + \omega_0^2)}.$$

Expanding this expression in partial fractions gives

$$V(s) = g_0\omega_0\left\{\frac{\dfrac{1}{(\gamma_2 - \gamma_1)(\gamma_1^2 + \omega_0^2)}}{(s + \gamma_1)} + \frac{\dfrac{1}{(\gamma_1 - \gamma_2)(\gamma_2^2 + \omega_0^2)}}{(s + \gamma_2)}\right.$$

$$\left. + \frac{\dfrac{1}{(\gamma_1 - i\omega_0)(\gamma_2 - i\omega_0)(-2i\omega_0)}}{(s + i\omega_0)} + \frac{\dfrac{1}{(\gamma_1 + i\omega_0)(\gamma_2 + i\omega_0)(2i\omega_0)}}{(s - i\omega_0)}\right\}.$$

The first two terms bring in the transient solution in terms of the characteristic modes of the differential equation. The second two terms provide the steady-state response in terms of the characteristic modes of $\sin \omega_0 t$. Inverting to the time domain, we can write down the total solution.

$$v(t) = g_0\omega_0\left\{\frac{e^{-\gamma_1 t}}{(\gamma_2 - \gamma_1)(\gamma_1^2 + \omega_0^2)} + \frac{e^{-\gamma_2 t}}{(\gamma_1 - \gamma_2)(\gamma_2^2 + \omega_0^2)}\right.$$

$$\left. + \frac{e^{i\omega_0 t}}{2i\omega_0(\gamma_1 + i\omega_0)(\gamma_2 + i\omega_0)} + \frac{e^{-i\omega_0 t}}{(-2i\omega_0)(\gamma_1 - i\omega_0)(\gamma_2 - i\omega_0)}\right\}U(t).$$

In closing, it is well to remark that the complex frequencies of the characteristic modes appear as poles in the complex s plane. Later, the reader will find the characteristics of a problem adequately described by listing the poles and by listing the zeros that give information about derivatives of the excitation and about the initial conditions. Our last example indicated two eigensolutions, γ_1 and γ_2, for the linear operator, and two characterstic modes, $\pm i\omega_0$, for the excitation. Thus, the representation of $V(s)$ in the s plane is provided by four poles at $-\gamma_1$, $-\gamma_2$, $i\omega_0$, and $-i\omega_0$. (See Fig. 15.) Here s has been written as the complex variable $s = \sigma + i\omega$, where σ is the real part of s and ω is the imaginary part. The poles $-\gamma_1$ and $-\gamma_2$ have been shown on the real axis. This is not necessary, since the γ could be complex. In general, passive physical systems give linear operators with real-positive coefficients, and if a root is complex, it always occurs with its complex conjugate. In other words, complex roots invariably appear in conjugate pairs.

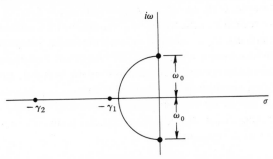

FIG. 15.   The complex s-plane diagram for an operator with characteristic frequencies γ_1 and γ_2 subjected to a sinusoidal excitation for which the frequency times 2π is ω_0. Poles are indicated by solid dots.

MATRICES

From the introductory remarks concerning circuits, we observe that networks of more than one loop will involve simultaneous linear equations in several unknowns.

For instance, in the last example of the first section, the two-loop circuit of Fig. 11 was described by two simultaneous integro-differential equations in two unknowns. If we had differentiated each of these equations once, we would have had

$$\frac{d}{dt}\, e_{11}(t) = L_{11}\frac{d^2 i_1}{dt^2} + \frac{i_1}{C_{12}} - \frac{i_1}{C_{12}}$$

and

$$0 = -\frac{i_1}{C_{12}} + \frac{i_2}{C_{12}} + R_{22}\frac{di_2}{dt}.$$

According to the remarks of the preceding section, we can write these equations operationally as

$$sE_{11}(s) = L_{11}s^2 I_1 + \frac{I_2}{C_{12}} - \frac{I_2}{C_{12}}$$

and

$$0 = -\frac{I_1}{C_{12}} + \frac{I_2}{C_{12}} + R_{22}sI_2.$$

We shall observe later that this particular operational form assumes that the initial values $i_j(0+)$ and $q_j(0+)$ are zero. This set of equations can be written as two simultaneous algebraic equations for I_1 and I_2, where the coefficients are functions of s. To assume some generality, let x_j represent the unknown terms; let y_k represent the driving functions (these will be polynomials in s); and represent the s-dependent coefficients as $A_{mn}(s)$. In this notation our set of equations assumes the form

$$A_{11}(s)x_1(s) + A_{12}(s)x_2(s) = y_1(s)$$

and

$$A_{21}(s)x_1(s) + A_{22}(s)x_2(s) = y_2(s).$$

Our special example, then, has $\gamma_1 = sE_{11}(s)$, and $A_{11} = L_{11}s^2 + 1/C_{12}$; etc.

Generally, if we regard an ordered set of N equations in N unknowns, the manipulation of these equations to a solution is systematically accomplished by matrix methods. In a sense, the matrix algebra achieves its greatest practical value from the concise nature of the notation and from the systematic method. Both formal proofs and practical problems are managed with greater ease.

Our purpose is served by outlining the method and notation to be used. For further information, the reader should consult special texts covering this subject.

Consider the set of N equations

$$\sum_{j=1}^{N} A_{kj}x_j = y_k;$$

or

$$A_{11}x_1 + A_{12}x_2 + A_{13}x_3 + \cdots + A_{1N}x_N = y_1,$$
$$A_{21}x_1 + A_{22}x_2 + A_{23}x_3 + \cdots + A_{2N}x_N = y_2,$$
$$A_{31}x_1 + A_{32}x_2 + A_{33}x_3 + \cdots + A_{3N}x_N = y_3,$$
$$\vdots$$
$$A_{N1}x_1 + A_{N2}x_2 + A_{N3}x_3 + \cdots + A_{NN}x_N = y_N.$$

The coefficients A_{jk} may be numbers, linear operators (such as integrals and derivatives), functions of a parameter (such as s); etc. We specify only that the A_{lm} are independent of the x_k. This set of equations can be represented in terms of the matrices $\mathbb{A}$, $\mathbf{x}$, and $\mathbf{y}$. We include the column vectors $\mathbf{x}$ and $\mathbf{y}$ in that class of mathematical objects denoted as matrices. In the expanded form, the set of equations appears as:

$$\begin{pmatrix} A_{11} & A_{12} & A_{13} & \cdots & A_{1N} \\ A_{21} & A_{22} & \cdots & \cdots & A_{2N} \\ A_{31} & \cdots & \cdots & \cdots & \cdots \\ \vdots & & & & \\ A_{N1} & A_{N2} & A_{N3} & \cdots & A_{NN} \end{pmatrix} \begin{bmatrix} x_1 \\ x_2 \\ x_3 \\ \vdots \\ x_N \end{bmatrix} = \begin{bmatrix} y_1 \\ y_2 \\ y_3 \\ \vdots \\ y_N \end{bmatrix}.$$

This equation can be written symbolically as

$$\mathbb{A} \cdot \mathbf{x} = \mathbf{y},$$

where

$$\mathbb{A} = \begin{pmatrix} A_{11} & A_{12} & A_{13} & \cdots & A_{1N} \\ A_{21} & A_{23} & \cdots & \cdots & A_{2N} \\ A_{31} & \cdots & \cdots & \cdots & \cdots \\ & & & & \vdots \\ A_{N1} & A_{N2} & \cdots & \cdots & A_{NN} \end{pmatrix}$$

and

$$\mathbf{x} = \begin{bmatrix} x_1 \\ x_2 \\ x_3 \\ \vdots \\ x_N \end{bmatrix}, \qquad \mathbf{y} = \begin{bmatrix} y_1 \\ y_2 \\ y_3 \\ \vdots \\ y_N \end{bmatrix}.$$

Inner products are taken by multiplying a column on the right by a row in the array appearing on the left-hand side of the product. The elements of a vector $\mathbf{y}$ formed from the inner product of a vector $\mathbf{x}$ and the matrix $\mathbb{A}$ are

$$y_k = \sum_{m=1}^{N} A_{km} x_m.$$

The subscripts of the element A_{km} indicate the position of A_{km} in the $N \times N$ array. A_{km} is in the kth row and mth column.

The inner product of two matrices $\mathbb{A}$ and $\mathbb{B}$ has elements that are formed by multiplying a column in the right matrix by a row in the left matrix. In other words, if

$$\mathbb{A} \cdot \mathbb{B} = \mathbb{C},$$

then

$$\sum_{m=1}^{N} A_{km} B_{mn} = C_{kn}.$$

if $\mathbb{M}$ is a transformation matrix, a vector $\mathbf{x}$ is transformed to $\mathbf{x}'$ according to

$$\mathbf{x}' = \mathbb{M} \cdot \mathbf{x}$$

or

$$x'_l = \sum_{n=1}^{N} M_{ln}x_n.$$

A matrix $\mathbb{A}$ is transformed by $\mathbb{M}$ according to the relation

$$\mathbb{M}^\dagger \cdot \mathbb{A} \cdot \mathbb{M} = \mathbb{A}'$$

where $\mathbb{M}^\dagger$ is the complex conjugate of the transpose of $\mathbb{M}$. The tranpose of $\mathbb{M}$ is formed by interchanging rows and columns in $\mathbb{M}$. In other words, the *lm* element of the matrix becomes the *ml* element of the tranpose. We designate the transpose by a tilde over the symbol. Thus, the tranpose of $\mathbb{M}$ is written $\mathbb{M}$, where the elements of $\mathbb{M}$ are written

$$\tilde{M}_{ml} = M_{lm}.$$

The vector has been written as a single column; thus, the tranpose of a column vector is a row vector. If

$$\mathbf{x} = \begin{bmatrix} x_1 \\ x_2 \\ \vdots \\ x_N \end{bmatrix},$$

then

$$\tilde{\mathbf{x}} = [x_1, x_2, \cdots, x_N].$$

The adjoint matrix, which we denoted as $\mathbb{M}^\dagger$, is the complex conjugate of the transpose of $\mathbb{M}$. The reader is reminded that our equations will generally involve the complex variable s; therefore, the arrays (vectors and matrices) will have complex elements. Considering the elements of $\mathbb{M}^\dagger$, we can write

$$M_{ml}^\dagger = (\tilde{M}_{ml})^* = M_{lm}^*.$$

The inner product between two vectors is defined as the product of an adjoint vector from the left and a vector from the right. This definition is useful because the inner product of a vector with itself is a real-positive number. The inner product of $\mathbf{x}$ and $\mathbf{y}$ is written

$$\mathbf{x}^\dagger \cdot \mathbf{y} = (\tilde{\mathbf{x}})^* \cdot \mathbf{y}$$

$$= [x_1^*, x_2^*, \cdots, x_N^*] \begin{bmatrix} y_1 \\ y_2 \\ \vdots \\ y_N \end{bmatrix}$$

and

$$\mathbf{x}^\dagger \cdot \mathbf{y} = x_1^* y_1 + x_2^* y_2 + \cdots + x_N^* y_N = \sum_{j=1}^{N} x_j^* y_j.$$

The magnitude squared of a vector is then $\mathbf{x}^\dagger \cdot \mathbf{x}$. A transformation that maintains the magnitude of a vector invariant is known as a *unitary* transformation. The most common example of a unitary transformation in real variables is a simple rotation. In this case, the vector $\mathbf{x}$ changes direction but not magnitude. Consider

$$\mathbf{x}' = \mathbb{M} \cdot \mathbf{x};$$

then

$$\mathbf{x}'^\dagger = \mathbf{x}^\dagger \cdot \mathsf{M}^\dagger$$

and

$$\mathbf{x}'^\dagger \cdot \mathbf{x}' = \mathbf{x}^\dagger \cdot \{\mathsf{M}^\dagger \cdot \mathsf{M}\} \cdot \mathbf{x}.$$

If the magnitude of the vector is invariant under the transformation, then

$$\mathbf{x}'^\dagger \cdot \mathbf{x}' = \mathbf{x}^\dagger \cdot \mathbf{x}$$

and

$$\mathsf{M}^\dagger \cdot \mathsf{M} = \mathbb{I}.$$

The matrix $\mathbb{I}$ is the unit matrix or identity transformation. Its elements are $+1$ on the diagonal and zero off the diagonal:

$$\mathbb{I} = \begin{pmatrix} 1 & 0 & 0 & 0 & \cdots & 0 \\ 0 & 1 & 0 & 0 & & \\ 0 & 0 & 1 & 0 & \cdots & 0 \\ \vdots & & & & & \\ 0 & 0 & 0 & \cdots & \cdots & 1 \end{pmatrix}.$$

$$\mathbb{I}_{lm} = \delta_{lm} = 1, \quad \text{if } l = m;$$
$$= 0, \quad \text{if } l \neq m.$$

The application of $\mathbb{I}$ in an inner product leaves the matrix unchanged:

$$\mathbb{I} \cdot \mathbf{x} = \mathbf{x}$$

and

$$\mathbb{I}^\dagger \cdot \mathbb{A} \cdot \mathbb{I} = \mathbb{A}, \quad (\mathbb{I}^\dagger = \mathbb{I}).$$

The magnitude of a square matrix is equal to the determinant of the matrix. If the magnitude is not zero, an inverse can be defined:

$$|\mathsf{M}| = \det \mathsf{M}.$$

If

$$|\mathsf{M}| \neq 0,$$

then

$$\mathsf{M}^{-1} \cdot \mathsf{M} = \mathbb{I}.$$

From the definition of the determinant, we can define the elements of M^{-1}, which are designated with a prime to indicate the inverse. The elements of M^{-1} are represented as M'_{lm}, where

$$M'_{jk} = \frac{(-1)^{j+k} \, \text{minor } M_{kj}}{|\mathsf{M}|}.$$

We observe that a unitary matrix has the special property that the adjoint of the matrix is equal to the inverse of the matrix:

$$\mathsf{M}^\dagger \cdot \mathsf{M} = \mathbb{I} \quad \text{(unitary)},$$
$$\mathsf{M}^{-1} \cdot \mathsf{M} = \mathbb{I} \quad \text{(definition of } M^{-1});$$

then

$$M^\dagger = \mathbb{M}^{-1} \qquad \text{(unitary)}.$$

Real matrices that are unitary are called *orthogonal matrices*. For these orthogonal transformations or rotations, as they are sometimes called, $\tilde{\mathbb{M}} = \mathbb{M}^{-1}$. Two matrices are summed by adding like elements. Consider

$$\mathbb{A} + \mathbb{B} = \mathbb{C};$$

then

$$A_{jk} + B_{jk} = C_{jk}.$$

When we discuss m-derived filters in the latter portion of the section on circuits, a transformation $\mathbb{M}$ will be employed which has magnitude 1, but is not unitary. The unitary transformation retains the magnitude of the matrix. In addition, it preserves the trace (or sum of the diagonal elements) and all the other coefficients of the λ^n in the characteristic polynomial

$$|\mathbb{A} - \lambda \mathbb{I}| = 0.$$

As we shall observe later, the matrix for "m-deriving" a filter matrix must maintain the magnitude of the filter matrix invariant, but m-deriving is different from the unitary operation in that it must maintain the symmetry properties of the matrix. It will be demonstrated that the operation which preserves the symmetry properties of the matrix preserves the geometric symmetry of the circuits. This means that if we begin with a symmetric T circuit, the transformed circuit will be a symmetric T. The details of this very special transformation will be left to the section that covers filter circuits.

FOURIER SERIES AND THE FOURIER TRANSFORM

The Fourier Series

The conventional expansion of an analytic function $f(z)$ is the Taylor's series. We expand $f(z)$ about z_0 according to

$$f(z) = \sum_{n=0}^{\infty} \frac{1}{n!} \left[\frac{d^n f}{dz^n} \right]_{z_0} (z - z_0)^n.$$

This series is quite restricted in that $f(z)$ must possess derivatives to all orders at the point z_0. Further, the convergence of the series depends upon the position of all the singularities in the complex z plane. The singular point nearest to z_0 determines the radius of convergence.

In our earlier discussion of the linear differential equation with constant coefficients, we observed that solutions could be expanded in the interval from 0 to ∞ on the real t axis in terms of the characteristic modes of the equation. When the interval of definition of the function $f(t)$ is finite or periodic, the function can be expanded in terms of the characteristic modes or eigenvectors of the operator $\{(d^2/dt^2)\} + \omega^2\}$, subject to the specific boundary conditions of the problem. Previously we did not concern ourselves unduly with boundary conditions. This had certain inherent disadvantages in that functions diverging for large t were not specifically excluded.

The Fourier series is more general than one might think if only eigenfunctions of the type $e^{\pm i\omega t}$ are considered. We shall profit from a brief glance at the general problem of complete orthogonal sets. Modern practice in circuit problems is not concerned solely with exponential sets. Often, other sets of functions are more useful in a specific problem.

To generate a set of functions, we consider solutions ϕ_n to the differential equation

$$\frac{d}{dz}\left[p(z)\frac{d}{dz}\phi_n(z)\right] + q(z)\phi_n(z) - \lambda_n w(z)\phi_n(z) = 0.$$

The solutions $\phi_k(z)$ are subject to the rigid boundary condition (on the real axis x):

$$\left[p(x)\phi_n(x)\frac{d\phi_m^*(x)}{dx}\right]_{\substack{x=a \\ x=b}} = \left[p(x)\phi_m^*(x)\frac{d\phi_n(x)}{dx}\right]_{\substack{x=a \\ x=b}}$$

Here the interval is $a \leqslant x \leqslant b$.

Under these conditions, the eigensolution $\phi_n(x)$ can form a complete orthogonal set in the interval $a \leqslant x \leqslant b$. The term *completeness* implies that any function $f(x)$ can be approximated in the mean if the function satisfies the Dirichlet conditions:

1. $f(x)$ has at most a finite number of discontinuities in the interval $a \leqslant x \leqslant b$.
2. $f(x)$ has a finite number of maxima and minima in the periodic interval.
3. The integral $\displaystyle\int_a^b |f(x)|^2 w(x)\, dx$ is finite. This is known as quadratic integrability.

We initiate the approximation by a sequence and an error function $\varepsilon_N(x)$:

$$f(x) = \sum_{n=1}^{N} a_n \phi_n(x) + \varepsilon_N(x).$$

Approximation in the mean implies that one-half the series evaluated at (x_0+), plus one-half the series evaluated at (x_0-), equals the value of the function at x_0.

Completeness is achieved if the quadratic integral of the function minus the quadratic integral of the series approaches zero as N approaches infinity. Define the integral $\mathcal{J}_N$ by the integral of $|\varepsilon_N|^2$:

$$\lim_{N\to\infty} \mathcal{J}_N = \lim_{N\to\infty} \int_a^b |\varepsilon_N(x)|^2 w(x)\, dx \xrightarrow[\text{if complete}]{} 0.$$

The expansion coefficients, or Fourier coefficients a_k, are chosen by minimizing $\mathcal{J}_N$ with respect to variations in a_k. To accomplish this, we set

$$\frac{\partial \mathcal{J}_N}{\partial a_m^*} = 0$$

and

$$\frac{\partial \mathcal{J}_N}{\partial a_l} = 0.$$

Working these derivatives out in detail from the original expression for $\mathcal{J}_N$ gives

$$a_m = \int_a^b \phi_m^*(x) f(x) w(x)\, dx$$

and

$$a_l^* = \int_a^b f^*(x)\phi_l(x)w(x)\,dx.$$

Substituting these values into $\mathscr{I}_N$, we obtain Parseval's relation, which must be satisfied if the $\phi_n(x)$ form a complete set; this is

$$\int_a^b |f(x)|^2 w(x)\,dx = \sum_{\text{all } n} |a_n|^2.$$

The $\phi_n(x)$ can be shown to be orthogonal. The functions can also be normalized such that the inner product of a function with itself is 1;

$$\int_a^b \phi_k^*(x)\phi_m(x)w(x)\,dx = \delta_{km},$$

where δ_{km} is called the *Kronecker delta function*. It has the values 1 if $k = m$; and 0 if $k \neq m$.

The exponential series is developed from the operator

$$\left\{\frac{d^2}{dt^2} + \omega^2\right\} \quad \text{or} \quad \left\{\frac{d^2}{dx^2} + m^2\right\}.$$

This is a special case in which $p(x) = 1$, $q(x) = 0$, $w(x) = $ the weight function $= 1$, and $\lambda = -\omega^2$, or m^2. In this, operator m is not specified. For a given m, we have seen that the characteristic modes or eigenvectors are e^{imx} and e^{-imx}. The function will be assumed to be periodic in the interval $-\pi \leqslant x \leqslant \pi$. The periodic boundary condition is less restricted and only requires that,

$$\left[e^{-imx}\frac{d}{dx}e^{inx}\right]_\pi = \left[e^{-imx}\frac{d}{dx}e^{inx}\right]_{-\pi}.$$

This equation implies, then, that

$$in\, e^{i(n-m)\pi} = in\, e^{-i(n-m)\pi}$$

and that m and n are integers. We can then represent a function $f(x)$ that satisfies the Dirichlet conditions and which is periodic in the interval 2π, or $-\pi \leqslant x \leqslant \pi$, as

$$f(x) = \frac{1}{\sqrt{2\pi}} \sum_{m=-\infty}^{\infty} a_m e^{imx},$$

with

$$a_m = \frac{1}{\sqrt{2\pi}} \int_{-\pi}^{\pi} f(y)\, e^{-imy}\, dy$$

and

$$\frac{1}{2\pi}\int_{-\pi}^{\pi} e^{imx}\, e^{-inx}\, dx = \delta_{mn}.$$

If $f(x)$ is real,

$$a_k = a_{-k}^*.$$

Sometimes a sine and cosine series is desired to accentuate the parity of the function. The Fourier series in sines and cosines is

$$f(x) = \frac{1}{\sqrt{2\pi}} \sum_{n=0}^{\infty} \{A_n \cos nx + B_n \sin nx\},$$

where the A_j and B_k are real if $f(x)$ is real:

$$A_0 = \frac{1}{\sqrt{2\pi}} \int_{-\pi}^{\pi} f(x)\, dx = a_0,$$

$$A_k = a_k + a_k^* = \sqrt{\frac{2}{\pi}} \int_{-\pi}^{\pi} f(x) \cos kx\, dx,$$

$$B_l = i(a_l - a_l^*) = \sqrt{\frac{2}{\pi}} \int_{-\pi}^{\pi} f(x) \sin lx\, dx.$$

One other form is sometimes useful. This series includes one of the coefficients as a phase shift:

$$f(x) = \frac{A_0}{\sqrt{2\pi}} + \frac{1}{\sqrt{2\pi}} \sum_{n=1}^{\infty} C_n \cos(nx - \Phi_n),$$

where

$$C_n = \sqrt{A_n^2 + B_n^2}$$

and

$$\Phi_n = \tan^{-1} \frac{B_n}{A_n}.$$

The periodic boundary condition allows periodic repetitions of $f(x)$ when the series is evaluated for $x < -\pi$ and $\pi < x$.

We have claimed that the Fourier series approximates certain functions in the mean. This implies that the series does not converge uniformly at discontinuities in $f(x)$. In fact, the series exhibits a nonphysical overshoot and undershoot at the point of the discontinuity. Mathematically, however, the mean value of the series at the discontinuity will have the appropriate value. This deviation at the discontinuity is called *Gibb's phenomenon*. A particularly simple example of this phenomenon is found in the series expansion of the periodic gate function:

$$g(x) = +1, \qquad \text{for} \quad 0 < x < \pi,$$

$$g(x) = 0, \qquad \text{for} \quad -\pi < x < 0,$$

where†

$$g(x_0) = \tfrac{1}{2}\{g(x_0+) + g(x_0-)\}.$$

See Fig. 16.

---

† The terms $(x+)$ and $(x-)$ have been employed repeatedly. The reader is reminded that $(x_0+) = \lim_{\Delta x \to 0} \{x_0 + |\Delta x|\}$ and $(x_0-) = \lim_{\Delta x \to 0} \{x_0 - |\Delta x|\}$.

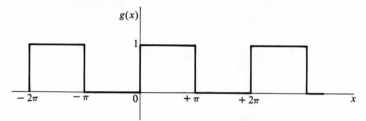

FIG. 16.   A periodic square wave.

In this example,

$$a_m = \frac{1}{\sqrt{2\pi}} \int_0^\pi e^{-imy}\, dy$$

and

$$g(x) = \sum_{m=-\infty}^{\infty} \left\{ \frac{\sin(m\pi/2)}{m\pi} \right\} e^{im[x-(\pi/2)]}.$$

All coefficients for even m vanish except for $m = 0$. The coefficients for odd m alternate in sign. The behavior of the series at the discontinuity (say, $x = 0$) can be studied by examining a finite sequence of terms and observing the behavior as the number of terms is allowed to increase to arbitrarily large values. Call the sequence of the first $(N + 1)$ terms s_N; then combining positive and negative exponentials,

$$s_N = \frac{1}{2} + \frac{2}{\pi} \sum_{n=0}^{N} \frac{\sin[(2n+1)x]}{(2n+1)}.$$

Writing this as an integral from zero to x,

$$s_N = \frac{1}{2} + \frac{1}{\pi} \int_0^x \sum_{n=0}^{N} \{ e^{i(2n+1)y} + e^{-i(2n+1)y} \}\, dy.$$

By factoring e^{iy} from each term, we can sum the series, using the relation for a geometric sequence:

$$\sum_{n=0}^{N} \xi^n = \frac{[\xi^{N+1} - 1]}{[\xi - 1]}.$$

Then

$$s_N = \frac{1}{2} + \frac{1}{\pi} \int_0^x \frac{2 \cos(N+1)y \, \sin(N+1)y}{\sin y}\, dy.$$

To examine this function near the discontinuity, we let x approach zero. This confines y to a very small interval. Then, $\sin y \to y$.

Define a new variable $\zeta = 2(N + 1)y$ and

$$s_N \xrightarrow[\text{small } x]{} \frac{1}{2} + \frac{1}{\pi} \int_0^{2(N+1)x} \frac{\sin \zeta}{\zeta}\, d\zeta.$$

A plot of s_N for various values of $x(x \text{ small})$ is shown in Fig. 17.

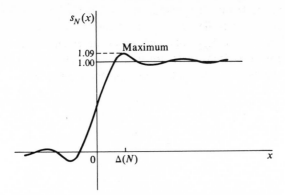

FIG. 17.   The Fourier sequence S_N at a discontinuity.

For a given N, the maximum of s_N appears for $x = \Delta(N)$; i.e.,

$$s_N(\max) \xrightarrow[x \text{ small}]{} \frac{1}{2} + \frac{1}{\pi} \int_0^{2(N+1)\Delta(N)} \frac{\sin \zeta}{\zeta} \, d\zeta = 1.09.$$

Therefore, if we allow N to become arbitrarily large in such a manner that $2(N + 1) \Delta(N)$ is constant [this determines the rate at which $\Delta(N) \to 0$], we see that the value of the function does not approach the value 1 just to the right of the discontinuity, but rather maintains the value 1.09.

If, on the other hand, we examine $s_N(0+)$, evaluated in the manner described above, this evaluation occurs for $2(N + 1)x \to \infty$, and

$$s_N \xrightarrow[\Delta(N) < x]{} \frac{1}{2} + \frac{1}{\pi} \left(\frac{\pi}{2} \right) = 1.$$

The overshoot and undershoot of the series approximation are illustrated in Fig. 18.

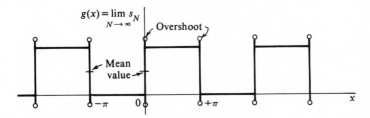

FIG. 18.   The approximation in the mean of a periodic square wave by a Fourier series.

The time-dependent functions are produced by allowing

$$x = \omega_0 t,$$

where ω_0 is the fundamental frequency of the distribution. Then the time-dependent expansion is

$$f(t) = \frac{1}{\sqrt{2\pi}} \sum_{n=-\infty}^{\infty} a_n e^{in\omega_0 t}.$$

A spectrum of the frequency components is provided by a tabulation of the a_n. In the terminology of our earlier discussion of the characteristic modes of a linear differential equation, we see, then, that each $n\omega_0$ is an eigenfrequency. Because of the boundary conditions, these frequencies form an infinite set of poles formed at discrete points on the imaginary axis of the complex s plane. See Fig. 19.

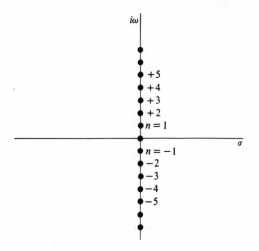

FIG. 19.   The s-plane plot of the poles of the Fourier series.

The amplitudes of the eigenfunctions $e^{in\omega t}$ can be obtained from the Fourier coefficients a_n. To illustrate these, consider the periodic gate just discussed. The series had the form

$$g(t) = \frac{1}{\sqrt{2\pi}} \sum_{n=-\infty}^{\infty} \sqrt{\frac{2}{\pi}} \left(\frac{\sin[n\pi/2]}{n} \right) e^{in[\omega_0 t - (\pi/2)]},$$

where $\omega_0 T/2 = \pi$, and $\omega_0 = 2\pi/T$. Also, we used the form

$$g(t) = \frac{1}{2} + \frac{2}{\pi} \sum_{n=1}^{\infty} \frac{\sin(2n+1)\omega_0 t}{2n+1}.$$

The magnitudes of the amplitudes are plotted in Fig. 20.

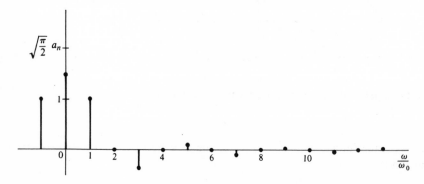

FIG. 20.   Spectrum of the amplitudes of the Fourier series for the periodic square wave of FIG. 18.

The Fourier Integral

In the preceding section, a function periodic in t was expanded in the interval $-\pi/\omega_0 \leqslant t \leqslant \pi/\omega_0$, or $-T/2 \leqslant t \leqslant T/2$. The resultant series is composed of eigenfrequencies spaced at regular intervals on the imaginary axis of the s plane. The separation between points specifying the characteristic modes is $\omega_0 = 2\pi/T$. As the width of the interval in the time domain increases, i.e., as T increases, the poles on the imaginary axis in the s plane get closer together. Thus, in the limit as the interval on the real t axis becomes arbitrarily large, the distribution of poles on the imaginary axis in the s plane becomes sufficiently dense to form a continous line. See Fig. 21.

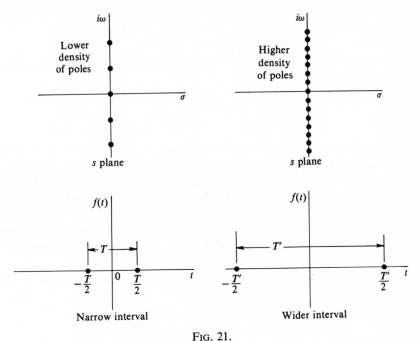

FIG. 21.

Thus, as $T \to \infty$ or $\omega_0 \to 0$ and the spacing between characteristic modes or eigenfrequencies decreases, the line spectrum of the a_n becomes a continuous function of the variable ω.

Starting with

$$f(t) = \frac{1}{\sqrt{2\pi}} \sum_{n=-\infty}^{\infty} a_n \, e^{in\omega t},$$

we can write

$$a_n = \frac{\omega}{\sqrt{2\pi}} \int_{-\pi/\omega}^{\pi/\omega} f(t) \, e^{-in\omega t} \, dt.$$

Since $\pi/\omega = T/2$,

$$a_n = \frac{\sqrt{2\pi}}{T} \int_{-T/2}^{T/2} f(t) \, e^{-in\omega t} \, dt.$$

In the limit as T becomes arbitrarily large,

$$\Delta\omega \doteq (n+1)\omega - n\omega = \omega = \frac{2\pi}{T}$$

and

$$\lim_{T\to\infty} \frac{2\pi}{T} \to d\omega.$$

Then the sum over n becomes an integral over ω between the limits Ω and $-\Omega$, with the limit as $\Omega \to \infty$ taken last. Substituting for a_n, and converting the sum,

$$f(t) = \lim_{\Omega\to\infty} \lim_{T/2\to\infty} \frac{1}{2\pi} \int_{-\Omega}^{\Omega} d\omega\, e^{i\omega t} \left\{ \int_{-T/2}^{T/2} f(t')\, e^{-i\omega t'}\, dt' \right\}.$$

The order of the limits is essential. If we take the limit $\Omega \to \infty$ first, we encounter the undefined integral

$$I = \frac{1}{2\pi} \int_{-\infty}^{\infty} e^{-i\omega(t'-t)}\, d\omega = \delta(t'-t).$$

If we regard the position of I in the integral for $f(t)$, we see that it is just the delta function $\delta(t'-t)$ that was discussed earlier. During the initial discussion of this function, we remarked that it is defined inside an integral. Thus, when it is introduced outside an integral, one must keep in mind the fact that invariably an integration must be imposed and a reordering of the improper change of taking limits must take place. In other words, the appearance of this improper function in an integral is acceptable because, in this situation, the order of taking limits can be inverted to give a proper integral.

Returning to the integral expression for $f(t)$, we first take the limit as $T \to \infty$, defining the Fourier transform of $f(t)$, as

$$a(\omega) = \mathscr{F}[f(t')] = \frac{1}{\sqrt{2\pi}} \int_{-\infty}^{\infty} f(t')\, e^{-i\omega t'}\, dt'.$$

Thus

$$f(t) = \lim_{\Omega\to\infty} \frac{1}{\sqrt{2\pi}} \int_{-\Omega}^{\Omega} a(\omega)\, e^{i\omega t}\, d\omega = \frac{1}{\sqrt{2\pi}} \int_{-\infty}^{\infty} a(\omega)\, e^{i\omega t}\, d\omega.$$

We designate this last integral as the *inverse* Fourier transform of $a(\omega)$; i.e.,

$$f(t) = \mathscr{F}^{-1}[a(\omega)] = \mathscr{F}^{-1}[\mathscr{F}[f(t)]].$$

To illustrate the use of $\mathscr{F}[f(t)]$, regard a unit-gate function defined in the infinite interval:

$$g(t) = +1, \quad \text{for } 0 < x < T;$$

and

$$g(t) = 0, \quad \text{for } x < 0 \text{ and } T < x.$$

See Fig. 22.

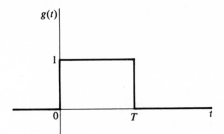

FIG. 22.   A unit-gate function.

For this example,

$$a(\omega) = \mathscr{F}[g(t)] = \frac{1}{\sqrt{2\pi}} \int_0^T e^{i\omega t'}\, dt' = \sqrt{\frac{2}{\pi}} \frac{\sin \omega T/2}{\omega}\, e^{-(i\omega T/2)}.$$

Thus

$$|a(\omega)| = \sqrt{\frac{2}{\pi}} \frac{|\sin \omega T/2|}{|\omega|}.$$

See Fig. 23.

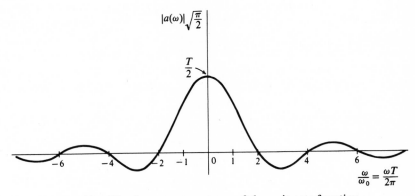

FIG. 23.   The frequency spectrum of the unit-gate function.

An important characteristic of frequency spectra appears here. The bandwidth of the central portion of the frequency spectrum is inversely proportional to the pulse width of the gate. Therefore, to achieve a wide time pulse a very narrow bandwidth of the frequency spectrum is required. Thus, a pulse of infinite time duration would require a zero bandwidth, which indicates a monochromatic frequency spectrum.

In closing, we should note that the Fourier transform of $f(t)$ can be separated into an even and an odd component, $a_E(\omega)$ and $a_O(\omega)$. By expanding the exponential

$$\mathscr{F}[f(t)] = a_E(\omega) + a_O(\omega) = \frac{1}{\sqrt{2\pi}} \int_{-\infty}^{\infty} f(t)\{\cos \omega t - i \sin \omega t\}\, dt,$$

where

$$a_E(\omega) = \frac{1}{\sqrt{2\pi}} \int_{-\infty}^{\infty} f(t) \cos \omega t\, dt = \sqrt{\frac{2}{\pi}} \int_0^{\infty} f_E(t) \cos \omega t\, dt$$

and

$$a_0(\omega) = \frac{-i}{\sqrt{2\pi}} \int_{-\infty}^{\infty} f(t) \sin \omega t \, dt = -i\sqrt{\frac{2}{\pi}} \int_{0}^{\infty} f_0(t) \sin \omega t \, dt.$$

The function $f(t)$ has been split into an even part $f_E(t)$ and an odd part $f_0(t)$ in the last two integrals.[†] This can be done because the integral $f_E(t) \sin \omega t$ vanishes and the integral of $f_0(t) \cos \omega t$ vanishes.

The Fourier transform has as its main advantage the fact that it can be employed to span the interval from $-\infty$ to $+\infty$. The Laplace transform is somewhat more convenient, although it is confined to functions that are zero for negative t.

When a system $H^{-1}(t)$ is subjected to an excitation $e(t)$, a response $v(t)$ is produced:

$$H^{-1}(t)v(t) = e(t).$$

If $H^{-1}(t)$ is a linear integral-differential operator,[††] we can employ our present technique to write $H^{-1}(t)$ as a factored, repeated product of first-order operators. If $H^{-1}(t)$ is of order N, then there are N characteristic modes for the operator $H^{-1}(t)$.

A simple differential operator will be used for convenience

$$H^{-1}(t)v_n(t) = \prod_{m=1}^{N} \left(\frac{d}{dt} + \gamma_m\right) v_n(t) = e_n(t).$$

A direct technique can be employed by setting

$$e(t) = \mathscr{F}^{-1}[a(\omega)] = \frac{1}{\sqrt{2\pi}} \int_{-\infty}^{\infty} a(\omega) \, e^{i\omega t} \, d\omega$$

and

$$v(t) = \mathscr{F}^{-1}[g(\omega)].$$

Then

$$H^{-1}(t)v(t) = \prod_{m=1}^{N} \left(\frac{d}{dt} + \gamma_m\right) \mathscr{F}^{-1}[g(\omega)] = e(t) = \mathscr{F}^{-1}[a(\omega)].$$

$H^{-1}(t)$ operates upon the exponential of $\mathscr{F}^{-1}[g(\omega)]$, giving

$$H^{-1}(t)\mathscr{F}^{-1}[g(\omega)] = \mathscr{F}^{-1}\left[\prod_{m=1}^{N} (i\omega + \gamma_m)g(\omega)\right] = \mathscr{F}^{-1}[a(\omega)].$$

Collecting terms under the integral sign, we obtain

$$\mathscr{F}^{-1}\left[\prod_{m=1}^{N} (i\omega + \gamma_m)g(\omega) - a(\omega)\right] = 0.$$

---

† An even function has the property that it has no change in sign upon reflection through the origin; $f_E(t) = +f_E(-t)$. The odd function changes sign: $f_0(t) = -f_0(-t)$.

†† In the example which will be employed the operator is only a differential operator. No generality is lost by this assumption because a differential plus integral operator also gives a polynomial in the denominator of $H(iw)$. The mixed operator also provides a polynomial in the numerator of $H(iw)$. This addition does not change the characteristics of the denominator.

A solution for this equation is

$$g(\omega) = \frac{a(\omega)}{\displaystyle\prod_{m=1}^{N}(i\omega + \gamma_m)} = H(i\omega)a(\omega).$$

Finally, then

$$v(t) = \mathscr{F}^{-1}[g(\omega)] = \mathscr{F}^{-1}[H(i\omega)a(\omega)].$$

The term $H(i\omega)$ is obtained directly in circuit analysis as the steady-state solution. Suppose the input excitation is applied to an LR circuit, with the response being the voltage across R. See Fig. 24.

$$L\frac{di(t)}{dt} + Ri(t) = e(t)$$

and

$$v(t) = Ri(t).$$

Then

$$\frac{L}{R}\frac{dv}{dt} + v = e(t).$$

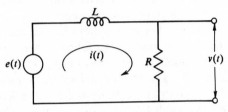

FIG. 24.

Transforming this equation, we get

$$\frac{L}{R}\mathscr{F}\left[\frac{dv}{dt}\right] + \mathscr{F}[v(t)] = \mathscr{F}[e(t)]$$

and

$$\frac{i\omega L}{R}g(\omega) + g(\omega) = a(\omega).$$

Solving for $g(\omega)$, we find the solution for $v(t)$:

$$v(t) = \mathscr{F}^{-1}\left[\frac{R}{(R + i\omega L)}a(\omega)\right] = \frac{1}{\sqrt{2\pi}}\int_{-\infty}^{\infty}\left\{\frac{R}{R + i\omega L}\right\}a(\omega)\,e^{iwt}d\omega.$$

In this example, then,

$$H(i\omega) = \frac{R}{(R + i\omega L)}$$

The reader will recognize in this example all the ingredients of the more elementary complex frequency representation of impedance.

LAPLACE TRANSFORMS

The Integral Transform

The method of Fourier transforms as applied to electrical circuits suffers from several disadvantages. As we have seen, the transient solutions are not conveniently expressed in terms of the initial conditions in the formalism of the Fourier transform; the initial conditions must be introduced as an extra consideration. The Fourier series and transforms often have the advantage that the eigenfunctions form an orthogonal set.

Laplace transforms, on the other hand, are nonzero for positive t only. As a result, the initial conditions are automatically introduced in conjunction with the characteristic modes of the transfer function. The Laplace representation clearly differentiates between transients caused by initial conditions imposed on the transfer function from those imposed by turning on the excitation. In addition to these fundamental assets, the step and the gate functions are expressed in a more apparent manner in the Laplace formalism.

Much of the complex algebra that will be introduced by the Laplace transform has already been anticipated by the earlier discussion of the algebraic nature of the linear differential operators with constant coefficients.

Many of the manipulations that were tedious in that analysis will appear in an elementary fashion in the formal methods to follow. There are several methods for introducing the $\mathscr{L}$T.† A convenient method consists of a transformation of the Fourier integrals to the two-sided $\mathscr{L}$T. The two-sided Laplace transform is not necessarily linear, although a number of contour integrations are conveniently evaluated with the two-sided integrals. The right-handed $\mathscr{L}$T is a special subset. These integrals are linear operators and represent the Laplace transforms that are customarily referred to.

Consider the set of Fourier transforms

$$f(t) = \mathscr{F}^{-1}[a(\omega)],$$

and

$$a(\omega) = \mathscr{F}[f(t)].$$

We now emphasize the class of functions

$$f(t)\, e^{-\sigma t} U(t).$$

The two-sided $\mathscr{L}$T can be avoided by the inclusion of the cutoff at $t = 0$, provided by $U(t)$. Therefore, we are specifically confining our attention to functions that are zero for $t < 0$ (or turned on at $t = 0$). The parameter σ is finite and positive. Also, we assume that the integral of $f(t)\, e^{-\sigma t} U(t)$ exists for all t.

$$\lim_{A \to \infty} \int_{-A}^{A} f(t)\, e^{-st} U(t)\, dt < \infty.$$

---

† We shall symbolize the name "Laplace transform" by the abbreviation $\mathscr{L}$T from this point.

This implies absolute convergence for the real part of s greater than a constant C $(C < \sigma)$. Then

$$a(\omega) = \frac{1}{\sqrt{2\pi}} \int_{-\infty}^{\infty} e^{-\sigma t} f(t) U(t) e^{-i\omega t} dt;$$

this integral defines the $\mathscr{L}$T of $f(t)$, $F(\sigma + i\omega) = F(s) = \mathscr{L}[f(t)]$;

$$F(\sigma + i\omega) = F(s) = \int_{0}^{\infty} f(t) e^{-(\sigma + i\omega)t} dt,$$

or

$$F(s) = \mathscr{L}[f(t)] = \int_{0}^{\infty} f(t) e^{-st} dt.$$

The inverse transform $\mathscr{L}^{-1}[F(s)]$, or $f(t)$, is then obtained from the inverse $\mathscr{F}$T†

$$e^{-\sigma t} f(t) U(t) = \frac{1}{2\pi} \int_{-\infty}^{+\infty} F(s) e^{i\omega t} d\omega.$$

Multiplying both sides by $e^{+\sigma t}$ and the integral by $U(t)$ to insure positive t,

$$f(t) = \mathscr{L}^{-1}[F(s)] = \frac{1}{2\pi i} \int_{\sigma - i\infty}^{\sigma + i\infty} F(s) e^{st} ds.$$

Ordinarily, the $U(t)$ is omitted; however, it must be understood. Since t is confined to the positive-real time axis, the contour integral in the s plane must be closed in the left-hand s plane. In many integrals the closure in the left-hand s plane will have a cut along the negative-real axis. These right-handed operators are linear and have the properties that

$$\mathscr{L}[f(t) + g(t)] = \mathscr{L}[f(t)] + \mathscr{L}[g(t)],$$

and

$$\mathscr{L}[Kf(t)] = K\mathscr{L}[f(t)].$$

Comparison of Laplace transform pairs to Fourier transform pairs will be left to the problems. We are now in a position to compute a number of $\mathscr{L}$T pairs.

First, the step function:

$$\mathscr{L}[U(t)] = \lim_{\alpha \to 0} \mathscr{L}[e^{-\alpha t} U(t)] = \lim_{\alpha \to 0} \int_{0}^{\infty} e^{-\alpha t} e^{-st} dt,$$

and

$$\mathscr{L}[U(t)] = \frac{1}{s}.$$

We also observe

$$\mathscr{L}[e^{-\alpha t} U(t)] = \frac{1}{(s + \alpha)}.$$

---

† The abbreviation $\mathscr{F}$T will be understood to mean Fourier Transform.

A diverging exponential $e^{-\sigma t}U(t)$ can be represented by adjusting σ to be greater than α:

$$\mathscr{L}[e^{+\alpha t}U(t)] = \frac{1}{(s-\alpha)}.$$

A large number of commonly used functions can be transformed. This will be left to the reader as an exercise. A few $\mathscr{L}$T pairs are shown in Tables 2a and 2b.

TABLE 2a

$f(t)$ for $t > 0$	$F(s) = \mathscr{L}[f(t)]$
$f(t)$	$F(s) = \int_0^\infty e^{-st} f(t)\, dt$
$af(t) + bg(t)$	$aF(s) + bG(s)$
$e^{at}f(t)$	$F(s-a)$
$f(at)$	$\dfrac{1}{a} F\left(\dfrac{s}{a}\right)$
$f'(t) = \dfrac{df}{dt}$	$sF(s) - f(0+)$
$f^{(n)}(t)$	$s^n F(s) - s^{n-1}f(0+) - s^{n-2}f'(0+)$ $- \cdots - f^{(n-1)}(0+)$
$\int_0^t f(t')\, dt'$	$\dfrac{1}{s} F(s)$
$t^n f(t)$; n a positive integer	$(-1)^n \dfrac{d^n}{ds^n} F(s)$
$\dfrac{f(t)}{t}$	$\displaystyle\int_s^\infty F(x)\, dx$
$U(t-T)f(t-T)$	$e^{-Ts}F(s)$
$f(t+T) = f(t)$	$\dfrac{1}{1-e^{-sT}} \displaystyle\int_0^T e^{-st} f(t)\, dt$

$f(t)$ for $0 < t$	$F(s) = \mathscr{L}[f(t)]$
$\delta(t)$	1
$U(t)$	$\dfrac{1}{s}$
$e^{-\alpha t}$	$\dfrac{1}{(s+\alpha)}$

TABLE 2a (*Continued*)

$f(t)$ for $0 < t$	$Fs = \mathscr{L}[f(t)]$
$e^{-\alpha t} - e^{-\beta t}$	$\dfrac{(\beta - \alpha)}{(s + \alpha)(s + \beta)}$
$\alpha e^{-\alpha t} - \beta e^{-\beta t}$	$\dfrac{(\alpha - \beta)s}{(s + \alpha)(s + \beta)}$
$(\beta - \gamma)e^{-\alpha t} + (\gamma - \alpha)e^{-\beta t} + (\alpha - \beta)e^{-\gamma t}$	$-\dfrac{(\alpha - \beta)(\gamma - \alpha)(\beta - \gamma)}{(s + \alpha)(s + \beta)(s + \gamma)}$
$\alpha(\beta - \gamma)e^{-\alpha t} + \beta(\gamma - \alpha)e^{-\beta t} + \gamma(\alpha - \beta)e^{-\gamma t}$	$\dfrac{(\alpha - \beta)(\beta - \gamma)(\gamma - \alpha)s}{(s + \alpha)(s + \beta)(s + \gamma)}$
$\alpha^2(\beta - \gamma)e^{-\alpha t} + \beta^2(\gamma - \alpha)e^{-\beta t} + \gamma^2(\alpha - \beta)e^{-\gamma t}$	$-\dfrac{(\alpha - \beta)(\beta - \gamma)(\gamma - \alpha)s^2}{(s + \alpha)(s + \beta)(s + \gamma)}$
$te^{-\alpha t}$	$\dfrac{1}{(s + \alpha)^2}$
$(1 - \alpha t)e^{-\alpha t}$	$\dfrac{s}{(s + \alpha)^2}$
$\dfrac{t^{n-1}}{(n-1)!} e^{-\alpha t}$	$\dfrac{1}{(s + \alpha)^n}$
$\sin \omega t$	$\dfrac{\omega}{(s^2 + \omega^2)}$
$\cos \omega t$	$\dfrac{s}{(s^2 + \omega^2)}$
$\sinh \alpha t$	$\dfrac{\alpha}{s^2 - \alpha^2}$
$\cosh \alpha t$	$\dfrac{s}{(s^2 - \alpha^2)}$
$1 - \cos \omega t$	$\dfrac{\omega^2}{s(s^2 + \omega^2)}$

Most of the expressions, Tables 2a and 2b, are demonstrated with some ease. For instance, the transform

$$\mathscr{L}[t^n] = \frac{n!}{s^{n+1}}$$

can be obtained by integrating $\mathscr{L}[t^n]$ by parts.

TABLE 2b

$f(t)$ for $0 < t$	$F(s) = \mathscr{L}[f(t)]$
$\omega t - \sin \omega t$	$\dfrac{\omega^3}{s^2(s^2 + \omega^2)}$
$e^{-\alpha t} \cos \omega t$	$\dfrac{(s + \alpha)}{[(s + \alpha)^2 + \omega^2]}$
$e^{-\alpha t} \sin(\omega t + \phi)$	$\dfrac{[(s + \alpha)\sin \phi + \omega \cos \phi]}{[(s + \alpha)^2 + \omega^2]}$
t	$\dfrac{1}{s^2}$
t^n	$\dfrac{n!}{s^{n+1}}$
$\dfrac{1}{\sqrt{\pi t}}$	$\dfrac{1}{\sqrt{s}}$
$\dfrac{1}{\sqrt{\alpha}} e^{\alpha t} \operatorname{erf} \sqrt{\alpha t}$	$\dfrac{1}{(s - \alpha)\sqrt{s}}$
$J_0(\alpha t)$	$\dfrac{1}{\sqrt{s^2 + \alpha^2}}$
$\dfrac{1}{\alpha t} J_1(\alpha t)$	$\dfrac{1}{s + \sqrt{s^2 + \alpha^2}}$
$\dfrac{\alpha}{2\sqrt{\pi t^3}} e^{-\alpha^2/4t}$	$e^{-\alpha \sqrt{s}}$, $(\alpha > 0)$
$\operatorname{erf}\left(\dfrac{\alpha}{2\sqrt{t}}\right)$	$\dfrac{1}{s} e^{-\alpha \sqrt{s}}$, $(\alpha \geqslant 0)$
$\dfrac{1}{\sqrt{\pi t}} e^{-\alpha^2/4t}$	$\dfrac{1}{\sqrt{s}} e^{-\alpha \sqrt{s}}$, $(\alpha \geqslant 0)$

The Shifting Theorem

Ideal delays of signals, i.e., delay without distortion, can be described in the $\mathscr{L}T$ formalism by the *shifting theorem*: If

$$\mathscr{L}[f(t)] = F(s),$$

then

$$\mathscr{L}[f(t - T)U(t - T)] = e^{-sT}F(s).$$

This is proved by shifting the origin of coordinates:

$$\mathcal{L}[f(t-T)U(t-T)] = \int_0^\infty f(t-T)U(t-T)\,e^{-st}\,dt$$

$$= \int_T^\infty f(t-T)\,e^{-st}\,dt.$$

By introducing a new variable $\xi = (t-T)$, we can write

$$\mathcal{L}[f(t-T)U(t-T)] = \int_0^\infty f(\xi)\,e^{-sT}\,e^{-s\xi}\,d\xi = e^{-sT}F(s).$$

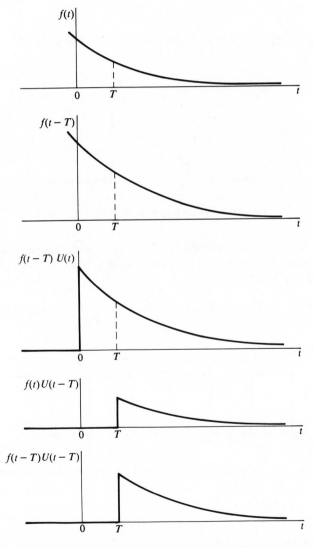

FIG. 25.   A comparison of the various products of $f(\tau)$ and $U(\tau)$.

The reader should be impressed by the fact that the shifted step, $U(t - T)$, must be incorporated in the product. One can demonstrate graphically the difference in the various combinations. See Fig. 25.

To illustrate this theorem, consider a gate function $g(t) = \{U(t) - U(t - T)\}$. The $\mathscr{L}$T of $g_T(t)$ can be written in the terms of the shifting function e^{-sT}:

$$\mathscr{L}[g_T(t)] = \mathscr{L}[U(t) - U(t - T)] = \frac{1}{s}\{1 - e^{-sT}\}.$$

A single sawtooth wave form can be formed by multiplying the gate $g(t)$ by a ramp function t/T:

$$f(t) = \frac{t}{T}\{U(t) - U(t - T)\} = \frac{t}{T}g_T(t)$$

and

$$\mathscr{L}[f(t)] = \mathscr{L}\left[\frac{t}{T}g_T(t)\right] = \frac{1}{Ts^2}\{1 - (1 + Ts)\,e^{-sT}\}.$$

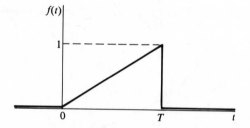

Fig. 26. A single sawtooth or ramp function.

Another useful role that the shift function plays is to represent the transforms of periodic functions. Regard first a periodic gate in which the "on" period equals the "off" period. See Fig. 27.

$$f(t) = U(t) - U(t - T) + U(t - 2T) - U(t - 3T) + \cdots + (-1)^{2n}U(t - nT) + \cdots.$$

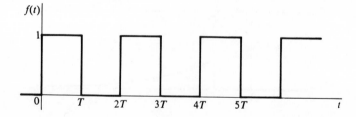

Fig. 27. A periodic gate; duration equal to one-half the period.

Transforming term by term,

$$\mathscr{L}[f(t)] = F(s) = \frac{1}{s}\{1 - e^{-sT} + e^{-2sT} - e^{-3sT} + \cdots + (-1)^n e^{-nsT} + \cdots\}.$$

This series is of the form

$$\lim_{N \to \infty} \sum_{k=0}^{N} x^k = \lim_{N \to \infty} \left(\frac{x^{N+1} - 1}{x - 1} \right) \xrightarrow[|x| < 1]{} \frac{1}{1 - x}.$$

Therefore

$$\sum_{k=0}^{\infty} x^k = \frac{1}{1 - x}; \qquad \text{if } |x| < 1.$$

In our series, $x = -e^{-sT}$ and

$$\mathscr{L}[f(t)] = \frac{1}{s} \sum_{m=0}^{\infty} [-e^{-sT}]^m = \frac{1}{s(1 + e^{-sT})}.$$

This result is the consequence of a more general theorem on periodic functions. Consider the repetitive function $f(t)$ with a period T such that

$$f(t) = f(t + T).$$

Then the definition of $F(s)$ can be written as

$$F(s) = \int_0^{\infty} e^{-st} f(t) \, dt = \int_0^{T} e^{-st} f(t) \, dt + \int_T^{\infty} e^{-st} f(t) \, dt.$$

With a change of variable $x = t - T$, the second integral becomes

$$\int_0^{\infty} e^{-s(x+T)} f(x + T) \, dx = e^{-sT} \int_0^{\infty} e^{-sx} f(x) \, dx$$

because $f(x + T) = f(x)$. Then

$$F(s) = \int_0^{T} e^{-st} f(t) \, dt + e^{-sT} F(s),$$

or the general result is

$$F(s) = \frac{1}{1 - e^{-sT}} \int_0^{T} e^{-st} f(t) \, dt.$$

It is sometimes convenient to define a function $f_p(s)$, which is equal to $f(t)$ in the interval $0 \leqslant t \leqslant T$ and zero everywhere else. Then

$$\int_0^{T} e^{-st} f(t) \, dt = \int_0^{\infty} e^{-st} f_p(t) \, dt = F_p(s),$$

where $f_p(t) = f(t)[U(t) - U(t - T)]$.

$$F(s) = \frac{F_p(s)}{1 - e^{-sT}}$$

As an example, consider a problem more complex than the preceding problem, namely, the pulse pictured in Fig. 28:

$$f(t) = U(t) - U(t - \tau) + U(t - T) - U(t - T - \tau)$$

$$+ \cdots + U(t - nT) - U(t - nT - \tau).$$

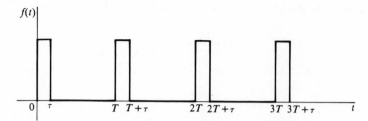

FIG. 28.   A periodic gate; duration less than one-half the period.

First we find

$$f_p(t) = U(t) - U(t - \tau),$$

which, by the shifting theorem, yields

$$F_p(s) = \frac{1 - e^{-s\tau}}{s}$$

Then

$$F(s) = \frac{1 - e^{-s\tau}}{s} \cdot \frac{1}{(1 - e^{-sT})}.$$

(Note that when $\tau = T/2$ and $T \to 2T$, the answer to the periodic gate is obtained.)
    If we describe a gate pulse of width τ as $g_\tau(t)$,

$$g_\tau(t) = U(t) - U(t - \tau),$$

then if each pulse of width τ is modulated by a function $h(t)$ and occurs with a period T, the resultant periodic wave form is

$$f(t) = h(t)g_\tau(t) + h(t - T)g_\tau(t - T) + \cdots h(t - nT)g_\tau(t - nT) + \cdots$$

and

$$f(t) = \sum_{n=0}^{\infty} h(t - nT)g_\tau(t - nT).$$

The transform of $f(t)$ is

$$\mathscr{L}[f(t)] = \sum_{n=0}^{\infty} \{\mathscr{L}[h(t)] \, e^{-nsT} - \mathscr{L}[h(t + \tau)] \, e^{-nsT} \, e^{-s\tau}\},$$

giving

$$\mathscr{L}[f(t)] = \frac{\mathscr{L}[h(t)]}{(1 - e^{-sT})} - \frac{\mathscr{L}[h(t - \tau)] \, e^{-s\tau}}{(1 - e^{-sT})}$$

$$= \frac{1}{1 - e^{-sT}} \{\mathscr{L}[h(t)] - e^{-s\tau} \mathscr{L}[h(t + \tau)]\}.$$

Often, when the response to a periodic excitation is obtained, a transient near $t = 0$ tends to mask the steady-state response. Steady-state behavior is obtained from our formalism by examining the solutions in the region of large n. Examples of this type of evaluation will be given in the discussion of circuit applications.

The shifting theorem has a practical application when we consider signals transmitted by a distortionless delay line. Consider a signal $e(t)$ applied to a line of delay T. See Fig. 29.

The $\mathscr{L}$T of the delay operator is e^{-sT}, and the response to an input excitation $e(t)$ is

$$v(t) = \mathscr{L}^{-1}[e^{-sT}\mathscr{L}[e(t)]] = e(t - T).$$

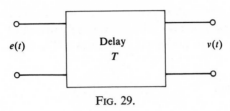

$e(t)$ Delay $v(t)$
                 T

FIG. 29.

The Differentiation Theorem

Previously we indicated the algebraic nature of the linear differential equations with constant coefficients. The algebraic properties that we developed at that time can be derived much more readily by direct Laplace transformation of the differential equation. In order to do this, we must establish the differentiation theorem and integration theorem. If

$$F(s) = \mathscr{L}[f(t)],$$

we consider

$$\mathscr{L}\left[\frac{df}{dt}\right] = \int_0^\infty \frac{df}{dt} e^{-st}\, dt.$$

Integrating by parts, we obtain

$$\mathscr{L}\left[\frac{df}{dt}\right] = sF(s) - f(0+).$$

Higher derivatives, when transformable, are obtained in the same manner:

$$\mathscr{L}\left[\frac{d^2f}{dt^2}\right] = s\mathscr{L}\left[\frac{df}{dt}\right] - f'(0+)$$
$$= s^2F(s) - sf(0+) - f'(0+).$$

Here, $f'(0+)$ means the first derivative of $f(t)$ evaluated at $(0+)$. In general, if transformable,

$$\mathscr{L}\left[\frac{d^nf}{dt^n}\right] = s^nF(s) - \sum_{m=1}^{n} s^{(n-m)}\left[\frac{d^{m-1}f}{dt^{m-1}}\right]_{0+}.$$

Thus, differentiation n times is equivalent to multiplication by s^n in the frequency domain or in the transform representation.

Consider the operator

$$\sum_{n=0}^{N} a_n \frac{d^n}{dt^n}$$

operating on $v(t)$ with $V(s) = \mathscr{L}[v(t)]$. Then

$$\mathscr{L}\left[\sum_{n=0}^{N} a_n \frac{d^n}{dt^n} v(t)\right] = \sum_{n=0}^{N} a_n \left\{ s^n V(s) - \sum_{m=1}^{n} s^{(n-m)} \left[\frac{d^{m-1}v}{dt^{m-1}}\right]_{0+} \right\}$$

$$= \sum_{n=0}^{N} a_n s^n V(s) - \sum_{n=0}^{N} \sum_{m=1}^{n} a_n s^{(n-m)} \left[\frac{d^{m-1}v}{dt^{m-1}}\right]_{0+}.$$

Therefore, the transformation produces a polynomial of order N times $V(s)$; and added to this, the transformation introduces a polynomial of degree $(N-1)$ whose coefficients are formed from the initial conditions of the problem.

The Integration Theorem

In practice, we shall be interested in operators that include single or multiple integrals. In the transform representation, the definite integral from $(0+)$ to t becomes a division by s. Again, if

$$F(s) = \mathscr{L}[f(t)],$$

consider the $\mathscr{L}$T of the integral of $f(t)$:

$$\mathscr{L}\left[\int_0^t f(t')\,dt'\right] = \int_0^\infty dt\, e^{-st} \int_0^t f(t')\,dt'.$$

We integrate by parts, and

$$\mathscr{L}\left[\int_0^t f(t')\,dt'\right] = -\left[\frac{e^{-st}}{s} \int_0^t f(t')\,dt'\right]_0^\infty + \frac{1}{s} F(s)$$

$$= \frac{F(s)}{s}.$$

This could have been obtained from the differentiation theorem. Let $f(t) = dg/dt$, and

$$\mathscr{L}\left[\int_0^t f(t')\,dt'\right] = \mathscr{L}[g(t) - g(0+)].$$

Consider

$$\mathscr{L}\left[\frac{dg}{dt}\right] = \mathscr{L}[f(t)] = s\mathscr{L}[g(t)] - g(0+).$$

Substituting into the expansion of the transform of the integral, we find that

$$\mathscr{L}\left[\int_0^t f(t')\,dt'\right] = \frac{\mathscr{L}[f(t)]}{s} + \frac{g(0+)}{s} - \frac{g(0+)}{s} = \frac{F(s)}{s}.$$

This demonstration does not add anything new to our proof. On the other hand, it demonstrates that the initial value of $g(t)$ does not appear in the transform of the definite integral.

The transform of the indefinite integral is obtained directly from the differentiation theorem:

$$\mathscr{L}\left[\int f(t)\,dt\right] = \mathscr{L}[g(t) - g(0+)] = \frac{F(s)}{s} + \frac{g(0+)}{s},$$

where

$$f(t) = \frac{dg}{dt}.$$

The Initial-Value Theorem

If $f(t)$ and its first derivative are Laplace-transformable, the initial value of $f(t)$ can be obtained from the transform according to

$$f(0+) = \lim_{t \to (0+)} f(t) = \lim_{s \to \infty} sF(s).$$

Proof:

$$\lim_{s \to \infty} sF(s) = \lim_{s \to \infty} \int_0^\infty \frac{df}{dt} e^{-st}\,dt + f(0+) = f(0+).$$

The Final-Value Theorem

This is the reciprocal theorem to the initial-value theorem. If $f(t)$ and df/dt are Laplace-transformable, then the value of $f(t)$ as t becomes arbitrarily large is given by

$$\lim_{t \to \infty} f(t) = \lim_{s \to 0} sF(s).$$

In this case,

$$\lim_{s \to 0} \{sF(s) - f(0+)\} = \lim_{s \to 0} \int_0^\infty \frac{df}{dt} e^{-st}\,dt = \int_0^\infty \frac{df}{dt}\,dt.$$

Then

$$\lim_{t \to \infty} f(t) = \lim_{s \to 0} sF(s).$$

Inverse Theorems

Because of the similarity in form between the $\mathscr{L}$T and its inverse, we might expect that multiplication of $f(t)$ by t would lead to a derivative of $F(s)$ by s. If

$$\mathscr{L}[f(t)] = F(s),$$

then

$$\mathscr{L}[tf(t)] = -\frac{dF}{ds}$$

and

$$\mathscr{L}\left[\frac{f(t)}{t}\right] = \int_s^\infty F(s')\,ds'.$$

Proof of these statements are left to the reader.

THE SOLUTION OF SIMULTANEOUS LINEAR DIFFERENTIAL EQUATIONS

To obtain a solution to a single linear differential-integral equation by transform methods, one first transforms both sides of the equation. The second step involves solving for the $\mathscr{L}$T of the unknown in terms of functions of s arising from the transform of the excitation function, the polynomial derived from the linear operator, and the polynomial set up by the initial conditions. In the discussion of the differentiation theorem, the general form of the transform of the differential operator was developed.

We consider a single equation involving a linear operator

$$H^{-1}(t)v(t) = e(t).$$

For our purposes, we can write $H^{-1}(t)$ as a linear combination of differential and integral operators:

$$H^{-1}(t) = \sum_{n=-M}^{N} a_n D^n;$$

where the operator D^n is the nth derivative d^n/dt^n, and negative values of n refer to integrals of order $-n$; i.e., $D^{-1} = \int dt$. For our purposes, we can cut this sum off at $n = 0$. Then, without loss of generality,

$$H^{-1}(t)v(t) = \sum_{n=0}^{N} a_n \frac{d^n}{dt^n} v(t) = e(t).$$

If the $\mathscr{L}$T of $v(t)$ and $e(t)$ are

$$\mathscr{L}[e(t)] = E(s)$$

and

$$\mathscr{L}[v(t)] = V(s),$$

we now transform the entire equation term by term, giving

$$\sum_{n=0}^{N} a_n s^n V(s) - \sum_{n=0}^{N} a_n \sum_{m=1}^{n} s^{(n-m)} [D^{m-1} v(t)]_{(0+)} = E(s).$$

Solving for $V(s)$ we obtain,

$$V(s) = \frac{E(s) + \sum_{n=0}^{N} a_n \sum_{m=1}^{n} s^{(n-m)} [D^{m-1}v]_{(0+)}}{\sum_{n=0}^{N} a_n s^n}.$$

If we include integrals of $v(t)$ in the operator $H^{-1}(t)$, the expression is altered in the following manner: Consider the highest multiple integral in $H^{-1}(t)$ to be M. Then the polynomial in the denominator on the right will be of degree $(N + M)$. In addition, the terms in the numerator will be multiplied by s^M, indicating that M differentiations of the equation will remove the highest integral. The initial conditions of the integrals will also be included in the polynomial of the numerator on the right. As an example, consider the special example

$$\left\{ a_1 \frac{d}{dt} + a_0 + a_{-1} \int dt \right\} v(t) = e(t).$$

After transformation we obtain

$$\left\{ a_1 s V(s) - a_1 v(0+) + a_0 V(s) + a_{-1} \frac{V(s)}{s} + a_{-1} \frac{[\int v \, dt]_{0+}}{s} \right\} = E(s),$$

where

$$v^{-1}(0+) = \left[\int v(t) \, dt \right]_{(0+)}.$$

Then, solving for $V(s)$ in this example,

$$V(s) = \frac{s E(s) + a_1 v(0+) s - a_{-1} [v^{-1}(0+)]}{a_1 s^2 + a_0 s + a_{-1}}.$$

Returning now to the general form of the solution for $V(s)$, we separate the terms on the right into two parts. The first term is the transform of the particular solution; the second is the transient introduced by the initial conditions

$$V(s) = \frac{E(s)}{\sum\limits_{n=0}^{N} a_n s^n} + \frac{\sum\limits_{n=0}^{N} a_n \sum\limits_{m=1}^{n} s^{(n-m)} [D^{m-1} v(t)]_{(0+)}}{\sum\limits_{n=0}^{N} a_n s^n}.$$

For convenience, the coefficients of the operator $H^{-1}(t)$ are normalized so that $a_N = 1$. This allows us to factor the polynomial in the denominator without renormalizing (by dividing by a_N); then

$$\sum_{n=0}^{N} a_n s^n = (s + \gamma_N)(s + \gamma_{N-1}) \cdots (s + \gamma_1) = \prod_{n=1}^{N} (s + \gamma_n) = \frac{1}{H(s)}.$$

The roots or eigenvalues γ_n are the same γ's as those employed in our earlier development of the operational method and the characteristic modes. Thus, the inverse of $\prod\limits_{n=1}^{N} (s + \gamma_n)$ is the operator $H(s)$ employed before. In general, $H(s)$ may be the ratio of two polynomials, however, we only need to emphasize the denominator.

Because the polynomial formed with the initial conditions as coefficients is of maximum order $N - 1$, the transient term is a rational fraction and can be expanded as N fractions of the type

$$\frac{A_n}{(s + \gamma_n)}$$

If $E(s)$ is a polynomial of degree less than or equal to N (which is for physical problems), the particular solution can also be expanded into N first-degree fractions:

$$V(s) = H(s) E(s) + H(s) \sum_{n=0}^{N} a_n \sum_{m=1}^{n} s^{(n-m)} [D^{m-1} v]_{(0+)}$$

and

$$v(t) = \mathscr{L}^{-1}[V(s)] = \mathscr{L}^{-1}[H(s)E(s)] + \mathscr{L}^{-1}\left[\sum_{n=1}^{N} \frac{A_n}{(s + \gamma_n)} \right].$$

Without specifying $E(s)$, we must leave $\mathscr{L}^{-1}[H(s)E(s)]$ for special values of E. The second term expands into a series of exponentials (characteristic modes of $H^{-1}(t)$)

with the coefficients A_n:

$$v(t) = \mathscr{L}^{-1}[H(s)E(s)] + \sum_{n=1}^{N} A_n e^{-\gamma_n t} U(t).$$

This, of course, has assumed no degeneracy in the γ_n.

THE HEAVISIDE EXPANSION COEFFICIENTS

The Nondegenerate Case

A rational fraction in s is given by an expression of the form

$$\frac{\sum_{m=0}^{M} b_m s^m}{\sum_{n=0}^{N} a_n s^n}.$$

The fraction is proper if $M < N$. In case $N \leq M$, the fraction is called *improper*. In real physical problems, the fraction corresponding to a physical operator is always proper. For the sake of simplicity in calculation, by neglecting small damping in some problems we employ relaxed inequalities between M and N such that $M \leq N$. All cases in which M is greater than N would provide solutions that are multiple derivatives of the delta function and as such are quite unphysical.

The polynomial of the denominator will be regarded as scaled with $a_N = 1$; using this rational fraction as a general response

$$V(s) = \frac{\sum_{m=0}^{M} b_m s^m}{\sum_{n=0}^{N} a_n s^n} = \frac{\sum_{m=0}^{M} b_m s^m}{\prod_{n=1}^{N} (s + \gamma_n)}; \qquad (M < N).$$

This expression can be expanded to be

$$V(s) = \sum_{n=1}^{N} \frac{B_n}{(s + \gamma_n)}.$$

To determine the B_k, multiply $V(s)$ by $(s + \gamma_k)$ and evaluate at $s = -\gamma_k$. Because all the γ_k are different, the only nonvanishing term after evaluating at $(-\gamma_k)$ is B_k:

$$B_k = [(s + \gamma_k)V(s)]_{s = -\gamma_k}.$$

Once the B_k have been evaluated, the inverse transformation of $v(s)$ to $v(t)$ can be performed by inspection. Because

$$\mathscr{L}^{-1}\left[\frac{1}{s + \gamma_n}\right] = e^{-\gamma_n t},$$

we can write

$$v(t) = \mathscr{L}^{-1}[V(s)] = \sum_{n=1}^{N} B_n \mathscr{L}^{-1}\left[\frac{1}{s + \gamma_n}\right] = \sum_{n=1}^{N} B_n e^{-\gamma_n t}.$$

As an example, consider

$$V(s) = \frac{(s + 4\alpha)}{(s + 2\alpha)(s + 3\alpha)}.$$

Using the procedure outlined above,

$$B_1 = [(s + 2\alpha)V(s)]_{(-2\alpha)} = 2,$$

and

$$B_2 = [(s + 3\alpha)V(s)]_{(-3\alpha)} = -1.$$

Then

$$\mathcal{L}^{-1}[V(s)] = \{2e^{-2\alpha t} - e^{-3\alpha t}\}U(t).$$

Operationally, the general result can be obtained by differentiating the denominator of $H(s)$. If

$$H(s) = \frac{P(s)}{A(s)},$$

where

$$A(s) = \prod_{n=1}^{N} (s + \gamma_n) = (s + \gamma_N)(s + \gamma_{N-1}) \cdots (s + \gamma_1),$$

then

$$\left[\frac{s + \gamma_r}{A(s)}\right]_{(-\gamma_r)} = \left[\frac{1}{dA/ds}\right]_{s = -\gamma_r} = \left[\frac{1}{A'}\right]_{s = -\gamma_r}.$$

This form has the advantage that one does not have to follow the grouping of the product terms $(s + \gamma_n)$ if the roots are known. In terms of the derivative of the denominator,

$$B_k = \frac{P(s = -\gamma_k)}{A'(s = -\gamma_k)}$$

or

$$B_k = \frac{[A(s)H(s)]_{s = -\gamma_k}}{A'(s = -\gamma_k)}.$$

Degenerate Roots

If a certain number of the eigenvalues or roots of the denominator are the same, the problem is said to have a degeneracy. When q of the roots are the same, the problem has a pole at γ_q of order q. This situation was encountered previously when the algebraic structure was investigated.

Assume that there is only one point of degeneracy and that the first q roots of the denominator of $H(s)$ are the same:

$$\gamma_1 = \gamma_2 = \cdots = \gamma_{q-1} = \gamma_q \ (q < N)$$

and

$$\gamma_q \neq \gamma_{q+1} \neq \cdots \neq \gamma_N.$$

Employing the same nomenclature,

$$V(s) = \frac{\displaystyle\sum_{m=0}^{M} b_m s^m}{(s + \gamma_1)^q (s + \gamma_{q+1})(s + \gamma_{q+2}) \cdots (s + \gamma_N)}.$$

We express this as a series in which the first q terms are ascending powers of $\{1/(s + \gamma_1)\}$.

$$V(s) = \frac{B_1}{(s + \gamma_1)} + \frac{B_2}{(s + \gamma_1)^2} + \cdots + \frac{B_q}{(s + \gamma_1)^q} + \frac{B_{q+1}}{(s + \gamma_{q+1})} + \cdots + \frac{B_N}{(s + \gamma_N)}.$$

The problem lies with the first q coefficients, since the nondegenerate ones can be obtained by multiplying by $(s + \gamma_r)$, $q < r$, and evaluating at $(-\gamma_r)$.

To obtain the coefficients of the degenerate terms, we proceed in steps. First multiply by $(s + \gamma_1)^q$ and evaluate at $(-\gamma_1)$;

$$B_q = [(s + \gamma_1)^q V(s)]_{(s = -\gamma_1)},$$

$$= [B_1(s + \gamma_1)^{q-1} + B_2(s + \gamma_1)^{q-2} + \cdots + B_q]_{-\gamma_1}.$$

To obtain B_{q-1}, we differentiate the product $\{(s + \gamma_1)^q V(s)\}$ once with respect to s and evaluate at $(-\gamma_1)$, giving

$$B_{q-1} = \left[\frac{d}{ds} (s + \gamma_1)^q V(s) \right]_{(s = -\gamma_1)}.$$

This can be done repeatedly to give the first q coefficients:

$$B_{q-l} = \frac{1}{l!} \left[\frac{d^l}{ds^l} \{(s + \gamma_1)^q V(s)\} \right]_{(s = -\gamma_1)} ; \qquad (l \leqslant q).$$

The inverse transform of the resultant series can also be performed by inspection, remembering that

$$\mathscr{L}^{-1}\left[\frac{1}{(s + \gamma_1)^l} \right] = \frac{t^{l-1}}{(l-1)!} e^{-\gamma_1 t} U(t).$$

Then, for the degenerate case,

$$v(t) = \mathscr{L}^{-1}[V(s)] = \sum_{n=1}^{q} B_n \mathscr{L}^{-1}\left[\frac{1}{(s + \gamma_1)^n} \right] + \sum_{n=q+1}^{N} B_n \mathscr{L}^{-1}\left[\frac{1}{s + \gamma_n} \right]$$

and

$$v(t) = \left\{ \sum_{n=1}^{q} B_n \frac{t^{n-1}}{(n-1)!} e^{-\gamma_1 t} + \sum_{n=q+1}^{N} B_n e^{-\gamma_n t} \right\} U(t).$$

If we recall the inverse theorems, this is to be expected, since

$$\mathscr{L}[t^k f(t)] = (-1)^k \frac{d^k}{ds^k} F(s).$$

The Improper Fraction $N \leqslant M$

When the highest power in the numerator is greater than or equal to the highest power appearing in the denominator, the solution will contain the delta function and derivatives of the delta function. This is a nonphysical result and is not encountered except in a few idealized problems for which $M = N$. Consider

$$V(s) = \frac{\sum_{m=0}^{M} b_m s^m}{\sum_{n=0}^{N} a_n s^n} = \frac{b_M \prod_{m=1}^{M} (s + \beta_m)}{\prod_{n=1}^{N} (s + \gamma_n)}; \qquad \text{with } N \leqslant M.$$

We evaluate this function as a power series in s plus a set of N partial fractions by splitting off the first $(M - N + 1)$ terms:

$$V(s) = \sum_{m=N}^{M} \frac{b_m s^m}{\prod_{n=1}^{N} (s + \gamma_n)} + \frac{\sum_{m=0}^{N-1} b_m s^m}{\prod_{n=1}^{N} (s + \gamma_n)}.$$

The first numerator can be factored to give

$$s^N \sum_{m=N}^{M} b_m s^{(m-N)} = s^N \prod_{m=1}^{M-N} (s + \beta_m).$$

Then

$$V(s) = \sum_{l=0}^{M-N} C_l s^l + \sum_{n=1}^{N} \frac{B_n}{(s + \gamma_n)},$$

where

$$C_k = \left[\frac{b_M s^N}{(s + \beta_k)} \frac{\prod_{m=1}^{M-N} (s + \beta_m)}{\prod_{n=1}^{N} (s + \gamma_n)} \right]_{(s = -\beta_k)}, \qquad \text{for } (k \neq 0);$$

and

$$C_0 = \sum_{m=1}^{M-N} \beta_m C_m.$$

The B_k are the proper coefficients;

$$B_k = \left[(s + \gamma_k) \frac{\sum_{m=0}^{N-1} b_m s^m}{\prod_{n=1}^{N} (s + \gamma_n)} \right]_{(s = -\gamma_k)}.$$

The inversion of the terms s^l gives the lth derivative of $\delta(t)$. Thus,

$$v(t) = \sum_{m=0}^{M-N} C_m \frac{d^m}{dt^m} \delta(t) + \sum_{n=1}^{N} B_n e^{-\gamma_n t}.$$

THE TRANSFER FUNCTION

Single Equations

We now return to the general problem of solving differential-integral equations. We see that the solution to a single equation generally results in a form

$$V(s) = H(s)E(s) + H(s)K_0(s),$$

where $K_0(s)$ is a polynomial resulting from the initial conditions. Returning to the case of the differential operator,†

$$H^{-1}(t) = \sum_{n=0}^{N} a_n \frac{d^n}{dt^n},$$

the polynomial $K_0(s)$ resulting from the Laplace transformation was

$$K_0(s) = \sum_{n=0}^{N} a_n \sum_{m=1}^{n} s^{(n-m)} [D^{(m-1)} v(t)]_{(t=0+)}$$

and

$$H(s) = \cfrac{1}{\displaystyle\sum_{n=0}^{N} a_n s^n} = \cfrac{1}{\displaystyle\prod_{n=1}^{N} (s + \gamma_n)} \xrightarrow{\text{in general}} \cfrac{P(s)}{\displaystyle\prod_{n=1}^{N} (s + \gamma_n)}.$$

The operator $H(s)$ is called the *transfer function* of the differential equation. $H(s)$ transfers the total excitation $\{E(s) + K_0(s)\}$ to a response function $V(s)$. The poles of $H(s)$ occur at the points $s = -\gamma_n$, and each pole corresponds to a characteristic mode of our initial differential operator. The γ_n correspond to the characteristic complex frequencies of the characteristic modes and are often called the *eigenfrequencies*.

The dimensions of $H(s)$, and particularly its inverse transform $h(t) = \mathcal{L}^{-1}[H(s)]$, are governed by the dimensions of the excitation $e(t)$ and the response $v(t)$, if the excitation is a voltage and the response is a voltage, $h(t)$ and $H(s)$ are dimensionless. If $e(t)$ is a voltage and $v(t)$ is a current, $h(t)$ will have the dimensions of an admittance, or $(\text{ohms})^{-1}$.

As a sample problem, consider the series LRC circuit shown in Fig. 30 to be excited by a step function $E_0 U(t)$. This could be a battery of emf E_0 switched in series at $t = 0$. The initial current through L and the initial charge on C are given by $i(0+)$ and $q(0+)$, respectively. See Fig. 30.

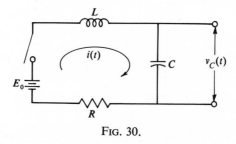

FIG. 30.

Kirchhoff's loop equation gives us

$$L \frac{di}{dt} + Ri + \frac{1}{C} \int i(t)\, dt = e(t).$$

---

† The presence of integral operators in $H^{-1}(t)$ will produce a polynomial $P(s)$ in the numerator of $H(s)$. In addition, the initial values of the integrals will appear in K_0. These terms will carry an s dependence which varies as $1/s^m$. The manipulations to expand $H(s)$ in terms of the roots of the denominator are the same as described in the preceding section.

The response $v(t)$ is the voltage across the capacitor C at any time $0 < t$:

$$v(t) = \frac{1}{C} \int i(t) \, dt.$$

Now set

$$I(s) = \mathscr{L}[i(t)].$$

Transforming the differential equation for $i(t)$ term by term, we get

$$LsI(s) - Li(0+) + RI(s) + \frac{I(s)}{Cs} + \frac{q_c(0+)}{Cs} = \frac{E_0}{s}.$$

Solving for $I(s)$, we obtain

$$I(s) = \frac{E_0 - (1/C)q_c(0+) + Li(0+)s}{L(s^2 + 2as + \omega_0^2)}.$$

We define the parameters: $2a = R/L$, and $\omega_0^2 = 1/LC$. Then

$$V(s) = \mathscr{L}[v(t)] = \frac{I(s) + q_c(0+)}{Cs} = \frac{\omega_0^2[E_0 - (1/C)q_c(0+) + Li(0+)s]}{s(s^2 + 2as + \omega_0^2)} + \frac{q_c(0+)}{Cs}.$$

Suppose we let $i(0+) = 0$ and $q(0+) = CE_0/2$. In addition, set $2a = (3/\sqrt{2})(\omega_0)$, and

$$V(s) = \frac{\omega_0^2 E_0}{2s(s + \sqrt{2}\omega_0)(s + (\sqrt{2}/2)\omega_0)} + \frac{E_0}{2s},$$

$$V(s) = \frac{\omega_0^2 E_0}{2} \left\{ \frac{1/\omega_0^2}{s} + \frac{1/\omega_0^2}{(s + \sqrt{2}\omega_0)} - \frac{2/\omega_0^2}{(s + (\sqrt{2}/2)\omega_0)} \right\} + \frac{E_0}{2s}.$$

Taking the inverse transform,

$$v(t) = \mathscr{L}^{-1}[V(s)] = \frac{E_0}{2} \{2 + e^{-\sqrt{2}\omega_0 t} - 2 e^{-(\sqrt{2}/2)\omega_0 t}\} U(t).$$

A sketch of the response $v(t)$ indicates that the far pole or characteristic mode at $s = -\sqrt{2}\omega_0$ causes $v(t)$ to rise rapidly for times of the order of $\{1/\sqrt{2}\omega_0\}$ while the near pole gives a slower rise at times greater than this. See Fig. 31.

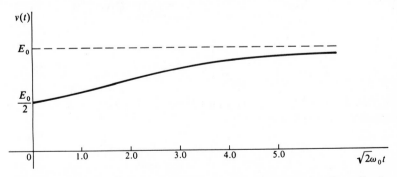

FIG. 31.   Voltage response across the capacitor in the LRC circuit when $i(0+) = 0$ and $q_c(0+) \neq 0$.

This result indicates the manner in which the initial conditions enter the problem. Appropriate accounting for $q(0+)$ provides a solution, which correctly gives $v(0+) = E_0/2$.

Simultaneous Integral-Differential Equations

Our attention can now be directed to problems that involve more than one Maxwell loop. The initial statement of a problem involving N loops and N loop currents will consist of N integral-differential equations in N unknowns. By Laplace-transforming each of the N equations, the system can be converted to N algebraic equations in N unknowns.

For orientation, the reader may consider the simple two-loop problem in two unknowns, shown in Fig. 32. The Maxwell loop equations for this problem are

$$L_{11}\frac{di_1}{dt} + R_{11}i_1 + \frac{1}{C_{12}}\int i_1(t)\,dt - \frac{1}{C_{12}}\int i_2(t)\,dt = e_{11}(t)$$

and

$$-\frac{1}{C_{12}}\int i_1(t)\,dt + \frac{1}{C_{12}}\int i_2(t)\,dt + R_{22}i_2(t) = 0.$$

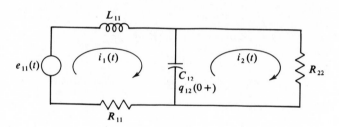

FIG. 32.

The $\mathcal{L}T$ of these equations are

$$\left\{L_{11}s + R_{11} + \frac{1}{C_{12}s}\right\}I_1 - L_{11}i_1(0+) + \frac{q_1(0+)}{C_{12}s} - \frac{I_2(s)}{C_{12}s} - \frac{q_2(0+)}{C_{12}s} = E_{11}(s)$$

and

$$-\frac{I_1(s)}{C_{12}s} - \frac{q_1(0+)}{C_{12}s} + \left\{\frac{1}{C_{12}s} + R_{22}\right\}I_2(s) + \frac{q_2(0+)}{C_{12}s} = 0.$$

The initial charge on C_{12} is $q_0(0+) = q_1(0+) - q_2(0+)$. One can write the equations above in a symbolic form as

$$H'_{11}(s)I_1(s) + H'_{12}(s)I_2(s) = E_1(s) + K_1(s)$$

and

$$H'_{21}(s)I_1(s) + H'_{22}(s)I_2(s) = E_2(s) + K_2(s).$$

These functions can be related to our special case:

$$H'_{11}(s) = \left\{ L_{11}s + R_{11} + \frac{1}{C_{12}s} \right\} = \sum_{\text{all } m} z_{1m}(s),$$

$$H'_{12}(s) = -\frac{1}{C_{12}s},$$

$$H'_{21}(s) = -\frac{1}{C_{21}s} = -\frac{1}{C_{12}s},$$

and

$$H'_{22}(s) = R_{22} + \frac{1}{C_{21}s} = \sum_{\text{all } k} z_{2k}(s).$$

Here we can think of the individual impedances as elements $z_{lm}(s)$, where l and m represent the fact that the element is common to loops l and m. The resultant matrices are symmetric. This is allowed by the fact that $z_{lm}(s) = z_{ml}(s)$ when the direction of the loop currents is taken in a consistent form.

The excitation transforms $E_m(s)$ represent the sum of the emfs in the mth loop, taken with appropriate signs. The transforms $K_m(s)$ are the excitations of the mth loop, brought about by the initial conditions of all the variables and the appropriate derivatives or integrals of the loops adjacent to the mth. In our example,

$$E_1(s) = \sum_{\text{all } m} E_{1m}(s) = E_{11}(s),$$

$$K_1(s) = L_{11}i_1(0+) + \frac{1}{C_{12}} \{q_1(0+) - q_2(0+)\},$$

while

$$E_2(s) = 0,$$

and

$$K_2(s) = -\frac{1}{C_{12}s} \{q_1(0+) - q_2(0+)\} = -\frac{q_c(0+)}{C_{12}s}.$$

The algebraic equations can then be represented in terms of matrices:

$$\begin{pmatrix} H'_{11}(s) & H'_{12}(s) \\ H'_{21}(s) & H'_{22}(s) \end{pmatrix} \begin{bmatrix} I_1(s) \\ I_2(s) \end{bmatrix} = \begin{bmatrix} E_1(s) \\ E_2(s) \end{bmatrix} + \begin{bmatrix} K_1(s) \\ K_2(s) \end{bmatrix};$$

or

$$\mathbb{H}^{-1}(s) \cdot \mathbf{I}(s) = \mathbf{E}(s) + \mathbf{K}(s).$$

This problem is solved by inverting $\mathbb{H}^{-1}(s)$ to $\mathbb{H}(s)$: multiplying by $\mathbb{H}(s)$ from the left, we obtain

$$\mathbf{I}(s) = \mathbb{H}(s) \cdot \{\mathbf{E}(s) + \mathbf{K}(s)\}.$$

The matrix $\mathbb{H}(s)$ is called the *transfer matrix*. For the example taken, $\mathbb{H}(s)$ would have the units of an admittance because we are generating a current vector $\mathbf{I}(s)$ by operating on a voltage vector $\mathbf{E}(s)$. If we were generating a voltage response from a voltage excitation, the transfer matrix elements would be dimensionless. This would be known then as the *voltage transfer matrix*.

The type of problem outlined can now be generalized to N loops or N simultaneous differential equations:

$$A'_{11}(t)v_1(t) + A'_{12}(t)v_2(t) + \cdots + A'_{1N}(t)v_N(t) = e_{11}(t) + e_{12}(t) + \cdots + e_{1N}(t),$$
$$A'_{21}(t)v_1(t) + A'_{22}(t)v_2(t) + \cdots + A'_{2N}(t)v_N(t) = e_{21}(t) + e_{22}(t) + \cdots + e_{2N}(t),$$
$$\vdots$$
$$A'_{N1}(t)v_1(t) + A'_{N2}(t)v_2(t) + \cdots + A'_{NN}(t)v_N(t) = e_{N1}(t) + e_{N2}(t) + \cdots + e_{NN}(t).$$

This time-dependent set of simultaneous linear integral-differential equations is quite general. The matrix elements $A'_{lm}(t)$ are linear operators of any order.

If we are dealing with N loops in circuit analysis, the form of the A'_{lm} depends upon the questions asked. In other words, the form depends upon whether $v_j(t)$ is a voltage or a loop current. Most examples consist primarily of loop-current equations. Then our A'_{lm} take very specific forms. The forms below are typical:

$$A'_{jk}(t) \rightarrow -L_{jk}\frac{d}{dt} - R_{jk} - \frac{1}{C_{jk}}\int dt, \qquad (j \neq k);$$

and

$$A'_{mm}(t) \rightarrow \sum_{\text{all } k}\left\{+ L_{mk}\frac{d}{dt} + R_{mk} + \frac{1}{C_{mk}}\int dt\right\}.$$

When the N equations are Laplace-transformed, they can be arranged to appear as

$$H'_{lm}(s)V_m(s) = \mathscr{L}[A'_{lm}(t)v_m(t)]$$

or

$$\begin{pmatrix} H'_{11}(s) & H'_{12}(s) & & H'_{1N}(s) \\ H'_{21}(s) & H'_{22}(s) & \cdots & H'_{2N}(s) \\ \vdots & & & \\ H'_{N1}(s) & H'_{N2}(s) & \cdots & H_{NN}(s) \end{pmatrix} \begin{bmatrix} V_1(s) \\ V_2(s) \\ \vdots \\ V_N(s) \end{bmatrix} = \begin{bmatrix} E_1(s) \\ E_2(s) \\ \vdots \\ E_N(s) \end{bmatrix} + \begin{bmatrix} K_1(s) \\ K_2(s) \\ \vdots \\ K_N(s) \end{bmatrix}.$$

As before, this is written as

$$\mathbb{H}^{-1}(s) \cdot \mathbf{V}(s) = \mathbf{E}(s) + \mathbf{K}(s).$$

Notice that $\mathbf{V}(s)$ is just a general response. It is $\mathbf{I}$ if the unknowns are the loop currents. Assuming that $|\mathbb{H}^{-1}| \neq 0$ and is defined, we compute $\mathbb{H}(s)$ and clear to give

$$\mathbf{V}(s) = \mathbb{H}(s) \cdot \{\mathbf{E}(s) + \mathbf{K}(s)\}.$$

To illustrate this operation, briefly consider the abstract problem

$$\frac{1}{\omega_0}\left(\frac{d}{dt} + \omega_0\right)v_1(t) - \frac{1}{\omega_0}\frac{d}{dt}v_2(t) = e_{11}(t),$$

$$-\frac{1}{\omega_0}\frac{d}{dt}v_1(t) + \frac{1}{\omega_0}\left(2\frac{d}{dt} + \omega_0\right)v_2(t) = 0,$$

with initial conditions

$$v_1(0+) = 0, \qquad v_2(0+) = E_0$$

and with

$$e_{11}(t) = E_0 U(t).$$

The $\mathscr{L}$T of this set is

$$\frac{1}{\omega_0}\begin{pmatrix} (s+\omega_0) & -s \\ -s & 2s+\omega_0 \end{pmatrix}\begin{bmatrix} V_1(s) \\ V_2(s) \end{bmatrix} = \begin{bmatrix} \dfrac{E_0}{s} \\ 0 \end{bmatrix} + \begin{bmatrix} -\dfrac{E_0}{\omega_0} \\ \dfrac{2E_0}{\omega_0} \end{bmatrix}.$$

The inverse of $\mathbb{H}^{-1}(s)$ is

$$\mathbb{H}(s) = \frac{\omega_0}{(s^2+3\omega_0 s+\omega_0^2)}\begin{pmatrix} \dfrac{(2s+\omega_0)}{s} & \dfrac{s}{(s+\omega_0)} \end{pmatrix},$$

where

$$|\mathbb{H}^{-1}| = \frac{1}{\omega_0}\begin{vmatrix} (s+\omega_0) & -s \\ -s & (2s+\omega_0) \end{vmatrix} = \frac{[s^2+3\omega_0 s+\omega_0^2]}{\omega_0}$$

and

$$H_{lm}(s) = \frac{(-1)^{l+m}\,\text{minor }H'_{ml}}{|\mathbb{H}^{-1}|}.$$

Multiplying the original matrix equation by $\mathbb{H}(s)$ we get

$$\begin{bmatrix} V_1(s) \\ V_2(s) \end{bmatrix} = \frac{\omega_0}{[s^2+3\omega_0 s+\omega_0^2]}\begin{pmatrix} 2s+\omega_0 & s \\ s & s+\omega_0 \end{pmatrix}\begin{bmatrix} \dfrac{E_0}{s}-\dfrac{E_0}{\omega_0} \\ \dfrac{2E_0}{\omega_0} \end{bmatrix},$$

or

$$V(s) = \mathbb{H}(s)\cdot\{E(s)+K(s)\}.$$

This form gives a complete solution for $V_1(s)$ and $V_2(s)$. Suppose we examine $V_2(s)$:

$$V_2(s) = \frac{\{(\omega_0-s)+2(s+\omega_0)\}E_0}{[s+\frac{1}{2}(3-\sqrt{5})\omega_0][s+\frac{1}{2}(3+\sqrt{5})\omega_0]}$$

and

$$v_2(t) = \mathscr{L}^{-1}[V_2(s)].$$

For convenience, call the roots of the denominator γ_1 and γ_2, where $\gamma_1 = \frac{1}{2}(3-\sqrt{5})\omega_0$ and $\gamma_2 = \frac{1}{2}(3+\sqrt{5})\omega_0$. Thus,

$$v_2(t) = E_0\left\{\left(\frac{3\omega_0-\gamma_1}{\gamma_2-\gamma_1}\right)e^{-\gamma_1 t} + \left(\frac{3\omega_0-\gamma_2}{\gamma_1-\gamma_2}\right)e^{-\gamma_2 t}\right\}U(t).$$

Returning now to the general form of $H_{lm}(s)$, we can see that in the usual problem in which the $v_k(t)$ are the loop currents,

$$H'_{lm}(s) \to -L_{lm}s - R_{lm} - \frac{1}{C_{lm}s}, \qquad (l \neq m),$$

$$H'_{mm}(s) \to \sum_{\text{all }k}\left\{L_{mk}s + R_{mk} + \frac{1}{C_{mk}s}\right\},$$

and $K_j(s)$ contains the initial currents and charges:

$$K_l(s) = \sum_{\text{all } k} \left\{ L_{lk} i_l(0+) - \frac{q_l(0+)}{C_{lk}s} \right\} - \sum_{\text{all } k \neq l} \left\{ L_{lk} i_k(0+) - \frac{q_k(0+)}{C_{lk}s} \right\}.$$

Again the initial charge in the lm branch is

$$q_{lm}(0+) = q_l(0+) - q_m(0+).$$

With these particular dimensions, the transfer function or matrix takes the units of an admittance and is often designated as $\mathbb{Y}(s)$ in place of $\mathbb{H}(s)$.

In conclusion, then, we have considered N simultaneous linear differential-integral equations in N unknowns, $v_j(t)$. The $\mathscr{L}$T of these equations provides N simultaneous algebraic equations in the variable s. Converting to a matrix equation, we invert the operator $\mathbb{H}^{-1}(s)$ and clear to give

$$\mathbf{V}(s) = \mathbb{H}(s) \cdot \{\mathbf{E}(s) + \mathbf{K}(s)\}.$$

The excitation $\mathbf{K}(s)$ is caused by the initial conditions, and in linear circuits $\mathbf{K}$ is a polynomial in s multiplied by $1/s$ if there are integrals in the original set of equations. Thus, the characteristic modes of $\mathbb{H}(s) \cdot \mathbf{K}(s)$ are governed completely by the denominator of $\mathbb{H}(s)$. Each element of $\mathbb{H}(s)$ has the common quantity $|\mathbb{H}^{-1}(s)|$ in the denominator.

As a consequence, we find that the zeros or roots of the polynomial $|\mathbb{H}^{-1}|$ determine the poles of $\mathbb{H}(s)$, i.e., the elements $H_{lm}(s)$. Thus, the portion of the solution that appears as $\mathbb{H}(s) \cdot \mathbf{K}(s)$ transforms to the time domain to give all the characteristic modes of $\mathbb{H}(s)$. Physically, we view this term ($\mathbb{H} \cdot \mathbf{K}$) as a quantity that expands that portion of the transient response which is caused by the initial conditions, in terms of the characteristic modes of the system. Thus, if the capacitor in an unexcited series LRC circuit is initially charged, this initial charge will produce oscillating currents at times greater than $(0+)$.

The product $\mathbb{H}(s) \cdot \mathbf{E}(s)$ is the response to the externally applied excitation. This excitation also causes a transient (or excites the characteristic modes of $\mathbb{H}(s)$) and produces a response that is also characterized by the characteristic modes of the excitation (poles of $\mathbf{E}(s)$). The component of the response that has as elements the characteristic frequencies of $\mathbf{E}(s)$ is normally called the *steady-state solution*.

To sum this last statement, we are saying that the expansion of a product of the type $\mathbb{H}(s) \cdot \mathbf{E}(s)$ will produce a series of partial fractions. One group of partial fractions, which contain all poles of $\mathbb{H}(s)$, represents the initial transient brought about by turning on the excitation. The second group of partial fractions contains terms involving the poles of $\mathbf{E}(s)$, and in the case of sinusoidal excitation is called the *steady-state solution*.

ROOTS OF THE TRANSFER FUNCTION

During the presentation of an earlier section (page 28), a number of important properties of the transfer function was introduced. We shall profit by mentioning some again and by expanding upon some of the properties.

We have seen that N equations in N unknowns can be reduced to a matrix equation of the type

$$\mathbf{V}(s) = \mathbb{H}(s) \cdot \{\mathbf{E}(s) + \mathbf{K}(s)\},$$

where $\mathbf{V}(s) = \mathscr{L}\mathrm{T}$ of the response

$\mathbb{H}(s) =$ inverse of the $\mathscr{L}\mathrm{T}$ of the differential integral operator (a matrix)

$\mathbf{E}(s) = \mathscr{L}\mathrm{T}$ of the applied excitation

$\mathbf{K}(s) = \mathscr{L}\mathrm{T}$ of the excitation provided by the initial conditions.

The importance of $\mathbb{H}(s)$ was stressed:

1. The term $\mathbb{H}(s) \cdot \mathbf{K}(s)$ gave the transient solution caused by the initial conditions of the problem. This transient contains the eigenfrequencies of the transfer operator $\mathbb{H}(s)$.
2. The term $\mathbb{H} \cdot \mathbf{E}$ gives *a* transient solution in terms of the eigenfrequencies of $H(s)$. This transient is caused by turning on the excitation.
3. The quantity $\mathbb{H}(s) \cdot \mathbf{E}(s)$ also gives a term involving the poles of $\mathbf{E}(s)$ or the characteristic frequencies of the excitation. If the excitation is sinusoidal, this is known as the steady-state solution.

The characteristics of $\mathbb{H}(s)$ can be described graphically by plotting the poles and zeros of $\mathbb{H}(s)$ in the complex s plane. This is equivalent to listing the characteristic modes (poles) and their amplitudes (the zeros). The zeros give the amplitudes of the characteristic modes under excitation by a delta function in the following manner: The amplitude of a given mode is the product of the distances between the appropriate pole and all zeros, divided by the product of the distances of that pole from all other poles. Obviously, then, if a zero is constructed to lie at the position of a pole, the net amplitude of that mode is zero (i.e., it is removed). See Fig. 33.

The product of the n_l divided by the product of all of the d_j is the strength of mode k in the final expansion.

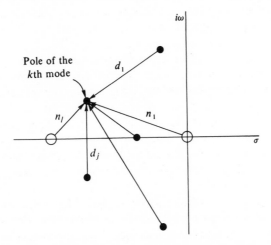

FIG. 33.   An example s-plane plot of the poles (characteristic modes) and zeros of a transfer function. The product of the n_l divided by the product of all the d_j is the relative strength of this mode in the final expansion.

In the s plane plot shown in Fig. 33 there are five poles but only three eigen-frequencies because a conjugate pair is counted as one frequency. This is a convention in which we consider positive and negative imaginary frequencies of the same magnitude as the same frequency. For ease of discussion, the authors have chosen to associate each pole with a separate characteristic mode.

Up to this point, questions of stability of the system represented by $H(s)$ have been avoided. Actually, we have implied that our discussions were in the main concerned with stable systems, since we referred only to poles in the left-hand complex s plane (poles with negative real parts).

Consider a scalar $H(s)$ of the type

$$H(s) = \frac{\sum\limits_{m=0}^{M} b_m s^m}{\sum\limits_{n=0}^{N} a_n s^n} = H_0 \frac{\prod\limits_{m=1}^{M} (s + \beta_m)}{\prod\limits_{n=1}^{N} (s + \gamma_n)}; \quad (M < N).$$

The expansion theorem enables us to evaluate the coefficients B_l in the expansion

$$H(s) = H_0 \sum_{n=1}^{N} \frac{B_n}{s + \gamma_n},$$

giving

$$h(t) = \mathscr{L}^{-1}[H(s)] = H_0 \sum_{n=1}^{N} B_n e^{-\gamma_n t}.$$

In their general form the roots $-\gamma_n$ are complex:

$$\gamma_n = \alpha_n + iW_n,$$

where α_n and w_n are real numbers (positive and negative). With the root sign convention chosen, the characteristic modes behave as $\exp(-\gamma_n t)$. Thus, if α_n in the expression above is negative, the exponential solution would have a positive-real part and would represent an undefined function for t arbitrarily large. These solutions (negative α_n) are poles in the right half-plane ($s = -\alpha_n - iw_n$) and are designated as unstable solutions.

If the α_n are zero, the poles lie upon the imaginary axis. These solutions are steady-state sustained oscillations. As such, they are pure sinusoidal wave forms of constant amplitude. The points on the imaginary axis represent the threshold of instability. Oscillators normally employ a nonlinear active device to prevent the exponential blowup that is present when the roots are in the right-hand plane. Ordinarily we are interested in stable transfer functions.

Finding the roots of a complicated $H(s)$ may be tedious and in some instances impracticable. To simplify the analysis, there are some elementary properties of polynomials that may be examined.

Regard the forms of the denominator of $H(s)$. The eigenvalues or characteristic frequencies of the characteristic modes occur as roots of the denominator, i.e., when the polynomial of the denominator vanishes. The same argument holds when the denominator is not a polynomial, except that the poles become branch points requiring special techniques to evaluate the inverse transform of $H(s)$. All passive networks and all active networks with which we are concerned are accounted for by polynomials in the denominator of $H(s)$. We write this polynomial as

$$H(s) = \frac{\sum\limits_{m=0}^{M} b_m s^m}{\sum\limits_{n=0}^{N} a_n s^n}, \qquad (M \leqslant N);$$

with $a_N = 1$, and

$$\sum_{n=0}^{N} a_n s^n = \prod_{n=1}^{N} (s + \gamma_n)$$

$$= s^N + \left\{ \sum_{n=1}^{N} \gamma_n \right\} s^{N-1} + \frac{1}{2} \left\{ \sum_{\substack{j=1 \\ j \neq k}}^{N} \sum_{k=1}^{N} \gamma_j \gamma_k \right\} s^{N-2} + \frac{1}{3} \left\{ \sum_{l \neq m \neq n} \sum_{m \neq n} \sum_{n} \gamma_l \gamma_m \gamma_n \right\} s^{N-3} + \cdots + \prod_{n=1}^{N} \gamma_n.$$

Thus, if all the coefficients of the polynomial a_n are real, the appearance of a complex root $-\gamma_k$ requires the presence of a second root, which is the complex conjugate of $-\gamma_k$ (see the coefficient of s^{N-1}). Therefore, for real coefficients, the complex roots will occur in conjugate pairs.

Our problem then concerns the real part of every root. A necessary (but not sufficient) condition that the real part of the roots $(-\gamma_n)$ be negative (i.e., α_n positive) is that all a_n have the same sign. A further necessary condition for negative roots is that all the a_n in a polynomial be nonzero. This would follow because of the indeterminant sign of a zero.

Preliminary inspection of a polynomial will tell whether or not it is possible to have stable solutions. If all the a_n are of the same sign and are nonzero, stability of the roots is still not guaranteed. A convenient test for stability is the Routh-Hurwitz criterion. We shall outline this test briefly. To set up the problem, we arrange the coefficients of the polynomial in rows, with the even shifts in the first row and the odd shifts in the second row. The remaining rows will be composed of terms formed from 2×2 determinants taken from the rows just preceding.

If the polynomial is

$$\sum_{n=0}^{N} a_n s^n,$$

we write (assume N even, for example)

a_N	a_{N-2}	a_{N-4}	$\cdots$	$\cdots$	a_2	a_0 ;	$\left\{ \left(\frac{N}{2} + 1 \right) \text{terms} \right\}$
a_{N-1}	a_{N-3}	a_{N-5}	$\cdots$	$\cdots$	a_1	$\cdots$;	$\left\{ \frac{N}{2} \text{ terms} \right\}$
a'_N	a'_{N-2}	a'_{N-4}	$\cdots$	$\cdots$	a'_2	$\cdots$;	$\left\{ \left(\frac{N}{2} - 1 \right) \text{terms} \right\}$
a''_{N-1}	a''_{N-3}	a''_{N-5}	$\cdots$	a''_3	$\cdots$	$\cdots$;	$\left\{ \left(\frac{N}{2} - 2 \right) \text{terms} \right\}$
$\vdots$							$\vdots$
$a'''_N {}^{\cdots\prime}$	$\cdots$	$\cdots$	$\cdots$	$\cdots$	$\cdots$	$\cdots$;	$\{1 \text{ term}\}$

Examine the signs of the first column.

The third row is formed by taking 2×2 determinants of the first two rows.

$$a_N' = -\frac{1}{a_{N-1}} \begin{vmatrix} a_N & a_{N-2} \\ a_{N-1} & a_{N-3} \end{vmatrix}; \quad a_{N-2}' = -\frac{1}{a_{N-1}} \begin{vmatrix} a_N & a_{N-4} \\ a_{N-1} & a_{N-5} \end{vmatrix}.$$

The fourth row is formed by taking 2×2 determinants from the elements of the two preceding rows, the second and third:

$$a_{N-1}'' = -\frac{1}{a_N'} \begin{vmatrix} a_{N-1} & a_{N-3} \\ a_N' & a_{N-2}' \end{vmatrix}; \quad a_{N-3}'' = -\frac{1}{a_N'} \begin{vmatrix} a_{N-1} & a_{N-s} \\ a_N' & a_{N-4}' \end{vmatrix}.$$

This procedure is carried out until there is but one term, $a_N'''^{\cdots'}$. If all terms in the first column have the same sign, the real part of the root is negative. Because our γ_n are the negatives of the roots, this means that α_n, the real part of γ_n, is positive.

A graphical study of the stability of $H(s)$ can be performed by regarding $H(s)$ as a transformation from the complex s plane to the complex $H(s)$ plane. To accomplish this, we write $H(s)$ as a complex function,

$$H(s) = u(\sigma, \omega) + iv(\sigma, \omega),$$

where

$$H(s) = H_0 \frac{\prod\limits_{m=1}^{M} (s + \beta_m)}{\prod\limits_{n=1}^{N} (s + \gamma_n)}.$$

One can map a contour C in the s plane directly into the $H(s)$ plane and study the stability in terms of the structure of the mapping. Unfortunately, we are interested in the poles of $H(s)$. A pole in the s plane is then mapped to a point at infinity in the $H(s)$ plane. Later we shall construct the open-loop transfer contour which passes near the origin in the s plane. A conformal mapping to $H(s)$ places the point $|s| \to \infty$ at the origin of the H plane.

To simplify this problem, we employ a mapping from the s plane to the *inverse* H plane or $H^{-1}(s)$. We define, then,

$$H^{-1}(s) = \frac{u(\sigma\,\omega)}{[u^2 + v^2]} - i\,\frac{v(\sigma, \omega)}{[u^2 + v^2]} = \xi(\sigma, \omega) + i\zeta(\sigma, \omega),$$

with

$$H^{-1}(s) = \frac{\prod\limits_{n=1}^{N} (s + \gamma_n)}{H_0 \prod\limits_{m=1}^{M} (s + \beta_m)}.$$

When a closed contour C in the s plane contains *one* pole of $H(s)$, the transformed contour C' in the $H^{-1}(s)$ plane encircles the origin once, in the same sense of circulation as that of C. See Fig. 34.

This characteristic of the transformation is apparent if we locate points on C relative to the pole $-\gamma_j$ by a polar vector $\rho_j e^{i\phi_j}$ and points on C relative to a zero $-\beta_k$ by a polar vector $R_k e^{i\theta_k}$. Then

$$H^{-1}(s \text{ on } C') = H_0 \frac{\rho_1 \rho_2 \cdots \rho_N}{R_1 R_2 \cdots R_M} e^{i(\phi_1 + \phi_2 + \cdots + \phi_N)} e^{-i(\theta_1 + \theta_2 + \cdots + \theta_M)}.$$

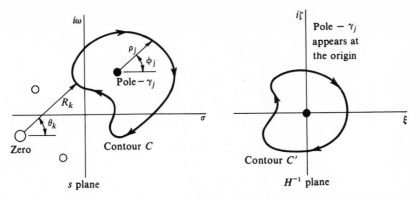

FIG. 34.   Transformation of a contour from the s-plane to the H^{-1} plane when C encloses
one pole.

Thus, one circuit about $-\gamma_j$ gives a total change in the phase ϕ_j of 2π and a total
change of phase about the origin of H^{-1} of $+2\pi$. The total phase change in one traversal of C due to poles and zeros outside C is zero. If the path C does not enclose a
pole or a zero, we notice that the contour C' does not contain the origin. If C encloses
n poles, C' makes n circuits about the origin in $H^{-1}(s)$. On the other hand, if C encloses n poles and m zeros, the contour C' makes $(m - n)$ circuits about the origin of
the $H^{-1}(s)$ plane in the direction of C if $n < m$. The example in Fig. 35 shows two poles
inside C.

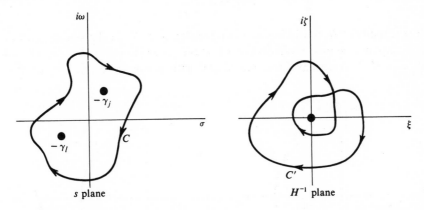

FIG. 35.   Transformation of a contour C from the s plane to the H^{-1} plane when C contains
two poles. In this example, C' makes two complete traversals about the origin in the H^{-1}
plane.

If C contains a zero $(-\beta_i)$, the variable $(s + \beta_i) = R_i\ e^{i\theta_i}$ causes C' in H^{-1} to
circle once in a direction opposite to the circulation in s.

A stability test for $H(s)$ can be constructed by forming a semicircular closed path
C encompassing the right-hand s plane as shown in Fig. 36. All encirclements of the
origin that are to occur in $H^{-1}(s)$ arise in the traversal of the imaginary axis in the s
plane. The graph of $-\infty < \omega < +\infty$, $\sigma = \lim_{\varepsilon \to 0} \varepsilon = 0 +$ is called the *open-loop transfer*
locus. A system is stable if the open-loop transfer locus does not pass through $H^{-1} = 0$

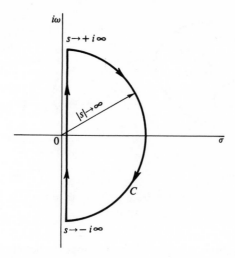

FIG. 36.   Contour of the open-loop transfer locus.

and if the number of counterclockwise encirclements of $H^{-1} = 0$ equals the number of zeros enclosed in C.

As an example, consider an elementary transfer function, which will be known as a *low-pass function*:

$$H(s) = \frac{\alpha}{(s + \alpha)}.$$

The stability of $H(s)$ will depend upon the sign of α. As an elementary illustration, we shall map the open-loop transfer locus C in the s plane to the H^{-1} plane. Obviously, in this case H^{-1} will behave as s, scaled and with the origin displaced. See Fig. 37.

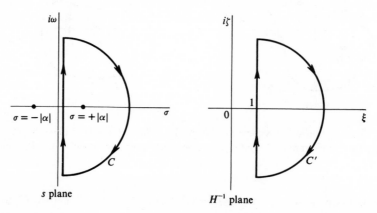

FIG. 37.   Transformation of the open-loop transfer contour in the case $H(s) = \alpha/(s + a)$.

Because $s = \sigma + i\omega$ and $H^{-1}(s) = (\sigma + \alpha)/\alpha] + i(\omega/\alpha)$, the contour C' is similar to C except for the shift along the real ξ axis, if α is a positive-real number. The case in which α is a negative-real number corresponds to a reflection about the vertical line at $\xi = +1$. See Fig. 38.

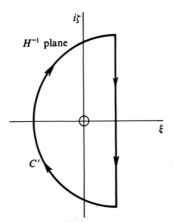

H^{-1} plane

C'

FIG. 38.   Open-loop transfer contour when the pole of $H(s)$ is in the right-hand portion of the s plane.

Again because a negative α corresponds to a pole at $\sigma = +|\alpha|$ on the positive-real axis of the s plane, this pole is then inside the contour; and the contour C' encircles the origin in H^{-1} in a clockwise fashion. This encirclement indicates that $H(s)$ is unstable for $\alpha < \sigma$.

We could also examine the polynomial $(s + \alpha)$ with the Routh-Hurwitz criterion. According to our procedure, $a_0 = 1$ and $a_{\cdot} = \alpha$. Grouping is trivial, but it gives the column

$$\begin{vmatrix} 1 \\ \alpha \end{vmatrix}.$$

The result obtained now becomes apparent. If α is positive, all of the signs are the same and the roots are negative-real parts. On the other hand, if α were negative, we would have a sign change in the column, indicating an instability.

Before completing this section we mention an added aspect of $H(s)$ when viewed as a conformal transformation. We deal directly with the transformation

$$H(s) = u(\sigma, \omega) + iv(\sigma, \omega).$$

Again consider the elementary low-pass transformation

$$H(s) = \frac{\alpha}{(s + \alpha)}.$$

Then

$$u = \frac{\alpha(\sigma + \alpha)}{[(\sigma + \alpha)^2 + \omega^2]}$$

and

$$v = \frac{-\alpha\omega}{[(\sigma + \alpha)^2 + \omega^2]}.$$

The frequency response of $H(s)$ is obtained from that portion of the open-loop transfer locus corresponding to $\sigma = 0+$ (where σ = a constant). Lines of constant σ

transformed to the H plane can be obtained by eliminating ω from u and v to give

$$v^2 + \left(u - \frac{\alpha}{2(\sigma + \alpha)}\right)^2 = \frac{\alpha^2}{4(\sigma + \alpha)^2}.$$

At $\sigma = 0$,

$$v^2 + (u - \tfrac{1}{2})^2 = \tfrac{1}{4};$$

this is a circle of radius $1/2$ with the center at $+1/2$.

The magnitude of H as a function of frequency ω is then the distance from the origin to the appropriate point on the circle. See Fig. 39.

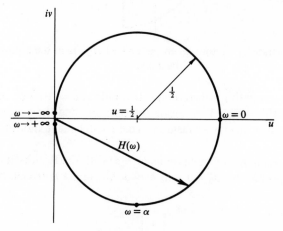

FIG. 39. $H(s)$ represented as a conformal transformation. The low-pass positive ω function is confined to the lower half-circle.

As ω varies from zero to $+\infty$, the corresponding points in the H plane move along the lower arc of the circle. $\omega = 0$ corresponds to $u = 1$, $v = 0$, if α is real. We shall observe that when the root is complex, the point corresponding to $\omega = 0$ lies on the lower arc of the circle, but not on the real axis u. The negative imaginary axis in the s plane corresponds to the upper arc of the circle.

As a second example, regard the high-pass function

$$H(s) = \frac{s}{(s + \alpha)}.$$

Then

$$u(\sigma, \omega) = 1 - \frac{\alpha(\sigma + \alpha)}{[(\sigma + \alpha)^2 + \omega^2]}$$

and

$$v(\sigma, \omega) = \frac{\alpha\omega}{[(\sigma + \alpha)^2 + \omega^2]}.$$

This form, as we would expect, is the earlier transfer subtracted from 1:

$$\frac{s}{(s + \alpha)} = 1 - \frac{\alpha}{(s + \alpha)}.$$

Consequently, the equation with ω eliminated and for $\sigma = 0$ is again

$$v^2 + (u - \tfrac{1}{2})^2 = \tfrac{1}{4}.$$

The big difference lies in the interval on the circle corresponding to $0 < \omega < \infty$. The positive imaginary axis $i\omega$ is now the upper half-circle, and the point for $\omega = 0$ lies at the origin, with the point for $\omega \to \infty$ at $u = +1$. See Fig. 40.

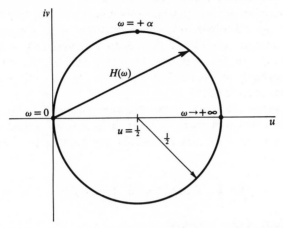

FIG. 40.   The high-pass transfer function represented as a conformal transformation.

THE RESPONSE OF $H(s)$ TO SPECIFIC EXCITATIONS

Experimentally, one is often faced with the problem of accounting for the properties of a system when the system details are not available to direct inspection. For instance, many experiments in physics are black-box experiments to the extent that our information is obtained by interrogating the system with a known excitation and measuring the response to this excitation. If this is done a number of times with different excitations, many properties of the system can be deduced.

In the next few sections we shall describe the manner in which the transfer function is related to the response under excitation by a known signal. Initially, an ideal delta function (or impulse) excitation will be discussed. We shall observe that the system-transfer function is the response to a delta function. Thus, the inverse transform of the transfer, $h(t) = \mathscr{L}^{-1}[H(s)]$, is the Green's function of the system operator.

After this idealized excitation has been discussed, we shall investigate the response to more realistic excitations such as step functions, gates, and sinusoids. In conclusion, then, we shall be interested to find out how much information about the transfer function can be gleaned from the responses to these excitations.

Response to an Impulse or Delta Function

At the outset of the discussion of the operational method, we introduced the delta function $\delta(t)$. We mentioned then that some controversy exists concerning the use of this function. This difficulty occurs because many authors inadvertently separate the function and its essential employment under an integral sign. We have exhibited the function often without an integral sign. On the other hand, the statement was made (and must be adhered to) that the integral is always carried in the "mind's eye" as an equation is read and manipulated.

If one blindly specifies the delta function as an object well defined outside the integral, certain mathematical discrepancies may result. However, when the order of integration and taking of limits is always clearly maintained, the delta function is a consistent and well-defined mathematical device.†

There are a number of ways in which this function can be specified. If the system is represented by an Nth-order differential equation, it is sufficient to construct a Green's function that has the $(N - 2)$th derivative represented as a function with a cusp at, say, t'. After two differentiations to achieve the Nth derivative, this function will exhibit a singularity at $t = t'$. [The derivative $(N - 1)$ will possess a jump discontinuity, of unit magnitude.]

Our method in the discussion of the algebraic nature of the linear equations with constant coefficients was somewhat more direct in that we started with the function $\Delta_T(t) = (1/T)(U(t) - U(t - T))$ and considered the limit of the integral of $\Delta_T(t)$ as $T \to 0$:

$$\lim_{T \to 0} \int_{-\infty}^{\infty} \Delta_T(t)\, dt = \lim_{T \to 0} \int_{0}^{\infty} \Delta_T(t)\, dt = 1, \qquad (0 \leqslant t).$$

We also noticed at that time that

$$\lim_{T \to 0} \int_{0}^{t+} \Delta_T(t' - t)\, dt' = 1, \qquad (t \geqslant 0).$$

This last result is essential because the delta function is a symmetric function; thus,

$$\lim_{T \to 0} \int_{0}^{t} \Delta_T(t' - t)\, dt' = \lim_{T \to 0} \int_{0}^{t} \Delta_T(t - t')\, dt' = 1, \qquad (0 \leqslant t).$$

The last integral in this expression is certainly 1, and by symmetry is equal to the integral on the left.

Other forms of $\delta(t' - t)$ that we can employ are

$$\delta(t' - t) \to \frac{1}{\sqrt{2\pi}}\, e^{-i\omega(t' - t)},$$

(when the exponential is integrated over all ω);

$$\delta(t' - t) \to \lim_{a \to 0} \cdots \frac{\sin\left(\dfrac{t' - t}{a}\right)}{\pi(t' - t)},$$

and

$$\delta(t' - t) \to \lim_{a \to 0} \cdots \frac{1}{a\sqrt{2\pi}}\, e^{-[(t' - t)^2/2a^2]}.$$

---

† See M. Lighthill, *Generalized Functions*, Cambridge University Press, 1959.

Notice that the direct equality has been avoided here in order to direct attention to the fact that limiting processes are indicated without integrating over t' first. This is an improper order, which must be kept in mind.

The convolution of a function $f(t)$ with the delta function gives the function evaluated at the point designated by the argument of the delta function:

$$\int_0^\infty \delta(t' - t)f(t')\, dt' = \int_0^t \delta(t' - t)f(t')\, dt' = f(t).$$

This property was demonstrated earlier. We can indicate a similar proof in the following manner:

$$\int_0^\infty f(t)\, \delta(t)\, dt = \lim_{T \to 0} \int_0^\infty f(t) \cdot \frac{1}{T} \cdot \{U(t) - U(t - T)\}\, dt$$

$$= \lim_{T \to 0} \int_0^T f(t) \cdot \frac{1}{T}\, dt.$$

To evaluate this integral, we expand $f(t)$ in a Taylor's series about zero; assuming, of course, that all derivatives of $f(t)$ exist at $t \to 0$. Then

$$\lim_{T \to 0} \int_0^T f(t) \frac{dt}{T} = \lim_{T \to 0} \int_0^T \{f(0) + [f'(0)]t + h.t.\} \frac{dt}{T}$$

$$= f(0).$$

Another way of writing this is

$$\int_0^t f(t')\, \delta(t' - t)\, dt' = \int_0^t f(t') \frac{dU(t' - t)}{dt'}\, dt' = \int_0^t f(t')\, dU(t' - t)$$

$$= f(t).$$

The Laplace transform of $\delta(t)$ is unity. This can be shown with any of the forms for $\delta(t)$. For instance,

$$\mathscr{L}[\delta(t)] = \lim_{T \to 0} \int_0^\infty \frac{1}{T} \{U(t) - U(t - T)\}\, e^{-st}\, dt$$

and

$$\mathscr{L}[\delta(t)] = \lim_{T \to 0} \frac{1}{T} \left\{ \frac{1}{s} - \frac{1}{s} e^{-sT} \right\} = 1.$$

In like manner,

$$\mathscr{L}^{-1}[1] = \delta(t).$$

remembering, of course, the essential integral and limit.

The Convolution Integral and the Green's Function

A very useful relation in the employment of the $\mathscr{L}T$ is the fact that the product of two Laplace transforms is equal to the $\mathscr{L}T$ of the convolution of the inverse transforms. If†

$$\mathscr{L}[f(t)] = F(s) \quad \text{and} \quad \mathscr{L}[g(t)] = G(s),$$

then

$$\mathscr{L}\left[\int_0^t f(t - t')g(t') \, dt'\right] = \mathscr{L}\left[\int_0^t f(t')g(t - t') \, dt'\right]$$

$$= F(s)G(s).$$

To prove this relation, we convert the integral on the right to an integral from 0 to ∞ by substituting a reverse step $U(t - t')$:

$$U(t - t') = 1, \quad \text{for } t' < t,$$

$$= 0, \quad \text{for } t < t'.$$

$$\mathscr{L}\left[\int_0^t f(t - t')g(t') \, dt'\right] = \int_0^\infty dt' \, g(t')\left\{\int_0^\infty f(t - t')U(t - t') \, e^{-st} \, dt\right\}$$

$$= \int_0^\infty dt' \, g(t')\left\{\int_{t'}^\infty f(t - t') \, e^{-s(t-t')} \, e^{-st'} \, dt\right\}.$$

The order of integration has been changed in the intermediate integral expression Now let $\tau = t - t'$; then

$$\mathscr{L}\left[\int_0^t f(t - t')g(t') \, dt'\right] = \int_0^\infty dt' \, g(t') \, e^{-st'} \int_0^\infty d\tau \, f(\tau) \, e^{-s\tau}$$

$$= F(s)G(s).$$

The convolution integral as described may be used to solve inhomogeneous equations; in other words, the particular response to an excitation $e(t)$ can be obtained in this manner. Although we have shown this before, the convolution theorem provides a short and elegant demonstration. Consider

$$H^{-1}(t)v(t) = e(t).$$

After transforming, this becomes

$$V(s) = H(s)E(s) + H(s)K(s).$$

For convenience, assume that the system is initially relaxed, i.e. $K(s) = 0$. We also show this as a scalar multiplication. The results can be readily generalized to the matrix form. In the preceding equation,

$$\mathscr{L}[v(t)] = V(s),$$

$$\mathscr{L}[h(t)] = H(s),$$

and

$$\mathscr{L}[e(t)] = E(s).$$

The product $H(s)E(s)$ can be converted to the time domain via the convolution theorem. Repeating the sequence of steps, we start with

$$V(s) = H(s)E(s).$$

---

† In this instance, $g(t)$ is any function of t, not the gate function necessarily.

Then, using the convolution theorem,†

$$v(t) = \mathcal{L}^{-1}[H(s)E(s)] = \int_0^t h(t - t')e(t')\, dt',$$

where

$$H^{-1}(t)v(t) = e(t).$$

The function $h(t)$, or $h(t - t')$, is the response to a delta function excitation and is called the *Green's function*. To prove this, we note that if

$$H^{-1}(t)h(t - t') = \delta(t' - t),$$

then Laplace-transforming both sides gives

$$\mathcal{L}[h(t)] = \mathcal{L}\left[\frac{\delta(t)}{H^{-1}(t)}\right] = H(s) \cdot 1.$$

Finally, we operate directly on the integral solution for $v(t)$:

$$H^{-1}(t)v(t) = H^{-1}(t)\int_0^\infty h(t - t')e(t')\, dt' = \int_0^\infty H^{-1}(t)h(t - t')e(t')\, dt'.$$

The step function $U(t - t')$ terminates the integral at t, giving

$$H^{-1}(t)v(t) = \int_0^t \delta(t' - t)e(t')\, dt' = e(t).$$

We should comment that $h(t - t')$ is often written as $h(t, t')$, particularly when $h(t, t')$ is represented in terms of products of the solutions of the operator that provide a cusp in the $(N - 2)$th derivative of h. In discussions, of circuits the Green's function $h(t - t')$ is ordinarily called the *impulse response*, for obvious reasons. If the response to a delta function excitation is designated by $v_\Delta(t) = \mathcal{L}^{-1}[V_\Delta(s)]$, we can write

$$V_\Delta(s) = H(s),$$

and

$$v_\Delta(t) = h(t).$$

In the second section of this chapter, we saw several examples of $h(t)$. A few, with the associated operators, are listed in Table 3.

TABLE 3

$H^{-1}(t)$	$H(s) = V_\Delta(s)$	$h(t) = v_\Delta(t)$
$\left(\dfrac{d}{dt} + \gamma_n\right)$	$\dfrac{1}{(s + \gamma_n)}$	$e^{-\gamma_n t}U(t)$
$\dfrac{1}{\omega_0}\left(\dfrac{d^2}{dt^2} + \omega_0^2\right)$	$\dfrac{\omega_0}{(s^2 + \omega_0^2)}$	$\sin \omega_0 t\, U(t)$
$\left(\dfrac{d^2}{dt^2} + 2\alpha\dfrac{d}{dt} + \alpha^2\right)$	$\dfrac{1}{(s + \alpha)^2}$	$(1 + \alpha t)e^{-\alpha t}U(t)$

† $h(t)$ in the $\mathcal{L}T$ representation contains $U(t)$. The convolution integral is terminated at the upper limit t because $U(t - t')$ is understood to have been included with $h(t - t')$. In the integration over t', $U(t - t')$ has the value $+1$ from $-\infty$ to t and zero for $t < t'$.

The matrix forms are handled in much the same manner. As an example, consider the following set of coupled equations:

$$f(t) + \int_0^t f(t')\, dt' - \int_0^t g(t')\, dt' = e_1(t),$$

$$-\int_0^t f(t')\, dt' + 2g(t) + \int_0^t g(t')\, dt' = e_2(t).$$

The $\mathscr{L}$T of these equations is

$$\left(1 + \frac{1}{s}\right)F(s) - \frac{1}{s}\, G(s) = E_1(s),$$

$$-\frac{1}{s}\, F(s) + \left(2 + \frac{1}{s}\right)G(s) = E_2(s).$$

In the matrix form,

$$\mathbb{H}^{-1}(s) \cdot \begin{bmatrix} F(s) \\ G(s) \end{bmatrix} = \begin{bmatrix} E_1(s) \\ E_2(s) \end{bmatrix} = \begin{pmatrix} \dfrac{(1+s)}{s} & -\dfrac{1}{s} \\ -\dfrac{1}{s} & \dfrac{(1+2s)}{s} \end{pmatrix} \begin{bmatrix} F(s) \\ G(s) \end{bmatrix}.$$

Inverting the matrix $\mathbb{H}^{-1}(s)$, we obtain

$$|\mathbb{H}^{-1}(s)| = \frac{(2s+3)}{s}$$

and

$$\mathbb{H}(s) = \begin{pmatrix} \left(\dfrac{2s+1}{2s+3}\right) & \dfrac{1}{(2s+3)} \\ \dfrac{1}{(2s+3)} & \left(\dfrac{s+1}{2s+3}\right) \end{pmatrix}.$$

The Green's function, or delta function response, is now a matrix instead of a scalar function. The inverse $\mathscr{L}$T to the time domain gives elements $h_{lm}(t - t')$:

$$\mathscr{L}^{-1}[\mathbb{H}(s)] = \begin{pmatrix} [\delta(t) - e^{-(3/2t)}U(t)] & \frac{1}{2}e^{-(3/2t)}U(t) \\ \frac{1}{2}e^{-(3/2t)}U(t) & [\frac{1}{2}\delta(t) - \frac{1}{4}e^{-(3/2t)}U(t)] \end{pmatrix}.$$

To see how this is employed, we carry out the matrix convolution

$$\begin{bmatrix} f(t) \\ g(t) \end{bmatrix} = \int_0^t \begin{pmatrix} h_{11}(t - t') & h_{12}(t - t') \\ h_{21}(t - t') & h_{22}(t - t') \end{pmatrix} \begin{bmatrix} e_1(t') \\ e_2(t') \end{bmatrix} dt',$$

giving, say,

$$f(t) = \int_0^t \{h_{11}(t - t')e_1(t') + h_{12}(t - t')e_2(t')\}\, dt'$$

or

$$f(t) = e_1(t) + e^{-(3/2t)} \int_0^t \{-e_1(t') + \tfrac{1}{2}e_2(t')\}e^{(3/2)t'}\, dt'.$$

This demonstrates the manner in which the Green's matrix can be employed.

In actual practice, it is often feasible to interrogate a system with an exciting pulse that is much shorter than the relaxation times (or one over the characteristic frequencies) of the system. The response to such an excitation can simulate the Green's function to a fair approximation.

As an example, consider a system described by $H^{-1}(t) = \{(d/dt) + \gamma\}$. The impulse response is

$$H(s) = V_\Delta(s) = \frac{1}{(s + \gamma)}$$

and

$$h(t) = e^{-\gamma t}U(t).$$

Suppose experimentally we can interrogate with a gate function $g_T(t)$, wherein the width of the gate, T, is much less than $1/\gamma$:

$$g_T(t) = \{U(t) - U(t - T)\}$$

and

$$T \ll \frac{1}{\gamma}.$$

Then

$$V_G(s) = H(s)\frac{1}{s}(1 - e^{-sT}) = \frac{1}{s(s + \gamma)}(1 - e^{-sT})$$

and

$$v_G(t) = \frac{1}{\gamma}(1 - e^{-\gamma t})U(t) - \frac{1}{\gamma}(1 - e^{-\gamma(t - T)})U(t - T).$$

For times somewhat longer than T,

$$v_G(t) \xrightarrow[T < t]{} \frac{1}{\gamma}e^{-\gamma t}(e^{\gamma T} - 1).$$

Because $T \ll 1/\gamma$, we can expand to first order, and

$$v_G(t) \xrightarrow[T < t]{} Te^{-\gamma t}.$$

Thus, to a normalization factor $1/T$ the response, to $g_T(t)$ for $T < t$ is essentially $h(t)$ if $T \ll 1/\gamma$.

$$Tv_G(t) \xrightarrow[T < t]{} e^{-\gamma t} \xrightarrow[T < t]{} h(t).$$

Therefore this is an extremely important concept. We are claiming that interrogation by a gate of width T (where T is less than the characteristic period of the system $1/\gamma$) gives a response that is a fair approximation of the Green's function (or impulse response).

A very short gate is often difficult to manufacture. The system operator can still be studied with other excitations. Experimentally, it is frequently possible to produce a step type excitation that has a short rise time as compared to the characteristic periods of the system.

Since the step function is the integral of the delta function, the transfer response $h(t)$ should be present in the response to a step excitation.

Response to a Step Excitation and the Superposition Integral

Consider an initially relaxed system described in terms of an impulse excitation and a response $h(t)$;

$$H^{-1}(t)h(t) = \delta(t).$$

This expression can be integrated once to give

$$\int_0^t H^{-1}(t)h(t - t')\, dt' = U(t)$$

or

$$H^{-1}(t) \int_0^t h(t - t')\, dt' = U(t).$$

If we Laplace-transform both sides of this equation, we obtain

$$\mathscr{L}\left[\int_0^t h(t - t')\, dt'\right] = \frac{H(s)}{s}$$

or

$$V_U(s) = \frac{H(s)}{s}.$$

The transform of the transfer function is then

$$H(s) = sV_U(s).$$

Thus, if one obtains the response to a step excitation, the transfer function can be obtained by differentiation:

$$h(t) = \mathscr{L}^{-1}[H(s)] = \frac{d}{dt} v_U(t) + v_U(0+)\delta(t), \qquad (v_U(t) = \mathscr{L}^{-1}[V_U(s)]),$$

We can represent the response to a general excitation in terms of the response to the step excitation:

$$V(s) = H(s)E(s) = sV_U(s)E(s).$$

This expression can be converted to the time domain by introducing the convolution of the product:

$$v(t) = \frac{d}{dt} \mathscr{L}^{-1}[V_U(s)E(s)] = \frac{d}{dt} \int_0^t v_U(t - t')e(t')\, dt'.$$

By regrouping the product expression for $V(s)$, we obtain this result in several different forms:

$$v(t) = \mathscr{L}^{-1}[V_U(s) \cdot s \cdot E(s)] = \int_0^t \mathscr{L}^{-1}[V_U(s)] \cdot \mathscr{L}^{-1}[sE(s)]\, dt'.$$

$$v(t) = \int_0^t v_U(t - t') \left\{ \frac{de(t')}{dt'} + e(0+) \, \delta(t') \right\} dt'$$

$$= e(0+)v_U(t) + \int_0^t v_U(t - t') \frac{de(t')}{dt'} \, dt'.$$

If s is associated with the $V_U(s)$ term,

$$v(t) = \mathscr{L}^{-1}[E(s) \cdot s \cdot V_U(s)] = v_U(0+)e(t) + \int_0^t e(t - t') \frac{dv_U}{dt'} \, dt'.$$

The graphical interpretation of these integrals is relatively straightforward. For instance, consider the second relation.

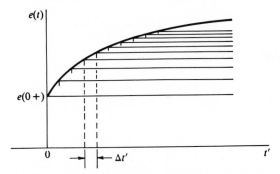

FIG. 41.   Illustration of the superposition integral.

The response to a unit step at $t = 0$ is $v_U(t)$; therefore, at any time t (see Fig. 41),

$$v(t) = e(0+)v(t) + \lim_{\Delta t' \to 0} \sum_{t'=0}^{t} \left[\frac{\Delta e(t')}{\Delta t'} \right] \Delta t' \, v_U(t - t').$$

In an interval $\Delta t'$ at t, the response changes by

$$\Delta v = \Delta e \cdot v_U(\Delta t).$$

Response to a Gate

The response to a gate ordinarily must be carried out in detail for the specific transfer function under consideration. One should keep in mind, however, the limiting situations.

As shown earlier, if the width of the gate is much shorter than the characteristic periods of the system, the response is quite similar to the delta function response. If the width of the gate is much longer than the characteristic periods of $H(s)$, the response is close to the step response $v_U(t)$.

There is a general problem that arises for many excitations, that is, the response of periodically excited systems for times long after the transient components of the wave form have become negligible. The periodic gate is an excitation that allows us to study the steady-state response with ease. For this reason, we incorporate a discussion of the response to periodic excitations in this section.

To begin with, let us consider the simplest case: the gate of amplitude 1 and with equal "off" and "on" periods. See Fig. 42.

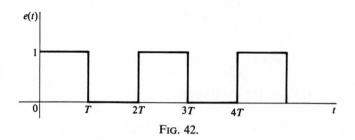

FIG. 42.

$$e(t) = \{U(t) - U(t - T) + U(t - 2T) + \cdots (-1)^n U(t - nT) + \cdots\}.$$

Then

$$E(s) = \mathcal{L}[e(t)] = \frac{1}{s(1 + e^{-Ts})}.$$

As a particular example, consider the response

$$V(s) = \frac{s}{(s + \alpha)} E(s).$$

Then

$$V(s) = \frac{1}{(s + \alpha)[1 + e^{-sT}]},$$

giving

$$v(t) = e^{-\alpha t} U(t) - e^{-\alpha(t - T)} U(t - T)$$
$$+ \cdots + e^{-\alpha(t - 2nT)} U(t - 2nT) - e^{-\alpha(t - (2n+1)T)} U(t - [2n + 1]T)$$
$$+ \cdots.$$

To find the steady-state response, we examine this series in the region of large n, We notice that in the first interval $(t < T)$, only $U(t)$ enters. In the interval $(t < 2T)$. both $U(t)$ and $U(t - T)$ enter.

Now consider the interval $(2n - 1)T < t < 2nT$; only terms from $U(t)$ to $U(t - (2n - 1)T)$ contribute. Thus, if we examine $v(t)$ in the interval $(2n - 1)T < t < 2nT$; one can write

$$v(t) \xrightarrow[(2n-1)T < t < 2nT]{} \{e^{-\alpha t} - e^{-\alpha(t - T)} + \cdots + e^{-\alpha(t - [2n-2]T)} - e^{-\alpha(t - [2n-1]T)}\},$$

or using the relation for the geometric series,†

$$v(t) \xrightarrow[(2n-1)T < t < 2nT]{} e^{-\alpha t} \left\{ \frac{[-e^{-\alpha T}]^{(2n-1)+1} - 1}{[-e^{-\alpha T}] - 1} \right\} = -e^{-\alpha t} \left(\frac{e^{2n\alpha T} - 1}{e^{\alpha T} - 1} \right).$$

If we now expand this, we find that one term becomes negligible for $t \to 2nT$ (when $T \gg 1/\alpha$):

$$v(t) \xrightarrow[t \to 2nT]{} - \frac{e^{-\alpha(t - 2nT)}}{e^{\alpha T} + 1} - \frac{e^{-\alpha t}}{e^{\alpha T} + 1}.$$

---

† $\sum\limits_{n=0}^{N} x^n = \dfrac{x^{N+1} - 1}{x - 1}.$

The second term in this expression can be dropped for large n when $t \to 2nT$:

$$v(t) \xrightarrow[\substack{t \to 2nT \\ n \text{ large}}]{} \frac{e^{-\alpha(t-2nT)}}{[e^{\alpha T} + 1]}.$$

See Fig. 43.

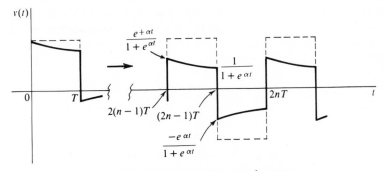

FIG. 43.   The approach to steady state.

Because of the symmetry about $v(t) = 0$, we observe that the d-c component of $v(t)$ has died out for large t.

As an exercise, a similar calculation can be performed for a periodic gate of width τ and period T. The analysis is performed in the same manner, and again we find that the form, for large t, drops out the d-c component.

Response to a Sinusoidal Excitation

One of the traditional methods of treating time-varying current circuits is the analysis of the response to a sinusoidal excitation. This method results in a representation in terms of complex impedances and complex amplitudes for the voltage and current variables. This approach to circuit response is limited. Pulse response and transient response are difficult to handle in detail with these techniques.

The magnitude and phase of the transfer function under sinusoidal excitation do, however, convey a great amount of information concerning the poles and zeros of $H(s)$. The logarithmic plot of the magnitude of the frequency response. $|H(i\omega)|$ is useful and will be employed often to characterize circuits. Before introducing this representation, however, the reader should be aware of its limitations.

In the sinusoidal response (complex impedance representation) the behavior of $H(s)$ is examined by regarding its form evaluated upon the imaginary $i\omega$ axis of the complex s plane. We employ scalar equations to illustrate the analysis.

The sinusoidal response refers to excitations of the type

$$E(s) \to \mathscr{L}[e^{i\omega t}] = \frac{1}{(s - i\omega)}.$$

This form is just one of the characteristic modes of a real sine or cosine excitation. Dealing with two excitation modes does not add to the analysis and complicates it by adding a characteristic mode on the negative $-i\omega$ axis. Computing the magnitude of $H(i\omega)$ (and its phase after evaluation) brings the analysis to that for a real excitation.

If the poles γ_n of $H(s)$ are N in number, the product $H(s)E(s)$ has the form [taking $E(s)$ as $(s - i\omega)^{-1}$]

$$V(s) = H(s)E(s) = \frac{P(s)}{\displaystyle\prod_{n=1}^{N}(s + \gamma_n)} \cdot \frac{1}{(s - i\omega)}.$$

where $P(s)$ is a polynomial of order M.

The Heaviside expansion theorem allows us to expand this form into $(N + 1)$ partial fractions; N of these represent the transient response setup by turning the excitation on. The other fraction is the steady-state response to the sinusoidal excitation:

$$v(t) = \mathcal{L}^{-1}\left[\sum_{n=1}^{N}\frac{A_n}{s + \gamma_n}\right] + \mathcal{L}^{-1}\left[\frac{P(i\omega)}{\displaystyle\prod_{n=1}^{N}(\gamma_n + i\omega)(s - i\omega)}\right]$$

and

$$v(t) = \sum_{n=1}^{N} A_n\, e^{-\gamma_n t} + H(i\omega)\, e^{i\omega t}.$$

Thus, the amplitude of the steady-state response to $e^{i\omega t}$ is $H(i\omega)$. We can write the complex function $H(i\omega)$ as a magnitude times a complex phase factor:

$$H(i\omega) = u(i\omega) + iv(i\omega) = \rho(\omega)\, e^{i\Phi(\omega)},$$

where $\Phi(\omega) =$ the phase response to the sinusoidal excitation.

The magnitude of the sinusoidal response is particularly useful to us because the product functions can be expanded by taking the logarithms of $|H(i\omega)|$, with the result that the products of characteristic one-dimensional operators become sums. A further advantage develops from the fact that the straight-line asymptotic behavior of the simple pole functions can be employed to describe the magnitude of the frequency response of the system.

As mentioned before, this does not represent a complete description. On the other hand, if one thinks in terms of the pole-zero diagram, the impulse response, and the frequency response in concert, all problems involving rational fractions can be understood quickly from a unified point of view.

A major advantage of the logarithmic plot of $|H(i\omega)|$ is that every problem involving a rational fraction is reduced to a *sum* of *elementary diagrams*. That is to say that the most complex polynomials can be reduced to a sum of first-order diagrams if one has the appropriate roots. This procedure is not unlike the analytic process of expanding the transfer function in terms of its characteristic modes or eigenfrequencies

The elementary first-order and second-order functions form a basis for the understanding of the higher-order functions. To form a consistent classification we designate two classes of functions:

1. Type I response. In these functions the eigenvalues are real and the poles fall on the negative real axis of the s plane.
2. Type II response. The roots of these functions are complex. Because complex poles occur in conjugate pairs, these functions will be of second order. By considering both members of a conjugate pair at the same time, it is easier to generalize the sinusoidal response.

With these classifications in mind we can introduce the elementary functions. The most general case will be treated at the conclusion.

Low-Pass Response, Type I

The low-pass response is a transfer function with one real pole and no zeros. We normalize to attain a transfer of 1 in the undistorted region. See Fig. 44.

$$H_{low}^{(I)}(s) = \frac{\alpha}{(s + \alpha)}.$$

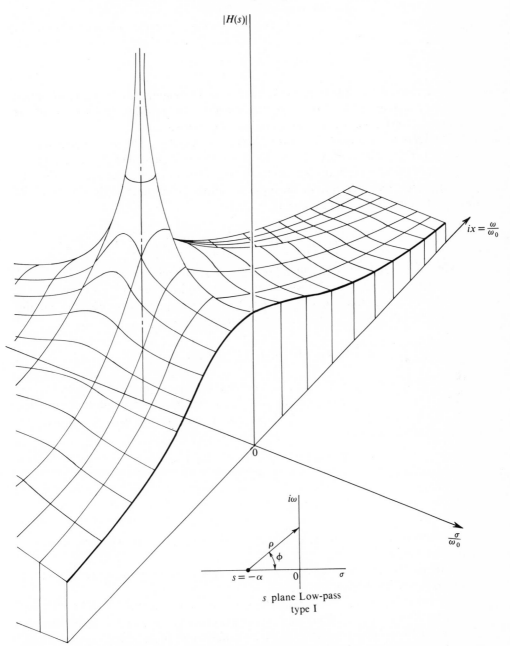

FIG. 44.   Pole diagram of the low-pass, type I, transfer function. The frequency response is shown as a cutaway along the imaginary axis.

The inverse transform of $H_{low}(s)$ in the time domain is a scaled characteristic mode;

$$h_{low}^{(1)}(t) = \mathscr{L}^{-1}[H_{low}^{(1)}(s)] = \alpha \, e^{-\alpha t} U(t).$$

The sinusoidal response is obtained by evaluating this function on the imaginary axis:

$$H_{low}^{(1)}(i\omega) = \frac{\alpha}{(i\omega + \alpha)} = \frac{1}{\sqrt{1 + (\omega/\alpha)^2}} \, e^{-i\phi} = \rho(\omega) \, e^{i\Phi(\omega)},$$

where

$$\tan \phi = \frac{\omega}{\alpha} = -\tan \Phi(\omega).$$

If we examine the logarithm to the base 10 of the magnitude of $|H(i\omega)|$, we obtain a relatively simple result in the asymptotic regions. In practice, to conform to the traditional description, we use the definition of decibels.

The *bel* is a measure of the power exchange of a system. The decibel is defined as $10 \log (P_{in}/P_{out})$, where P_{in} is the power put into the system and P_{out} is the power taken out of the system. If an electric circuit has the input impedance equal to the output impedance, then the ratio of the input to output power goes as the square of the ratio of the input voltages or currents. Therefore,

$$10 \log_{10} \frac{P_{in}}{P_{out}} = 20 \log_{10} \frac{V_{in}}{V_{out}} = 20 \log_{10} \frac{I_{in}}{I_{out}}$$

Since the quantities ordinarily represented were voltages or currents, a factor of 2 was introduced to provide a power measure (i.e., $10 \log_{10} |H|^2$).If a quantity has a value 10, we say that the ratio or change is 20 db. If the quantity (or ratio) is 100, the value in decibels is 40. Then our response function becomes

$$20 \log_{10} |H(i\omega)| = -10 \log_{10}\left(1 + \frac{\omega^2}{\alpha^2}\right).$$

As ω approaches zero, the log plot has a horizontal asymptote of magnitude zero. At large values of ω ($\alpha \ll \omega$), the log plot has a straight-line asymptote of negative slope. The value of the slope is -6 db per octave (an octave is twice or one-half the fundamental frequency):

$$20 \log |H(i\omega)| \xrightarrow[\text{or } \omega \ll \alpha]{\omega \to 0} 20 \log 1 = 0;$$

$$20 \log |H(i\omega)| \xrightarrow[\alpha \ll \omega]{} -20 \log \frac{\omega}{\alpha}.$$

The function $-20 \log(\omega/\alpha)$ changes by approximately 6 db when the ratio ω/α changes by 2.

A frequency response can be created in terms of these asymptotes by plotting $20 \log |H|$ against $\log(\omega/\alpha)$. See Fig. 45.

The behavior of the actual response curve is shown in the region of the cusp formed by the asymptotes. These are universal curves because of the normalization. Thus, the numbers shown can be used often in analyzing a more complicated response. The relatively large low-frequency response compared to the response at frequencies above $\omega = \alpha$ is responsible for the name "low pass."

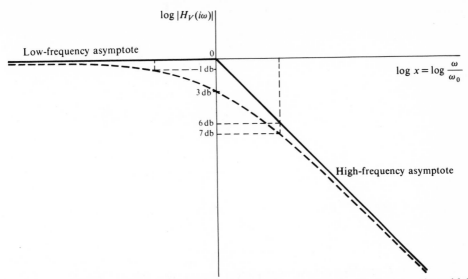

FIG. 45. Asymptotes of the low-pass transfer function compared with the true sinusoidal response.

The phase of this response function can also be generalized. At $\omega = 0$, the slope of $\Phi(\omega)$ is -1, and at high frequencies,

$$\Phi(\omega) \xrightarrow[\alpha \ll \omega]{} -\frac{\pi}{2}$$

See Fig. 46.

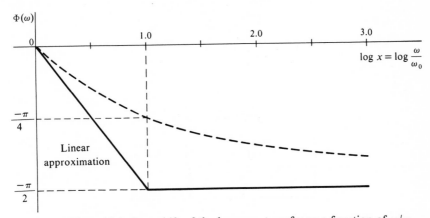

FIG. 46. Sinusoidal phase shift of the low-pass transfer as a function of ω/ω_0.

The phase shift varies from 0 to $-\pi/2$ as ω increases from zero to values large compared with α. At $\omega = \alpha$, $\Phi(\omega) = -\pi/4$.

The two examples in passive circuits of this transfer function occur in the RC circuit and the LR circuit. We consider the voltage across the capacitor C in the RC circuit. See Fig. 47. Assume that the circuit is initially relaxed ($q_c(0+) = 0$). Then

$$Ri(t) + \frac{1}{C} \int_0^t i(t')\,dt' = e(t),$$

giving

$$V(s) = \frac{I(s)}{Cs} = \frac{\alpha}{(s + \alpha)} \mathscr{L}[e(t)],$$

where

$$\alpha = \frac{1}{RC}.$$

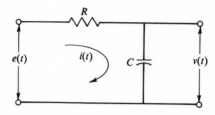

FIG. 47.   The RC circuit connected as a low-pass voltage transfer.

The voltage across the resistor in a passive LR circuit has a low-pass transfer. Again consider the initially relaxed case. See Fig. 48.

$$L \frac{di}{dt} + Ri = e(t)$$

and

$$V(s) = \frac{\alpha}{(s + \alpha)} E(s),$$

where

$$\alpha = \frac{R}{L}.$$

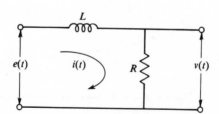

FIG. 48.   The LR circuit employed in a low-pass voltage transfer configuration.

High-Pass Response, Type I

The transfer function with one pole at $s = -\alpha$ and one zero at the origin behaves as a high-pass function in that the low-frequency response is suppressed relative to the high-frequency response. This function has the form

$$H_{high}^{(1)}(s) = \frac{s}{s + \alpha} = 1 - H_{low}^{(1)}(s),$$

with

$$h^{(I)}_{high}(t) = \mathscr{L}^{-1}[H^{(I)}_{high}(s)] = \{\delta(t) - \alpha\, e^{-\alpha t} U(t)\}.$$

See Fig. 49.

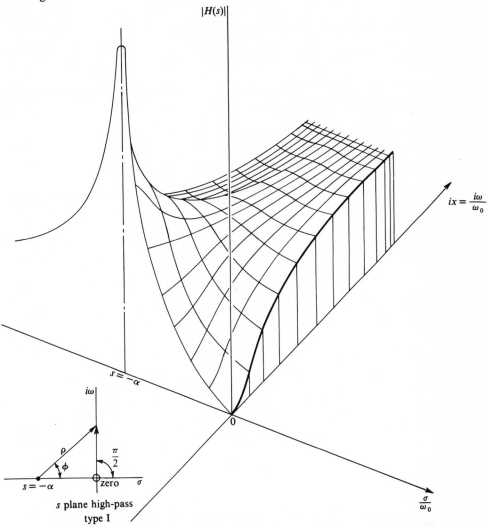

FIG. 49.   Pole-zero diagram of the high-pass, type I, transfer function. The frequency response is shown as a cutaway along the imaginary axis.

This function is not independent of the low-pass function, since both have the same characteristic eigenvalue, $-\alpha$. As shown in the equation above, $H^{(I)}_{high}(s)$ as defined is merely $(1 - H^{(I)}_{low})$. Physically, this form implies that a high-pass function is a flat response minus a low-pass function.

The sinusoidal response is

$$H^{(I)}_{high}(i\omega) = \frac{1}{\sqrt{1 + (\alpha/\omega)^2}}\, e^{i[(\pi/2) - \phi]}.$$

The total phase, $\Phi(\omega) = \pi/2 - \tan^{-1}(\omega/\alpha)$.

The asymptotes for $|H(i\omega)|$ are obtained as before:

$$|H(i\omega)| \xrightarrow[\omega \ll \alpha]{} + 20 \log \frac{\omega}{\alpha}$$

(dropping at $+6$ db per octave), and

$$|H(i\omega)| \xrightarrow[\alpha \ll \omega]{} 0.$$

The magnitude of $H(i\omega)$ and the phase as a function of (ω/α) are shown in the accompanying diagrams. See Figs. 50a and 50b.

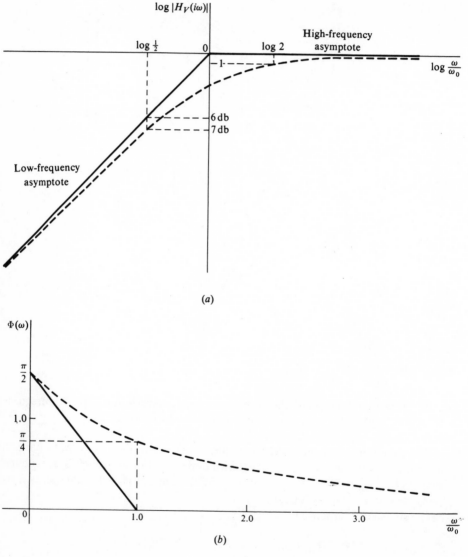

(a)

(b)

FIG. 50. (a) Log of the magnitude of the response of a high-pass, type I, transfer to a sinusoidal excitation. (b) Phase response of the high-pass, type I, transfer.

The voltage across R in a CR circuit gives a typical high-pass response:

$$V_R(s) = \frac{s}{(s + \alpha_c)} E(s),$$

with

$$\alpha_c = \frac{1}{RC}.$$

See Fig. 51.

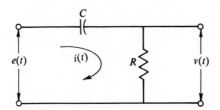

FIG. 51.   An RC circuit connected as a high-pass voltage transfer.

The voltage across the inductance in the RL circuit also gives this transfer:

$$V_L(s) = LsI(s) = \frac{s}{(s + \alpha_L)} E(s),$$

where

$$\alpha_L = \frac{R}{L}.$$

See Fig. 52.

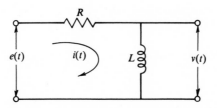

FIG. 52.   An LR circuit connected as a high-pass voltage transfer.

Compound Response, Type I

A linear combination of a low-pass and a high-pass function with the same characteristic pole gives a function with one zero on the real axis and one pole on the negative-real axis. This type of function appears as

$$H(s) = \frac{(s + \beta)}{(s + \alpha)} = \frac{s}{(s + \alpha)} + \frac{\beta}{\alpha} \frac{\alpha}{(s + \alpha)}.$$

$$H(s) = H_{high}^{(I)}(s) + \frac{\beta}{\alpha} H_{low}^{(I)}(s)$$

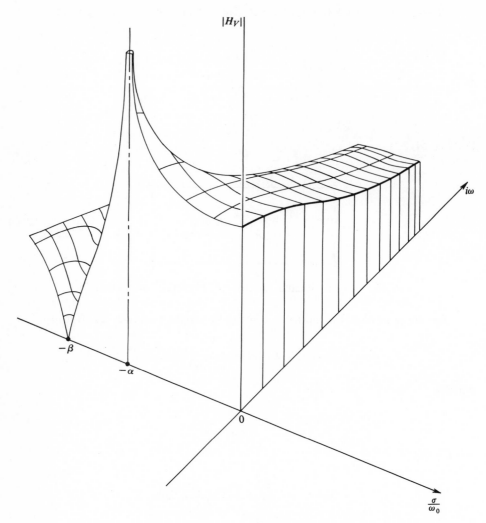

FIG. 53.   A compound, low-pass, type I, pole-zero configuration.

(see Fig. 53); and

$$h(t) = \mathscr{L}^{-1}[H(s)] = \delta(t) + (\beta - \alpha)\, e^{-\alpha t} U(t).$$

This addition can produce either a high-pass or low-pass type of response, depending upon the relative magnitude of β and α.

If α is less than β ($\alpha < \beta$), the zero is farther from the origin than the pole. Thus, the major effect should be that of a low-pass device. The log of the magnitude of the frequency response exhibits a falling characteristic at $\omega = \alpha$. The term $(s + \beta) \rightarrow (i\omega + \beta)$ in the numerator produces a rising function at $\omega = \beta$. The net logarithmic response is (see Figs. 54 and 55).

$$20 \log |H| = 20 \log \frac{\beta}{\alpha} + 10 \log\left(1 + \frac{\beta^2}{\omega^2}\right) - 10 \log\left(1 + \frac{\omega^2}{\alpha^2}\right),$$

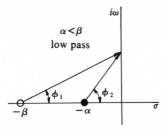

FIG. 54.   Pole-zero diagram for a compound transfer for which the pole is nearest to the origin. This has a low-pass characteristic.

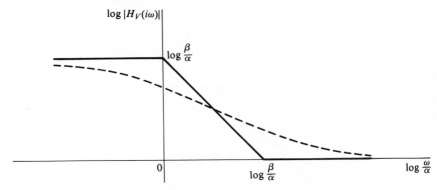

FIG. 55.   A compound low-pass sinusoidal response.

The phase is

$$\Phi(\omega) = \phi_1(\omega) - \phi_2(\omega) = \tan^{-1}\frac{\omega}{\beta} - \tan^{-1}\frac{\omega}{\alpha}.$$

At ω near zero, the phase is approximately zero. The phase has a minimum (greater than $-\pi/2$) between α and β, returning to zero at large ω. (See Fig. 56).

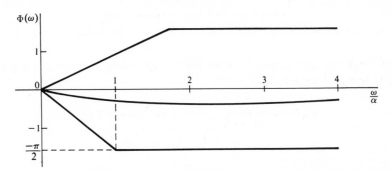

FIG. 56.   Phase response of a compound low-pass device for which $\beta_\alpha = 1\cdot75$.

If β is less than α ($\beta < \alpha$), the zero is nearest the origin, and the response should simulate a high-pass characteristic. The functional form of $H(i\omega)$ is the same in both cases. In fact, the high-frequency response in both cases is unity. The difference arises from the normalization $20 \log_{10} \beta/\alpha$. In this case, this factor is less than 1. See Fig. 57.

Now the phase increases in a positive direction for $0 < \omega$, peaking between β and α, at a value less than $\pi/2$. See Fig. 58.

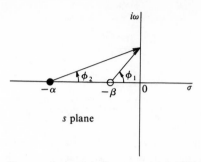

FIG. 57.   A pole-zero diagram for a type I, compound, high-pass transfer function.

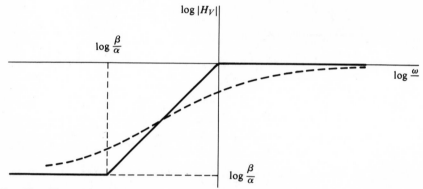

FIG. 58.   Sinusoidal response for a compound, high-pass, type I, transfer function.

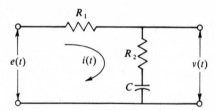

FIG. 59.   An *RC* voltage dividing circuit that acts as a compound, low-pass device.

A resistance voltage divider in series with a capacitor is a physical example of the compound low-pass circuit. See Fig. 59.

$$V_{RC}(s) = \frac{R_2}{[R_1 + R_2]} \frac{(s + 1/R_2C)}{\left(s + \dfrac{1}{(R_1 + R_2)C}\right)} E(s).$$

Here,

$$\alpha = \frac{1}{(R_1 + R_2)C} < \beta = \frac{1}{R_2C}.$$

The resistance voltage divider in series with an inductance is an example of a compound high-pass device. See Fig. 60.

$$V(s) = \frac{[s + R_2/L]}{[s + (R_1 + R_2)/L]} E(s).$$

Now
$$\beta = \frac{R_2}{L} < \alpha = \frac{(R_1 + R_2)}{L}.$$

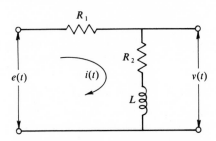

FIG. 60.   An example of a compound, high-pass device.

Quadratic Product Response, Type I

LOW PASS, TYPE I

In this example, the transfer function has a quadratic denominator with two real poles. See Fig. 61.

$$H(s) = \frac{\alpha_1}{(s + \alpha_1)} \cdot \frac{\alpha_2}{(s + \alpha_2)},$$

with

$$h(t) = \frac{\alpha_1 \alpha_2}{(\alpha_2 - \alpha_1)} \{e^{-\alpha_1 t} - e^{-\alpha_2 t}\} U(t).$$

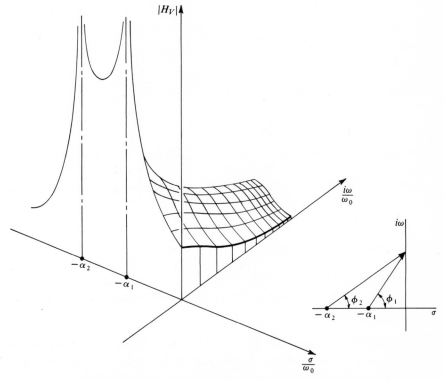

FIG. 61.   Pole-zero diagram for the quadratic low-pass, type I, transfer function.

The log of the sinusoidal response is particularly useful in the product responses. The product becomes a sum in the logarithmic representation of elementary responses. In the example under consideration, the total log response is the sum of two low-pass log functions:

$$20 \log_{10} |H(i\omega)| = -10 \log\left(1 + \frac{\omega^2}{\alpha_1^2}\right) - 10 \log\left(1 + \frac{\omega^2}{\alpha_2^2}\right),$$

with

$$\Phi(\omega) = -\tan^{-1}\frac{\omega}{\alpha_1} - \tan^{-1}\frac{\omega}{\alpha_2}.$$

Assume $\alpha_1 < \alpha_2$; then the log $|H|$ is formed of the three straight-line asymptotes, as shown in Fig. 62.†

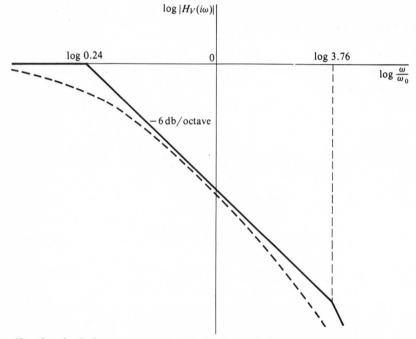

FIG. 62.   Quadratic low-pass, type I. Here, $Q = 1/4$; thus, $\alpha_1 = 0.24\omega_0$ and $\alpha_2 = 3.76\omega_0$.

When the frequency is much higher than α_1 or α_2,

$$20 \log H \xrightarrow[\text{large } \omega]{} 20 \log \frac{\omega^2}{\alpha_1\alpha_2},$$

a high-frequency asymptote that falls at 12 db per octave.

The phase varies from zero to $(-\pi)$ as ω increases. We shall investigate circuits in some detail in a later section. This response is encountered several times. The first will be as the voltage across the capacitor in an overdamped series *LRC* circuit.

HIGH PASS, TYPE I

It is reasonable to anticipate that this function is the product of two high-pass elementary functions with poles on the real axis in the *s* plane. See Fig. 63.

---

† The Q value mentioned refers to the quadratic $s^2 + 2as + \omega_0^2$. In the pages which follow,

$$Q = \frac{\omega_0}{2a} = \frac{\sqrt{\alpha_1\alpha_2}}{(\alpha_1 + \alpha_2)}.$$

$$H(s) = \frac{s}{(s + \alpha_1)} \cdot \frac{s}{(s + \alpha_2)}, \quad \text{with} \quad h(t) = \delta(t) + \frac{1}{(\alpha_2 - \alpha_1)} \{\alpha_1^2 \, e^{-\alpha_1 t} - \alpha_2^2 \, e^{-\alpha_2 t}\} U(t).$$

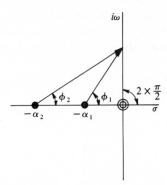

FIG. 63.   The pole-zero diagrams for an overdamped, type I, high-pass function.

In the same manner as the previous case,

$$20 \log |H(i\omega)| = -10 \log\left(1 + \frac{\alpha_1^2}{\omega^2}\right) - 10 \log\left(1 + \frac{\alpha_2^2}{\omega^2}\right)$$

and

$$\Phi(\omega) = \pi - \tan^{-1} \frac{\omega}{\alpha_1} - \tan^{-1} \frac{\omega}{\alpha_2}.$$

See Fig. 64.

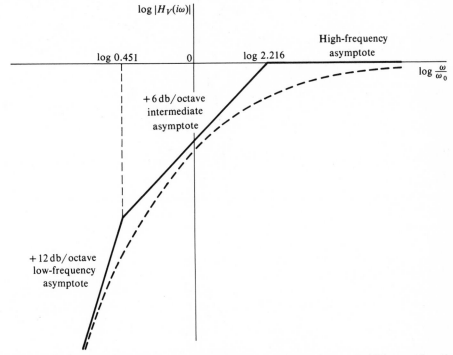

FIG. 64.   The sinusoidal response of a quadratic overdamped, type I, high-pass function. In this diagram, $Q = 3/8$.

A physical example showing this response would be the voltage across the inductor in a series overdamped LRC circuit.

RESONANCE, TYPE I

This function is the only variation left to us in the quadratic transfers with real poles. It consists of a low-pass elementary function multiplied by an elementary high-pass function. The physical systems that produce this response are the class of systems having an overdamped resonance response such as the voltage across the resistor in an overdamped series *LRC* circuit:

$$H(s) = \frac{(\alpha_1 + \alpha_2)s}{(s + \alpha_1)(s + \alpha_2)} \quad \text{and} \quad h(t) = -\frac{(\alpha_2 + \alpha_1)}{(\alpha_2 - \alpha_1)}\{\alpha_1 e^{-\alpha_1 t} - \alpha_2 e^{-\alpha_2 t}\}U(t)$$

See Fig. 65

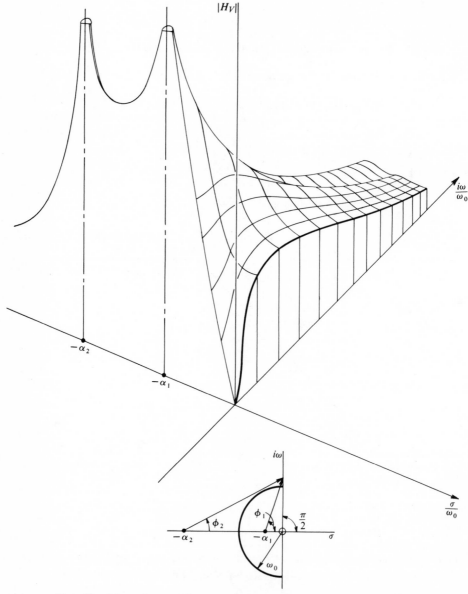

FIG. 65.   The pole-zero diagram of the overdamped resonant transfer.

The log of the magnitude of the sinusoidal response is (here we take into account the fact that $\alpha_1 < \alpha_2$ in our example)

$$20 \log |H(i\omega)| = 20 \log\left(1 + \frac{\alpha_1}{\alpha_2}\right) - 10 \log\left(1 + \frac{\omega^2}{\alpha_2^2}\right) - 10 \log\left(1 + \frac{\alpha_1^2}{\omega^2}\right).$$

The magnitude of $H(i\omega)$ can be written in another form to illustrate the properties that we shall emphasize

$$H(i\omega) = \frac{2ai\omega}{[\omega_0^2 - \omega^2 + 2ai\omega]} \quad \text{and} \quad |H(i\omega)| = \frac{2a\omega}{\sqrt{(\omega_0^2 - \omega^2)^2 + 4a^2\omega^2}}.$$

In this form

$$2a = \alpha_1 + \alpha_2$$

and

$$\omega_0^2 = \alpha_1\alpha_2.$$

The normalization that we have chosen places the value of $H(i\omega)$ at 1 when $\omega = \omega_0$. The asymptotes of the high-frequency cutoff intercept the vertical axis (at $\omega = \omega_0$) at a point $20 \log 2a/\omega_0$. These same asymptotes intercept the $|H| = 0$ horizontal axis at $\pm \log (2a/\omega_0)$ if the plot is in terms of the ratio (ω/ω_0). The frequencies corresponding to the negatives of the roots α_1 and α_2 occur within the interval $\pm \log (2a/\omega_0)$. See Fig. 66.

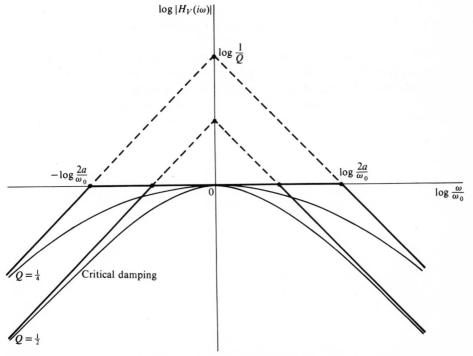

FIG. 66.   Logarithm of the magnitude of a sinusoidal response of an overdamped resonant transfer and a critically damped resonant transfer. The asymptotes are emphasized to illustrate the symmetry in the log plot.

The parameter $2a/\omega_0 = (\alpha_1 + \alpha_2)/\alpha_1\alpha_2$ is a universal term employed to provide a figure of merit for resonant systems. It is the inverse of the Q value:

$$Q = \frac{\omega_0}{2a} = \frac{\sqrt{\alpha_1\alpha_2}}{(\alpha_1 + \alpha_2)}.$$

The phase varies from $+\pi/2$ to $-\pi/2$ as ω is increased. At resonance $\omega = \omega_0 = \sqrt{\alpha_1\alpha_2}$ the phase is zero (another unique property of the point $\omega = \omega_0$).

$$\Phi(\omega) = \frac{\pi}{2} - \tan^{-1}\frac{\omega}{\alpha_1} - \tan^{-1}\frac{\omega}{\alpha_2}$$

See Fig. 67.

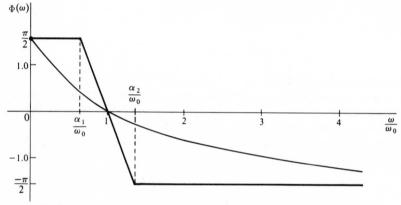

FIG. 67.   Phase shift in an overdamped resonant transfer. In this example, $Q = \sqrt{2}/3$.

When the roots are degenerate $\alpha_1 = \alpha_2$, the two poles are at the same point on the negative-real axis. In a physical system, this unique situation is called *critical damping*. More will be said about this in the section on circuits. See Fig. 68.

The transition configuration, which is called critical damping between two real poles, and that with two complex poles conjugate to one another, has a Q value of $1/2$.

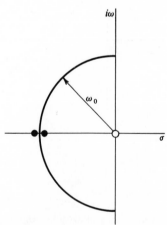

FIG. 68.   Pole-zero diagram of a resonant transfer near the condition for critical damping.

Type II Responses

When the roots of the transfer function are real, it is possible to consider first-order functions (with a single root). It is also possible to generalize the problem of one complex root. The results are, however, somewhat tedious and unnecessary.

Because the complex roots of a physical system invariably appear in conjugate pairs, it is simpler and more convenient from the beginning to discuss quadratic transfer functions that incorporate both members of a conjugate pair.

We call elementary functions with a pair of conjugate roots a type II response. Later, we shall observe that transfer functions of order higher than 2 (quadratic) can be manufactured from components that are elementary type I and elementary type II functions.

This view of the transfer function allows us to describe the frequency response of complicated transfer functions in terms of the asymptotic diagrams of the component elementary functions.

LOW PASS, TYPE II

This transfer function is similar to the quadratic low-pass function with real poles (type I) except that the two roots in this case form a conjugate pair, $-\gamma$ and $-\gamma^*$.

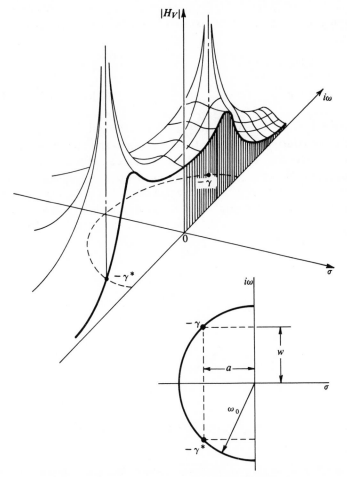

FIG. 69.   Pole-zero diagram for an underdamped, type II, low-pass transfer.

The type II low-pass function is (see Fig. 69):

$$H_{low}^{(II)}(s) = \frac{\omega_0^2}{(s^2 + 2as + \omega_0^2)}$$

$$= \frac{\omega_0}{(s + \gamma)} \cdot \frac{\omega_0}{(s + \gamma^*)}.$$

The roots $-\gamma$ and $-\gamma^*$ are given by

$$\gamma = a - iw = a - i\sqrt{\omega_0^2 - a^2}$$

and

$$\gamma^* = a + iw.$$

Transforming to the time domain, we obtain

$$h_{low}^{(II)}(t) = \frac{\omega_0^2}{w} e^{-at} \sin wt.$$

The response of this system to a sinusoidal excitation is somewhat more involved than the case of real roots. Complex roots most often produce an overshoot in the frequency response. Departure of the roots from the real axis occurs when the damping is less than critical, which implies that the Q value or figure of merit is greater than $1/2$.

To simplify our notation, we shall write $20 \log|H(i\omega)|$ as $B(\omega)$. Then, for the type II low-pass function,

$$B(\omega) = 20 \log_{10} |H(i\omega)|$$

$$= 40 \log \frac{\omega_0}{a} - 10 \log\left[1 + \left(\frac{\omega - w}{a}\right)^2\right] - 10 \log\left[1 + \left(\frac{\omega + w}{a}\right)^2\right].$$

The high-frequency asymptote ($\omega_0 \ll \omega$) is a straight line of slope -12 db per octave. The low-frequency asymptote ($\omega \ll \omega_0$) is a horizontal line, and $B(\omega)$ has the value 0 at low frequencies. This corresponds to a unit amplitude at $\omega \ll \omega_0$ for $H(i\omega)$. The spectrum near the cusp formed by the high-frequency asymptote and the low-frequency asymptote is complicated by the fact that $B(\omega)$ has the value $20 \log Q$ at ω_0 and has a higher value of $20 \log(\omega_0^2/2aw)$ at a frequency less than ω_0. This frequency, corresponding to the maximum of the function, is denoted as ω_m. The value of ω_m is $\sqrt{\omega_0^2 - 2a^2}$.

$$B(\omega) \xrightarrow[\omega \ll \omega_0]{} 0,$$

$$B(\omega) \xrightarrow[\omega_0 \ll \omega]{} -40 \log \frac{\omega}{\omega_0},$$

while

$$B(\omega_0) = 20 \log \frac{\omega_0}{2a} = 20 \log Q,$$

and

$$B\left(\omega = \sqrt{w^2 - a^2}\right) = B_{max} = 20 \log \frac{\omega_0^2}{2aw},$$

$$\omega_{max} = \sqrt{w^2 - a^2} = \omega_0 \sqrt{1 - \frac{1}{2Q^2}}.$$

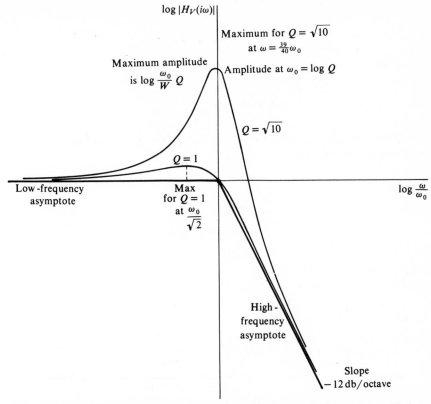

FIG. 70.   The magnitude of the response to a sinusoid of an underdamped, type II, low-pass transfer function. Two curves are shown, one for $Q = 1$ and another for $Q = \sqrt{10}$.

The phase response of this circuit has a particularly simple form. The phase $\Phi(\omega)$ varies from zero at low frequencies to $-\pi$ at high frequencies. At $\omega = \omega_0$, the phase is $-\pi/2$. This phase diagram goes through the values $-\pi/4$ and $-3\pi/4$ at sideband frequencies ω_1 and ω_2. The separation $\omega_2 - \omega_1 = 2a$; thus (see Fig. 71),

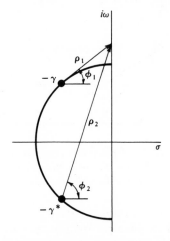

FIG. 71.   The pole-zero diagram for the underdamped low-pass transfer, showing the angles involved in the phase response.

$$\frac{\omega_2 - \omega_1}{\omega_0} = \frac{2a}{\omega_0} = \frac{1}{Q}.$$

$$\Phi(\omega) = -\phi_1(\omega) - \phi_2(\omega).$$

Rewriting this in terms of $\tan \Phi$,

$$\tan \Phi(\omega) = -\frac{2a\omega}{(\omega_0^2 - \omega^2)}.$$

This last form indicates that $\tan \Phi = \pm 1$ at $\{\sqrt{\omega_0^2 + a^2} - a\}$, and $\{\sqrt{\omega_0^2 + a^2} + a\}$, respectively. See Fig. 72.

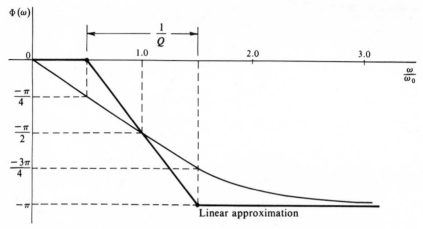

FIG. 72.   Phase response to a sinusoidal excitation for an underdamped low-pass transfer. Curve is shown for the case $Q = 1$.

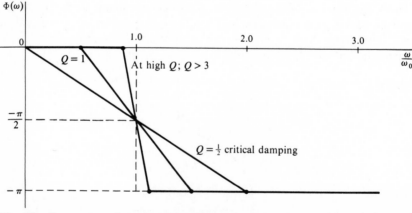

FIG. 73.   The linear approximation of the phase response for different Q values. Notice in Fig. 72 that the curve for $Q = 1$ has the closest approximation to a linear-phase response at frequencies less than ω_0.

The slope of $\Phi(\omega)$ near ω_0 behaves as $-(1/Q)$ or $-(2a/\omega_0)$ when $\Phi(\omega)$ is plotted as a function of (ω/ω_0). The sideband frequencies can be written in terms of Q, showing that $(\omega_2 - \omega_1)/\omega_0$ is exactly $1/Q$. Therefore, the phase diagram (see Fig. 73) can be blocked in also in terms of the asymptotes of zero slope and a straight-line section approximating the region between ω_1 and ω_2. We notice that the true values of $\Phi(\omega)$ at the sideband frequencies ω_1 and ω_2 are $-\pi/4$ and $-3\pi/4$, the interval between the asymptotes (in this case, between $\Phi = 0$ and $\phi = -\pi$).

HIGH PASS, TYPE II

This transfer is the analogue of the type I quadratic high-pass response. It has a pair of conjugate complex poles and a double zero at the origin. (see Fig. 74).

$$H^{(II)}_{high}(s) = \frac{s^2}{(s^2 + 2as + \omega_0^2)} = \frac{s}{(s + \gamma)} \cdot \frac{s}{(s + \gamma^*)},$$

with

$$h^{(II)}_{high}(t) = \mathscr{L}^{-1}[H^{(II)}_{high}] = \delta(t) + \frac{\omega_0^2}{w} e^{-at} \sin wt.$$

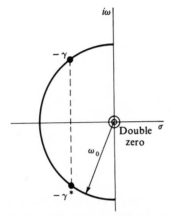

FIG. 74.   The pole-zero diagram for the underdamped, type II, high-pass transfer function.

The frequency response can be blocked out with the relation

$$B_{high}(\omega) = 20 \log |H(i\omega)|$$

$$= 40 \log \frac{\omega}{a} - 10 \log\left[1 + \left(\frac{\omega - w}{a}\right)^2\right] - 10 \log\left[1 + \left(\frac{\omega + w}{a}\right)^2\right].$$

To obtain the shape of this curve, we can observe that this log response is the low-pass type II response minus $40 \log(\omega_0/a)$ plus $40 \log(\omega/a)$. This indicates that the two curves are identical at $\omega = \omega_0$. The 12-db per octave rise in $40 \log(\omega/a)$ causes a flat response at high frequency with an asymptote falling at 12 db per octave at low frequencies.

The maximum in this curve occurs at $\omega = \omega_0$. One would not expect this function to be a perfect reflection of $\log|H_{low}|$ because it is formed by multiplying H_{low} by ω^2. See Fig. 75.

The amplitude of the peak is equal to $20 \log Q$. The phase of this response is just the phase of the two zeros at the origin $(+\pi)$ minus the low-pass phase characteristic. Thus, as ω varies from zero to values much greater than ω_0, the phase varies from π to 0. The asymptotic phase plot has characteristics similar to that of the low-pass function (see Fig. 76).

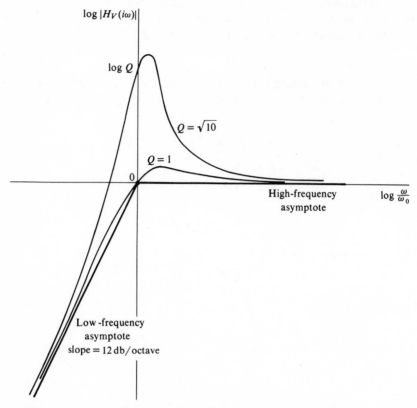

FIG. 75.   Logarithmic plot of the response to a sinusoidal excitation of an underdamped, type II, high-pass transfer function.

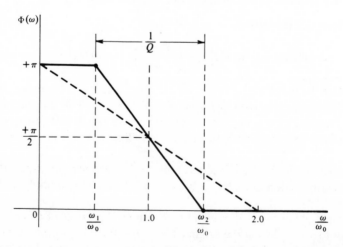

FIG. 76.   A linear approximation of the phase response in the case of an underdamped high-pass transfer function. The half-power points are separated by ω_0/Q and determine the position of the cusps in the linear approximation.

RESONANCE, TYPE II

The $\mathscr{L}T$ representation provides a symmetry in the elementary transfer functions. In the quadratic functions, the sum of the three possible characteristic functions is equal to 1. See Fig. 77.

$$H_{\text{low}}^{(\text{II})}(s) + H_{\text{high}}^{(\text{II})}(s) + H_{\text{res}}^{(\text{II})}(s) = 1.$$

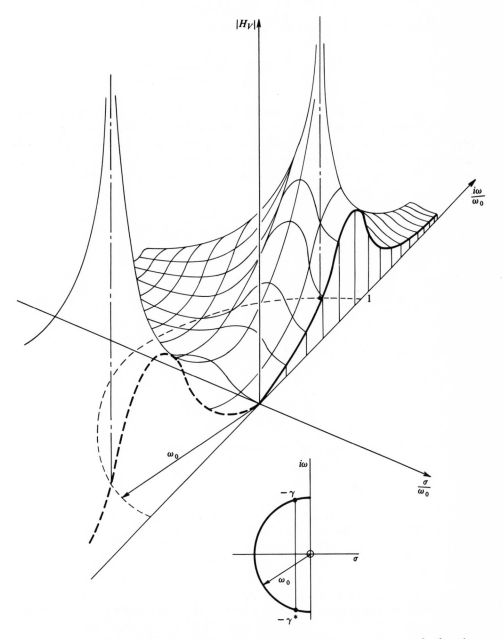

FIG. 77.   The pole-zero diagram of the underdamped, type II, resonance transfer function.

As in the type I overdamped case,

$$H_{res}^{(II)}(s) = \frac{2as}{(s^2 + 2as + \omega_0^2)} = \frac{2as}{(s + \gamma)(s + \gamma^*)},$$

with

$$h_{res}^{(II)}(t) = \frac{2a\omega_0}{w} e^{-at} \sin\left\{wt - \tan^{-1}\frac{w}{a}\right\} U(t).$$

The magnitude of H_R (s) on the imaginary axis is

$$|H_R(i\omega)| = \frac{2a\omega}{\sqrt{(\omega_0^2 - \omega^2)^2 + 4a^2\omega^2}},$$

which is the classical resonance characteristic. This function assumes a particularly simple asymptotic form in the log $|H|$ plot. At resonance ($\omega = \omega_0$), the amplitude of $H(i\omega)$ is a maximum and has the value 1. The high-frequency asymptote is a straight line of slope -6 db per octave, and the low-frequency, straight-line asymptote has a slope of $+6$ db per octave. These asymptotes intersect at $\omega = \omega_0$ at a point $-20 \log Q$ or $20 \log Q$ below the peak. See Fig. 78.

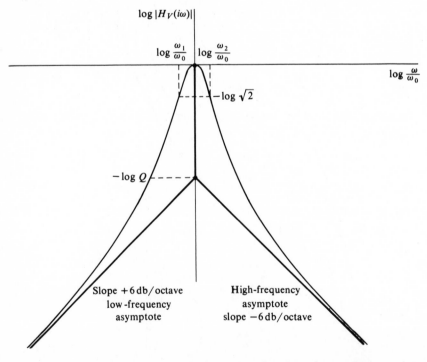

FIG. 78.   The log plot with asymptotes of the transfer function of an underdamped, type II, resonant device. This particular example illustrates the resonance response to a sinusoidal excitation when $Q = \sqrt{10}$.

To locate points on the actual function relative to the asymptotes, we note that the function is down by a factor $1/\sqrt{2}$ at the half-power points ω_1 and ω_2. The function $|H(i\omega)|$ is down by $1/\sqrt{2}$ when

$$\frac{\omega}{\omega_0} = \left\{ 1 + \frac{1}{2Q^2} \pm \frac{1}{Q} \sqrt{1 + \frac{1}{4}Q^2} \right\}^{12},$$

where, as before,†

$$Q = \frac{\omega_0}{2a}.$$

The half-power points are separated from one another by $(1/Q)\omega_0$.

$$\omega_2 - \omega_1 = \frac{\omega_0}{Q}.$$

These frequencies correspond to the frequencies at which the phase has the values $\pm \pi/4$ relative to the phase at the resonant frequency ω_0. The half-power result is to be expected because the transfer function is real at resonance, dropping to a magnitude of $1/\sqrt{2}$ of the peak when the relative phase changes by $\pi/4$ radians. These sideband frequencies are approximately

$$\frac{\omega_2}{\omega_0} \xrightarrow[Q \text{ large}]{} \left(1 + \frac{1}{2Q} \right)$$

and

$$\frac{\omega_1}{\omega_0} \xrightarrow[Q \text{ large}]{} \left(1 - \frac{1}{2Q} \right).$$

As an example of a typical problem, regard a resonant type II circuit (underdamped) excited by a unit gate pulse of width T. The response $\mathscr{L}T$ is

$$V(s) = \frac{2as}{(s + \gamma)(s + \gamma^*)} \cdot \frac{1}{s} (1 - e^{-sT}).$$

This can be expanded and expressed in terms of the low-pass type II transfer function, giving

$$v(t) = \mathscr{L}^{-1}[V(s)] = \frac{2a}{\omega_0^2} \{ h_{\text{low}}^{(\text{II})}(t) - h_{\text{low}}^{(\text{II})}(t - T) \}$$

or

$$v(t) = \frac{2a}{w} \{ e^{-at} \sin wt U(t) - e^{-a(t-T)} \sin w(t-T) U(t-T) \}.$$

See Fig. 79. The phase varies from $(\pi/2)$ to $(-\pi/2)$ as ω increases. See Fig. 80.

---

† Q is one-half the cosecant of the angle between the complex pole and the imaginary axis.

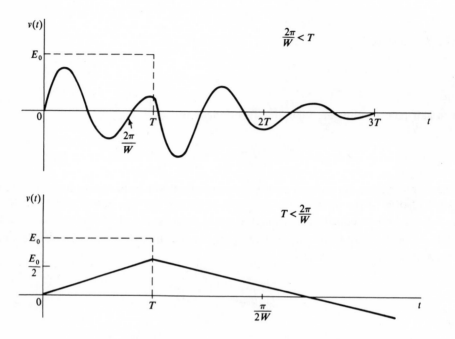

FIG. 79.   The response of an underdamped resonant transfer function to a gate excitation of duration T. In the first graph, the period of the resonant circuit is less than T, whereas the period of the circuit in the second graph is greater than the gate width T.

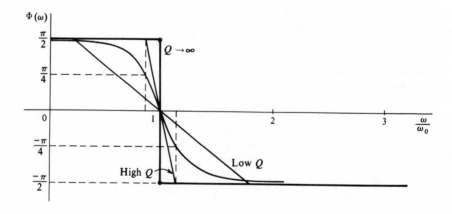

FIG. 80.   Phase response to a sinusoid of an underdamped resonant transfer. The linear approximation is indicated for three Q values and the true phase response is shown for the high-Q case.

General Response to a Sinusoid

The general transfer function $H(s)$ (when a rational fraction) can be written in terms of the elementary functions. If

$$H(s) = \frac{\prod_{m=1}^{M} (s + \beta_m)}{\prod_{n=1}^{N} (s + \gamma_n)},$$

then

$$H(s) = \left\{ \prod_{m=1}^{M} \left(\frac{s + \beta_m}{s + \gamma_m} \right) \right\} \cdot \left(\frac{1}{\prod_{n=M+1}^{N} (s + \gamma_n)} \right).$$

The result is independent of the grouping. The fact that $H(s)$ has this unique property was obvious when it was shown by the expansion theorem that $H(s)$ could be represented as a sum of the individual characteristic modes.

The log of the sinusoidal response is easily manipulated to exhibit the elementary diagrams:

$$20 \log_{10} |H(i\omega)| = \sum_{m=1}^{M} 20 \log |i\omega + \beta_m| - \sum_{n=1}^{N} 20 \log |i\omega + \gamma_n|.$$

To show a special case, consider the zeros and poles to be real; then

$$20 \log |H(i\omega)| = \sum_{m=1}^{M} \left\{ 20 \log \beta_m + 10 \log \left(1 + \frac{\omega^2}{\beta_m^2} \right) \right\} - \sum_{n=1}^{N} \left\{ 20 \log \gamma_n + 10 \log \left(1 + \frac{\omega^2}{\gamma_n^2} \right) \right\}.$$

As an example, consider the special case (see Fig. 81).

$$H(s) = \frac{6a^3}{[s^3 + 6as^2 + 11a^2 s + 6a^3]}.$$

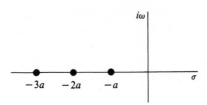

FIG. 81.   The pole-zero diagram for the low-pass function with three poles at $-a$, $-2a$, and $-3a$.

This corresponds to three diagrams:

$$H(s) = \frac{3a}{(s + 3a)} \cdot \frac{2a}{(s + 2a)} \cdot \frac{a}{(s + a)}$$

The sinusoidal response has the form

$$20 \log_{10} |H(i\omega)| = -10 \log \left(1 + \frac{\omega^2}{9a^2} \right) - 10 \log \left(1 + \frac{\omega^2}{4a^2} \right) - 10 \log \left(1 + \frac{\omega^2}{a^2} \right),$$

giving the response curve shown in Fig. 82.

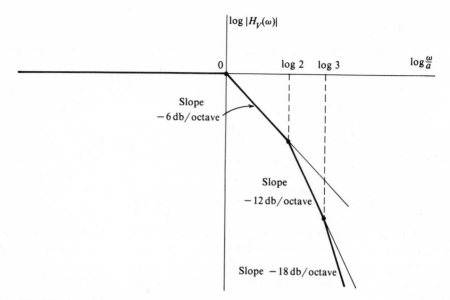

FIG. 82.   The logarithm of the magnitude of the underdamped low-pass transfer function with three poles on the negative-real axis.

We observe that for all practical purposes the system is controlled by the pole nearest the origin. In the next section it will be shown that the time delay of this system is to first order, $11/6a$.

TIME DELAY OF THE TRANSFER FUNCTION

The Exponential Approximation

The ideal time-delay function in $\mathscr{L}T$ is the shifting function e^{-sT}. Every transfer function approximates this exponential to some degree. At the elementary level, we observe that the primary effect of a transfer function is to impose amplitude distortion or phase distortion upon a function. The word "distortion" may not convey the appropriate meaning, since we may be interested in selectivity that entails the suppression of certain components of an excitation.

Higher-order transfer functions may have an increased similarity to the shifting exponential. In many cases, we shall be able to represent the transfer polynomial as a shift in time, characteristic of the polynomial, multiplied by an attenuating factor that represents the distortion of the signal. When a pulse is delayed in a circuit formed of lumped elements, usually the function $H(s)$ has distorted the high-frequency components of the pulse in some manner, either amplitude distortion (suppression in this case) or phase distortion. Thus, we shall expect to observe time lags in the *low-pass* functions. The time delay in "minimum phase" networks having lumped components is connected to the rise time of the response. Therefore, at the conclusion of the discussion of the shifting property of a function $H(s)$, we shall relate the shifting properties to the same parameters that alter the rise time of a signal. The differentiation between lumped networks and spatially distributed networks is quite clear in this section. When the dimensions of a network are long compared with the wavelengths of the signal, one can produce delays caused by transit time primarily. The lumped network relies on the charging time of capacitors and inductors to simulate a delay.

These arguments also indicate to us that high-pass functions may not produce an apparent delay in a lumped network. The characteristics of a high-pass function produce distortions and phase shifts of the low-frequency components of a signal. These distortions produce sag in the tops of square pulses and, in some cases, an apparent advance of the first centroid of the signal.

As an example, consider the low-pass quadratic function

$$H_{\text{low}}(s) = \frac{\omega_0^2}{[s^2 + 2as + \omega_0^2]}.$$

This function can be rewritten to exhibit the initial portion of an exponential series in the denominator:

$$H_{\text{low}}(s) = \frac{1}{[1 + (2a/\omega_0^2)s + (s^2/\omega_0^2)]}.$$

For simplicity, let us consider the special case $a = \omega_0/\sqrt{2}$. Here the poles of $H(s)$ are complex and make angles of 45 deg relative to the negative-real axis in the s plane. The polynomial in the denominator of $H(s)$ now represents the first three terms in an exponential expansion. See Fig. 83.

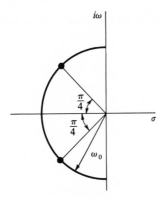

FIG. 83.   The pole configuration for the example low-pass delay function. In the example, $a = \omega_0/\sqrt{2}.$

Define $W = \omega_0/\sqrt{2}$, with $a = \omega_0/\sqrt{2}$; then

$$H(s) = \frac{1}{[1 + x + \frac{1}{2}x^2]},$$

where

$$x = \frac{s}{W}.$$

The function $H(s)$ can now be written in a form that displays the shifting function:

$$H(s) = \frac{e^{-x}}{\left\{1 - e^{-x}x^3 \displaystyle\sum_{n=0}^{\infty} \frac{x^n}{(n-3)!}\right\}} = \mathscr{D}\left(\frac{s}{W}\right)e^{-s/W}.$$

As long as we can neglect the power series in x in the denominator, $H(s)$ can be viewed as a shift of the excitation by a time of the order $1/w = \sqrt{2}/\omega_0$. The function $\mathcal{D}(s/W)$ is a distorting term that provides a measure of the deviation of the shape of the response from that of the excitation. If the characteristic times of the input signal are greater than $\sqrt{2}/\omega_0$, this circuit approximates a pure shifting function. This is another way of saying that $H(s) \sim e^{-x}$ if x is small.

The Average Value of t

Various criteria can be employed to estimate the delay time which a transfer function introduces into the response to a signal. We have just examined a convenient mathematical method which studies the deviation of $H(s)$ from the exponential form. When the response function is examined experimentally, the shifting-function component is not apparent in an obvious form.

For long delays (delays longer than the signal width), it is possible to study the shift in time of, say, the front edge of a pulse. An equivalent and more general technique is provided by measurements of the shift of the first centroid of a gate. To remove the sign uncertainty that may be present when the distortion is high, one can utilize the shift of the second moment. All these are related as well as the rise-time measurement. By far the simplest technique lies in the measure of the shift of the first centroid of a gate.

To simplify the development, let us define some new symbols. Denote the average value of t in a function $g(t)$ by

$$\langle tg(t) \rangle = \int_0^\infty tg(t)\, dt$$

and

$$\langle g(t) \rangle = \int_0^\infty g(t)\, dt.$$

Then the average value of t is

$$\langle t \rangle = \frac{\langle tg(t) \rangle}{\langle g(t) \rangle}.$$

If $e(t)$ is the excitation and $v(t)$ is the response, the delay can be defined as τ_d, where

$$\tau_d = \langle t \rangle_{\text{out}} - \langle t \rangle_{\text{in}} = \frac{\langle tv(t) \rangle}{\langle v(t) \rangle} - \frac{\langle te(t) \rangle}{\langle e(t) \rangle}.$$

We have stipulated that τ_d should be greater than or equal to zero in order to exclude situations that appear as an advance. Thus, if a calculation indicates a negative τ_d, we shall interpret this as a zero delay. Some high-pass transfers give a negative value for τ_d in this approximation. This occurs because the removal of the low-frequency components of a gate pulse pushes the centroid to smaller values.

This definition of τ_d is not useful if $H(s)$ has poles or zeros at the origin. If $H(s)$ has poles or zeros at $s = 0$, the function has zero delay.

For the functions $H(s)$ that show a delay, we can perform a very simple manipulation to demonstrate that the delay is basically given by the constant term and the coefficients of s in the two polynomials. The reader will perceive that this is equivalent to approximating the shifting exponential by the two leading terms in the series.

To evaluate $\langle tg(t) \rangle$ in a convenient fashion, we use the inverse transform;

$$tg(t) = -\mathscr{L}^{-1}\left[\frac{dG}{ds}\right],$$

where

$$G(s) = \mathscr{L}[g(\ )].$$

Then

$$\langle tg(t) \rangle = -\int_0^\infty \mathscr{L}^{-1}\left[\frac{dG}{ds}\right] dt = -\frac{1}{2\pi i}\int_0^\infty dt \int_{\sigma-i\infty}^{\sigma+i\infty} \frac{dG}{ds} e^{st} \, ds.$$

The derivative of $G(s)$ is particularly simple when $G(s)$ is a rational fraction. If

$$G(s) = \frac{\displaystyle\prod_{m=1}^{M}(s + \beta_m)}{\displaystyle\prod_{n=1}^{N}(s + \gamma_n)},$$

then

$$\frac{dG}{ds} = G(s)\left\{\sum_{m=1}^{M}\frac{1}{(s + \beta_m)} - \sum_{n=1}^{N}\frac{1}{(s + \gamma_n)}\right\}.$$

We write this as

$$\frac{dG}{ds} = G(s)R(s).$$

Returning to the integral, we invert the order of integration and take into account the fact that†

$$\delta(s) = \int_0^\infty \frac{e^{st}}{2\pi i} \, dt.$$

Thus,

$$\langle tg(t) \rangle = -\int_{\sigma-i\infty}^{\sigma+i\infty} G(s)R(s)\,\delta(s) \, ds = -G(0)R(0)$$

and

$$\langle g(t) \rangle = +\int_{\sigma-i\infty}^{\sigma+i\infty} G(s)\,\delta(s) \, ds = +G(0).$$

These forms make the expressions for $\langle t \rangle_{\text{out}}$ and $\langle t \rangle_{\text{in}}$ very simple. We write

$$V(s) = H(s)E(s);$$

---

† The proof of this identity can be performed by direct substitution:

$$\int_{\sigma-i\infty}^{\sigma+i\infty} G(s')\delta(s'-s) \, ds' = \int_{\sigma-i\infty}^{\sigma+i\infty} ds'G(s')\cdot\frac{1}{2\pi i}\int_0^\infty e^{t(s'-s)} \, dt = \int_0^\infty g(t)e^{-st} \, dt = G(s).$$

then

$$\frac{dV}{ds} = H(s)E(s)\{R_H(s) + R_E(s)\}.$$

This expression has both the sum of the partial fractions of $H(s)$, namely,

$$\sum_{m=1}^{M} \frac{1}{(s + \beta_m)} - \sum_{n=1}^{N} \frac{1}{(s + \gamma_n)}$$

and the sum of the first-order operators of $E(s)$, which will have the form

$$R_E(s) = \sum_{l} \frac{1}{(s + \xi_l)} - \sum_{k} \frac{1}{(s + \zeta_k)}.$$

The ξ_l are the zeros of $E(s)$ and the ζ_k are the poles.

In the same manner,

$$\frac{dE(s)}{ds} = E(s)R_E(s).$$

Finally, we use the expansion of $\langle tg(t) \rangle$ to give

$$\tau_d = \langle t \rangle_{out} - \langle t \rangle_{in} = - \frac{H(0)E(0)\{R_H(0) + R_E(0)\}}{H(0)E(0)} + \frac{E(0)R_E(0)}{E(0)}$$

or

$$\tau_d = - R_H(0) = \sum_{n=1}^{N} \frac{1}{\gamma_n} - \sum_{m=1}^{M} \frac{1}{\beta_m}.$$

We may now refer to the expansion of a polynomial in terms of its roots. By writing the polynomial in the series form instead of as a product,

$$H(s) = H_0 \left\{ \frac{s^M + b_{m-1}s^{M-1} + \cdots b_1 s + b_0}{s^N + a_{N-1}s^{N-1} + \cdots a_1 s + a_0} \right\}.$$

We then see that

$$\tau_d = \sum_{n=1}^{N} \frac{1}{\gamma_n} - \sum_{m=1}^{M} \frac{1}{\beta_m} = \frac{a_1}{a_0} - \frac{b_1}{b_0}.$$

As we stated before, this is equivalent to approximating the shifting exponential by the first two terms in the series. To see this, we rewrite $H(s)$ as

$$H(s) = H_0 \left\{ \frac{b_0}{a_0} \right\} \left\{ \frac{1 + (b_1/b_0)s + \cdots}{1 + (a_1/a_0)s + \cdots} \right\} \longrightarrow H_0 \frac{b_0}{a_0} e^{(b_1/b_0)s} e^{-(a_1/a_0)s}.$$

As an example of a simple delay, we consider again the low-pass function

$$H_{low}(s) = \frac{\omega_0^2}{[s^2 + \sqrt{2}\omega_0 s + \omega_0^2]};$$

using the result for τ_d,

$$\tau_d = \frac{\sqrt{2}\omega_0}{\omega_0^2} = \frac{\sqrt{2}}{\omega_0}.$$

This is the same result as we obtained when approximating with an exponential. A function with a zero at the origin will not delay. This can be shown by assuming the form,

$$H(s) = sG(s),$$

where $G(s)$ has no zeros or poles at the origins. Then

$$H(s) = \mathscr{L}\left[\frac{dg}{dt}\right] + g(0+)$$

and

$$h(t) = \frac{dg}{dt} + g(0+)\,\delta(t).$$

The presence of the $\delta(t)$ in the function $h(t)$ indicates that there will be no delay. The quadratic high-pass function with a single term s^2 in the numerator will obviously not show a delay by our definition.

The Mean Square Value

Another method for defining the delay is to employ the mean square value of t in a function $g(t)$:

$$\langle t^2 \rangle = \frac{\langle t^2 g(t) \rangle}{\langle g(t) \rangle}.$$

Techniques similar to those used for $\langle tg(t) \rangle$ can be introduced again. We note that

$$t^2 g(t) = \mathscr{L}^{-1}\left[\frac{d^2 G}{ds^2}\right].$$

If the transform of $g(t)$, $G(s)$, is again a rational fraction with no poles or zeros at the origin,

$$\frac{dG}{ds} = G(s)R(s)$$

and

$$\frac{d^2 G}{ds^2} = G(s)\frac{dR(s)}{ds} + \frac{dG}{ds}R(s) = G(s)\left\{\frac{dR}{ds} + R^2(s)\right\}.$$

Carrying out the integration and evaluating the expression,

$$\tau_d = \sqrt{\langle t^2 \rangle_{\text{out}}} - \sqrt{\langle t^2 \rangle_{\text{in}}}$$

does not eliminate the excitation function because of the square of $R(s)$, among other things. Because of its complexity, this definition of τ_d is not particularly convenient. To indicate the general form, we notice that when

$$V(s) = H(s)E(s),$$

$$\frac{\langle t^2 v(t) \rangle}{\langle v(t) \rangle} = \left[\frac{d}{ds}\{R_H(s) + R_E(s)\} + \{R_H(s) + R_E(s)\}^2\right]_{s=0},$$

then

$$\tau_d = \left[\frac{d}{ds} R_H(s) + R_H^2 + 2R_H R_E \right]_{s=0}$$

The Phase Shift

The phase shift of a response to a sinusoidal excitation is essentially the same problem as the preceding one. As has been shown, the response to an excitation $e^{-i\omega t}$ is $H(i\omega)$. The phase shift of the response is obtained directly by writing $H(i\omega)$ in the polar form:

$$H(i\omega) = \rho(\omega)\, e^{i\Phi(\omega)}.$$

Phase distortion arises when $\Phi(\omega)$ is not a linear function of ω. Thus, the ideal transfer function with no phase distortion has the form

$$H(i\omega) = \rho(\omega)\, e^{i\omega\tau}.$$

Real systems always deviate from the ideal to some extent. The quality of a system is measured by the relative amount of the deviation.

Let $\phi_j(\omega)$ be the phase of the jth pole relative to a point on the imaginary $i\omega$ axis. Take $\Theta_k(\omega)$ as the phase of the kth zero from that point. The total phase shift of a transfer function (see Fig. 84),

$$H = H_0 \frac{\displaystyle\prod_{m=1}^{M} (s + \beta_m)}{\displaystyle\prod_{n=1}^{N} (s + \gamma_n)},$$

is then

$$\Phi(\omega) = \sum_{m=1}^{M} \Theta_m(\omega) - \sum_{n=1}^{N} \phi_n(\omega).$$

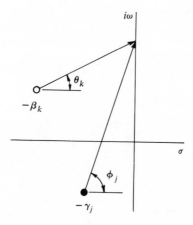

FIG. 84.   An illustration of the contribution of a pole and a zero to the sinusoidal phase shift.

To illustrate a situation, consider a low-pass function described by two poles γ and γ^* (no zeros). This is a quadratic type II low-pass function; the total phase is

$$\Phi(\omega) = -\tan^{-1}\frac{2a\omega}{[\omega_0^2 - \omega^2]}.$$

This particular phase function is fairly linear for frequencies up to $\omega_0/2$. As we have seen, the variations in phase become quite marked near resonance. If a is large, the phase shift per unit frequency near zero is large. A large Q value, on the other hand, provides linearity with a small value of τ, the phase shift per unit frequency. In the example given above, at any frequency ω,

$$\tau \simeq \frac{d\Phi}{d\omega} = -\frac{2a(\omega_0^2 + \omega^2)}{(\omega_0^2 - \omega^2)^2 + 4a^2\omega^2} \xrightarrow[\text{small } \omega]{} -\frac{2a}{\omega_0^2} = -\frac{1}{Q\omega_0}.$$

The relation between the time delay τ_d and the linear component of the phase response is obvious. They are equal in magnitude and opposite in sign.

The Rise Time

There are several ways of defining the rise-time response of an electronic device. The simplest method is to measure the slope of the response to a step excitation. Variations in definition occur from the different ways in which slopes can be taken. A partial list of the different definitions is given below.

1. The extrapolation of the slope of the response at $t = 0$ to the final steady-state height. This method is poor because in many instances this slope may be close to zero. See Fig. 85a.
2. The extrapolation of the slope at the point where the function is one-half its final steady-state value. See Fig. 85b.
3. The time required for the response to vary in height from 10 percent to 90 percent of its final value. This value is quite close to that of (2), usually. See Fig. 85c.

The slope of the response can be expanded by transform techniques. To make the calculations general, we scale $H(s)$ so that the amplitude of the response equals the amplitude of the step excitation for large t:

$$v(t) = \mathscr{L}^{-1}[H(s)E_U(s)] \xrightarrow[\text{large } t]{} 1.$$

Because $e(t) = U(t)$,

$$v_U(t) = \mathscr{L}^{-1}\left[\frac{H(s)}{s}\right].$$

Now

$$\frac{dv_U(t)}{dt} = \mathscr{L}^{-1}[H(s)] - v(0+)\delta(t) = \mathscr{L}^{-1}[H(s)]$$

and

$$\left[\frac{dv}{dt}\right]_{t=T} = h(T).$$

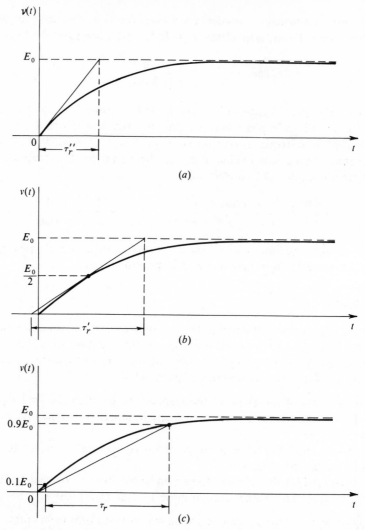

FIG. 85. Three methods by which a measure of the rise time can be defined. The first (a) employs the slope of the response at $t = 0$. The second (b) utilizes the slope at half-minimum. The third (c) is the conventional definition, which uses the time interval between points corresponding to 0.1 and 0.9 of the final value.

We can also note that

$$v_U(t) = \int_0^t h(t')\, dt'.$$

The value T can be defined from the relation

$$v_U(T) = \int_0^T h(t')\, dt' = \tfrac{1}{2}.$$

Finally,

$$\tau_{\text{rise}} = \frac{1}{h(T)}.$$

This method is somewhat cumbersome because the value of T is close to τ_r and is approximately τ_d, the delay that was developed in the preceding section.

The most convenient measure of τ_r, experimentally is the time required for the pulse to rise from 10 percent to 90 percent of its final value.

This rise time and the others are closely related to the half-power point $\omega_{1/2}$, which in an elementary function is the frequency corresponding to the pole nearest the origin. The standard definition relates τ_r to $\omega_{1/2}$ (or $|\gamma|_1$, the nearest pole) by

$$\tau_r = \frac{0.35}{f_{1/2}} = \frac{2.2}{\omega_{1/2}}.$$

When several units are cascaded [each having a transfer function $H_j(s)$,] the overall rise time T_R is approximately the square root of the sum of the squares of the individual τ_r:

$$T_R = \left\{ \sum_j \tau_r(j) \right\}^{1/2}.$$

In this equation, the expression $\tau_r(j)$ is the rise-time response of the jth unit.

If all the units are identical and there are N of them,

$$T_R = \sqrt{N}\,\tau_r.$$

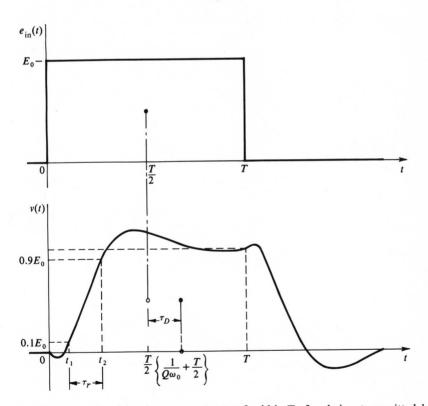

FIG. 86. The apparent delay in a square gate of width T after being transmitted by an underdamped low-pass transfer of $Q = 1$ and $\omega_0 = 5\pi/\sqrt{3}T$. Notice that τ_D and τ_r are essentially the same.

Numerical examples have been worked out, and the results are shown in Table 4. The gain per stage was normalized to 1. The reader will observe that a slightly more accurate form of T_R is

$$T_R = 1.1\sqrt{N}\,\tau_r.$$

A square gate whose width is long compared with the delay time and rise time was used to compute the values shown. (Diagrams of the parameters are shown in Fig. 86.)

TABLE 4

Number of Sections	$\dfrac{H(s)}{s}$	$v(t)$	t_1	t_2	τ_r	$\sqrt{N}\,\dfrac{2.2}{\omega_0}$	τ_d	$\dfrac{v(\tau_d)}{\%}$
1	$\dfrac{\omega_0}{s(s+\omega_0)}$	$(1 - e^{-\omega_0 t})$	$\dfrac{0.1}{\omega_0}$	$\dfrac{2.3}{\omega_0}$	$\dfrac{2.2}{\omega_0}$	$\dfrac{2.2}{\omega_0}$	$\dfrac{1}{\omega_0}$	63.3
2	$\dfrac{\omega_0^2}{s(s+\omega_0)^2}$	$\{1 - (1+\omega_0 t)e^{-\omega_0 t}\}$	$\dfrac{0.55}{\omega_0}$	$\dfrac{3.88}{\omega_0}$	$\dfrac{3.35}{\omega_0}$	$\dfrac{3.1}{\omega_0}$	$\dfrac{2}{\omega_0}$	59.5
3	$\dfrac{\omega_0^3}{s(s+\omega_0)^3}$	$\left\{1 - \left(1 + \omega_0 t + \dfrac{\omega_0^2 t^2}{2}\right)e^{-\omega_0 t}\right\}$	$\dfrac{1.1}{\omega_0}$	$\dfrac{5.3}{\omega_0}$	$\dfrac{4.2}{\omega_0}$	$\dfrac{3.8}{\omega_0}$	$\dfrac{3}{\omega_0}$	57.5

CHAPTER 3

PASSIVE LINEAR NETWORKS

Linear analysis and linear systems were investigated in terms of the general properties in previous sections. Much of the detail of the problems of one-loop circuits is contained in these developments of the basic response functions. The RC circuit, the LR circuit, and the series LRC circuit have in practice been covered as type I and type II responses. The results, on the other hand, should be summarized for each particular case in order that we may obtain a table of characteristic and responses of our most elementary combinations of passive components.

Before considering the specific circuits, we shall regard a few general theorems: the theorem of duality, Thévenin's theorem, and Norton's theorem.

DUALITY

The algebraic form of the relation between current and voltage in the three passive elements is symmetric under the exchange of elements and current and voltage. This is to say that the operations of integration, scaling, and differentiation are present symmetrically in the operations of the three lumped, passive elements. A capacitor integrates the current and differentiates the voltage appearing across its terminals. On the other hand, the inductance differentiates its current and integrates the voltage. Table 5 illustrates the duality.

It follows, then, that every voltage-excited circuit has a duel circuit that is current-excited or current-driven. Algebraically, the dual is achieved by converting the initial circuit equation. Therefore, if we initially consider a voltage-driven LRC circuit, the defining equation takes the form

$$v_L(t) + v_R(t) + v_C(t) = e(t).$$

In other words, we consider a loop equation (see Fig. 87), stating that the sum of the instantaneous drops about a loop equals the applied emf, $e(t)$.

The dual of this equation will be constructed if $e(t)$ becomes a current source $i(t)$, and if each voltage is changed to a current through a reciprocal element. Then

$$i_{C'}(t) + i_{G'}(t) + i_{L'}(t) = i(t).$$

TABLE 5

Element	Voltage Excited	Current Excited
Capacitor $i(t)$ C $v_C(t)$	$i(t) = C\dfrac{dv_c}{dt}$ $I(s) = \mathcal{L}[i(t)] = Cs\,V_c(s)$ $\qquad\qquad - Cv_c(0+)$	$v_c(t) = \dfrac{1}{c}\displaystyle\int i(t')dt'$ $V_c(s) = \dfrac{I(s)}{Cs} + \dfrac{v_c(0+)}{s}$
Resistor $i(t)$ R $v_R(t)$	$i(t) = Gv_R(t) = \dfrac{v_R}{R}$ $I(s) = GV_R(s) = \dfrac{V_R(s)}{R}$	$v_R(t) = Ri(t) = \dfrac{i(t)}{G}$ $V_R(s) = RI(s) = \dfrac{I(s)}{G}$
Inductance $i(t)$ L $v_L(t)$	$i(t) = \dfrac{1}{L}\displaystyle\int v_L(t')dt'$ $I(s) = \dfrac{V_L(s)}{Ls} + \dfrac{i(0+)}{s}$	$v_L(t) = L\dfrac{di(t)}{dt}$ $V_L(s) = LsI(s) - Li(0+)$

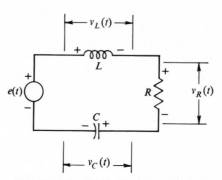

FIG. 87.   A series LRC circuit, voltage excited.

This is the current conservation equation for a circuit consisting of three branches, C', G', and L', being fed by a current generator. See Fig. 88.

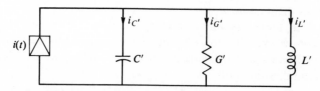

FIG. 88.   The current dual to the series LRC circuit is a parallel $C'G'L'$ arrangement.

To construct a dual circuit, then, we must follow these rules:

1. A series resistance R becomes a parallel conductance G' in the dual.
2. A series capacitor C becomes a parallel inductance L'.
3. The series inductance L of the original circuit becomes a parallel capacitor C' in the dual.

4. Voltage generators become current sources in the dual.
5. Open switches in a series circuit become closed parallel switches in the dual, and vice versa.

The reader is reminded that an ideal voltage generator has zero internal impedance, whereas an ideal current generator has an infinite internal impedance. This is an obvious duality.

To convert a loop to a parallel dual, then, we can employ some very simple graphical techniques (see Fig. 89). After placing a point A inside the loop to be con-

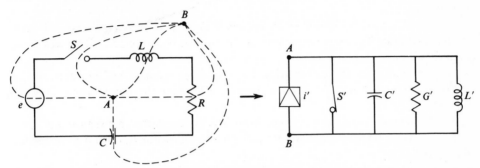

FIG. 89.   Graphic technique for conversion of the series voltage-excited circuit to its dual.

verted and a point outside (B in the diagram), we pass a line from A to B through each element, switch, and generator in the loop. The lines become the branches of the dual, and the corresponding elements in the original take the dual role in the final circuit.

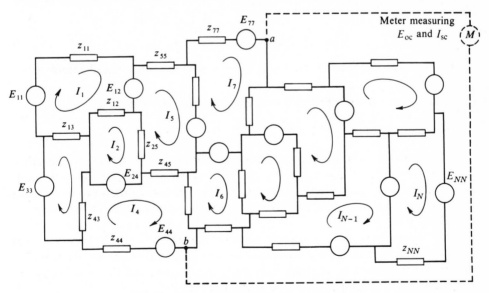

FIG. 90.   General flat network illustrating the two-point extraction preliminary to substitution by a Thévenin equivalent circuit.

There are several other general theorems that we should take note of before considering specific circuits. In the next section, we shall derive Thévenin's theorem. It is interesting to find that this theorem has a dual called *Norton's theorem*.

THÉVENIN'S THEOREM

In a circuit of any complexity, consisting only of passive linear elements and linear generators, the characteristics between any two points in the network can be replaced by a single, active, voltage generator in series with an impedance $Z_{int}(s)$.

The output of the generator is equal to the open-circuit voltage $E_{oc}(s)$ between the two points. By measuring or computing the current $I_{sc}(s)$ flowing in the short circuit when the two points are shorted, the internal impedance $Z_{int}(s)$ can be computed as $E_{oc}(s)/I_{sc}(s)$.

When this theorem is applied to the imaginary axis of the s plane (i.e., a Fourier series), a separate Thévenin equivalent circuit must be constructed for each individual frequency component.

By initiating our discussion with the $\mathscr{L}T$ of the voltages and currents, we can avoid the extra tedium of the Fourier series. Consider the flat network shown in Fig. 90.

The theorem states that a linear branch $\mathbf{Z}_L(s)$ connected between a and b will respond as if the points a and b were in series with a generator $E_{oc}(s)$ and an impedance $Z_{int}(s)$. See Fig. 91.

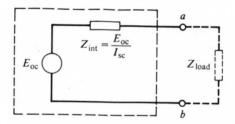

FIG. 91.   The Thévenin equivalent circuit connected to an external load impedance.

The loaded terminals deliver a load current $I_L(s)$, determined by

$$\{Z_{int}(s) + Z_L(s)\}I_L(s) = E_{oc}(s).$$

Some care must be exercised in the interpretation of $E_{oc}(s)$. Unless the initial conditions in each branch are to be respected at every new connection, we must assume a steady-state form for $E_{oc}(s)$ and $I_{sc}(s)$. Otherwise, the variations in transients make the problem quite difficult. Therefore, we may assume that the elements are initially relaxed.

The flat network does not imply a restriction. The theorem holds for nonflat networks. We employ flatness here because the matrix development is relatively simple. A flat network of N loops with the terminals a, b, and the load impedance $Z_L(s)$ in the Nth (exterior) loop are shown in Fig. 92.

The branch impedances $z_{lm}(s)$ have been appropriately combined to form the lumped matrix element $Z_{kj}(s)$. The method was developed in an earlier section (p. 8).

$$Z_{ll}(s) = \sum_{\text{all } k} z_{lk}(s);$$

$$Z_{lm}(s) = z_{lm}(s), \qquad (l \neq m).$$

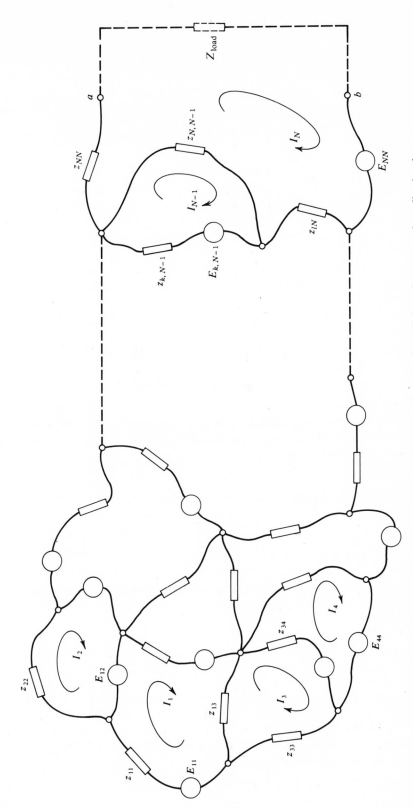

FIG. 92. A flat network of N loops with the load impedance in the Nth loop but external to all other loops.

The matrix equation for the loop currents in terms of the loop emfs is

$$\begin{pmatrix} Z_{11}(s) & Z_{12}(s) & \cdots & Z_{1N}(s) \\ Z_{21}(s) & Z_{22}(s) & \cdots & Z_{2N}(s) \\ \vdots & & & \\ Z_{N1}(s) & Z_{N2}(s) & \cdots & [Z_{NN} + Z_L] \end{pmatrix} \begin{bmatrix} I_1(s) \\ I_2(s) \\ \vdots \\ I_N(s) \end{bmatrix} = \begin{bmatrix} E_1(s) \\ E_2(s) \\ \vdots \\ E_N(s) \end{bmatrix}.$$

We have separated $Z_{NN}(s)$ and $Z_L(s)$ to indicate that $Z_L(s)$ is variable and exterior to the terminals a, b. A projection operator $\mathbb{N}$ can be employed to separate $Z_L(s)$ from the interior matrix $\mathbb{Z}_0(s)$, where

$$\mathbb{N} = \begin{pmatrix} 0 & 0 & 0 & \cdots & 0 \\ 0 & 0 & 0 & \cdots & 0 \\ \cdots & 0 & 0 & \cdot & \cdots \\ \vdots & & & \ddots & \vdots \\ 0 & 0 & 0 & \cdots & 1 \end{pmatrix}.$$

Then

$$\mathbb{Z} \cdot \mathbf{I}(s) = \{\mathbb{Z}_0 + Z_L(s)\mathbb{N}\} \cdot \mathbf{I}(s) = \mathbf{E}(s),$$

with

$$\mathbb{Z}_0(s) = \begin{pmatrix} Z_{11} & Z_{12} & \cdots & Z_{1N} \\ Z_{21} & Z_{22} & & \cdots \\ \vdots & & & \vdots \\ Z_{N1} & Z_{N2} & \cdots & Z_{NN} \end{pmatrix}.$$

The solution that is sought obviously lies in finding an expression for $I_N(s)$ in terms of the loop emf $E_{jk}(s)$. This is found by computing the inverse Z operator. It turns out that the steps are more apparent if this inversion is done in two stages First we multiply from the left by $\mathbb{Y}_0(s) = \mathbb{Z}_0^{-1}(s)$, and

$$\{\mathbb{I} + Z_L(s) \, \mathbb{Y}_0 \cdot \mathbb{N}\} \cdot \mathbf{I}(s) = \mathbb{Y}_0 \cdot \mathbf{E}(s).$$

The matrix on the left is quite simple, with

$$\{\mathbb{I} + Z_L\mathbb{Y}_0 \cdot \mathbb{N}\} = \begin{pmatrix} 1 & 0 & 0 & 0 & \cdots & Z_L Y_{N1} \\ 0 & 1 & 0 & 0 & \cdots & Z_L Y_{N2} \\ 0 & 0 & 1 & 0 & \cdots & Z_L Y_{N3} \\ \vdots & & & & & \\ 0 & 0 & 0 & 0 & \cdots & (1 + Z_L Y_{NN}) \end{pmatrix}.$$

The inverse is

$$\{\mathbb{I} + Z_L\mathbb{Y}_0 \cdot \mathbb{N}\}^{-1} = \begin{pmatrix} 1 & 0 & 0 & \cdots & & \cdots \\ 0 & 1 & 0 & \cdots & & \cdots \\ \vdots & & & & & \\ 0 & 0 & 0 & \cdots & & \dfrac{1}{1 + Z_L Y_{NN}} \end{pmatrix}.$$

The important aspect of the inverse matrix is that the last row of this inverse has all elements equal to zero except for the NN element, which is $1/(1 + Z_L Y_{NN})$.

Solving for the total vector, we can write

$$\mathbf{I}(s) = \{\mathbb{I} + Z_L\mathbb{Y}_0 \cdot \mathbb{N}\}^{-1} \cdot \mathbb{Y}_0 \cdot \mathbf{E}(s).$$

Expanding this to obtain the load current $I_N(s)$, we get

$$I_N(s) = \frac{\sum\limits_{k=1}^{N} Y_{Nk}E_k(s)}{[I + Z_L Y_{NN}]}.$$

The open-circuit voltage is

$$E_{oc}(s) = \lim_{Z_L \to \infty} Z_L I_N = \frac{\sum\limits_{k=1}^{N} Y_{Nk}E_k}{Y_{NN}}.$$

The short-circuit current is

$$I_{sc}(s) = \lim_{Z_L \to 0} I_N(s) = \sum_{k=1}^{N} Y_{Nk}E_k(s).$$

With these identifications, the general expression for $I_N(s)$ can be written as

$$\left\{\frac{1}{Y_{NN}} + Z_L(s)\right\}I_N(s) = \frac{\sum\limits_{k=1}^{N} Y_{Nk}E_k}{Y_{NN}}$$

or

$$\{Z_{int}(s) + Z_L(s)\}I_N(s) = E_{oc}(s).$$

We see that

$$Z_{int}(s) = \frac{E_{oc}}{I_{sc}} = \frac{1}{Y_{NN}(s)}.$$

This demonstrates our theorem. We notice in closing that when $s \to i\omega_0$, the constraint mentioned for the Fourier series is apparent.

To illustrate the method, we regard the following three-loop circuit from the point of view of Thévenin's theorem. The generator in this case is a gate (see Fig. 93):

$$g_T(t) = E_0\{U(t) - U(t - T)\}.$$

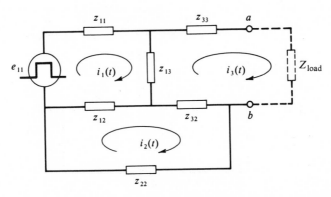

FIG. 93.   The three-loop circuit used as an example of the application of Thévenin's theorem.

In the $\mathscr{L}T$ notation,

$$\mathbb{Z}_0 = \begin{pmatrix} z_{11} + z_{12} + z_{13} & -z_{12} & -z_{13} \\ -z_{21} & z_{21} + z_{22} + z_{23} & -z_{23} \\ -z_{31} & -z_{32} & z_{31} + z_{32} + z_{33} \end{pmatrix},$$

and

$$(\mathbb{Z}_0 + Z_L \mathbb{N}) \cdot \mathbf{I}(s) = \mathbf{E}(s).$$

This detail illustrates the starting form with $\mathbb{Z}_0(s)$, $\mathbb{N}$, and $Z_L(s)$ represented in detail.
If the forms of $Z_{lm}(s)$ are given, $\mathbb{Y}_0(s)$ can be computed in detail. Assume the special example in Fig. 94. The characteristic impedance is

$$\mathbb{Z}_0 = \begin{pmatrix} 2R\left(\dfrac{s+a}{s}\right) & -R & -\dfrac{1}{Cs} \\ -R & 3R & -R \\ -\dfrac{1}{Cs} & -R & 2R\left(\dfrac{s+a}{s}\right) \end{pmatrix},$$

with

$$|\mathbb{Z}_0| = \frac{8R^3(s+2a)}{s},$$

where

$$a = \frac{1}{2RC}.$$

The inverse $\mathbb{Z}_0^{-\prime} = \mathbb{Y}_0$ is

$$\mathbb{Y}_0(s) = \frac{1}{|\mathbb{Z}_0|} \begin{pmatrix} \dfrac{R^2}{s}(5s + 6a) & \dfrac{2R^2(s+2a)}{s} & R^2\left(\dfrac{s+6a}{s}\right) \\ \dfrac{2R^2(s+2a)}{s} & \dfrac{4R^2}{s}(s+2a) & \dfrac{2R^2}{s}(s+2a) \\ R^2\left(\dfrac{s+6a}{s}\right) & \dfrac{2R^2}{s}(s+2a) & \dfrac{R^2}{s}(5s+6a) \end{pmatrix}.$$

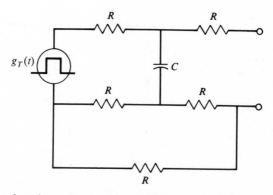

FIG. 94.   The three-loop circuit with specific assignments for the z_{lm} and $e_{ll}(t)$.

With this information and the fact that the only nonvanishing $E_j(s)$ is E_1, we can write

$$I_{sc}(s) = \sum_{k=1}^{3} Y_{Nk}E_k = Y_{31}E_1 = \frac{E_0(s + 6a)(1 - e^{-sT})}{8Rs(s + 2a)},$$

$$Z_{int}(s) = \frac{1}{Y_{33}} = \frac{8R(s + 2a)}{5(s + \frac{6}{5}a)},$$

and

$$E_{oc}(s) = \frac{E_0(s + 6a)(1 - e^{-sT})}{5s(s + \frac{6}{5}a)}$$

The internal circuit adds a characteristic mode ($\frac{6}{5}a$) to the equivalent generator. Take the case when the load is $Z_L = R$. See Fig. 95.

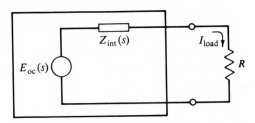

FIG. 95.   A Thévenin equivalent circuit with a resistive load.

The load current I_L is

$$I_L(s) = \frac{E_{oc}(s)}{[Z_{int}(s) + R]} = \frac{E_0(s + 6a)(1 - e^{-sT})}{13Rs(s + \frac{22}{13}a)}.$$

$Z_{int}(s)$ is correlated with $E_{oc}(s)$ and shifts the additional characteristic mode when loaded.

If this particular set of terminals were to be investigated, say, using an oscilloscope, it would require two independent measurements, an open circuit and a short circuit. We would observe (see Fig. 96)

$$i_{sc}(t) = \frac{E_0}{8R} \left\{ (3 - 2e^{-2at})U(t) - (3 - 2e^{-2a(t-T)})U(t - T) \right\}.$$

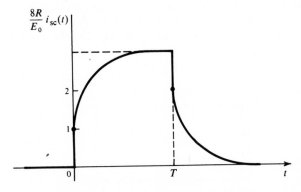

FIG. 96.   The short-circuit current wave form from the example circuit of Fig. 94.

The time-domain representation of $i_{sc}(t)$ could then be obtained from the oscillo-scope measurement. The open-circuit voltage would appear with longer time constants. See Fig. 97.

$$e_{sc}(t) = E_0\{(1 - \tfrac{4}{5}e^{-(6/5)at})U(t) - (1 - \tfrac{4}{5}e^{-(6/5)a(t-T)})U(t - T)\}.$$

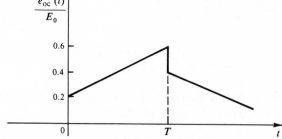

FIG. 97.   The open-circuit voltage wave form from the example circuit.

Using as good a time representation as possible for the wave forms, we could then transform to get $I_{sc}(s)$ and $E_{oc}(s)$. The ratio of these two would indicate that $Z_{int}(s)$ has the form shown in Fig. 98.

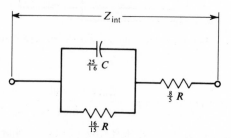

FIG. 98.   The equivalent internal impedance for the example circuit.

NORTON'S THEOREM

The dual of Thévenin's theorem is that of Norton, which states that a linear mesh viewed from any two points (a and b) can be simulated by a constant-current generator in parallel with an internal admittance $Y_{int}(s)$. If all the generators are periodic, and if a Fourier representation is used, we must have a separate equivalent for each frequency. On the other hand, we can, as in Thévenin's theorem, work in the complex frequency domain with a single equivalent network. The flat network employed for the general development of Thévenin's theorem (Fig. 91) can be used again. The equivalent Norton circuit is shown in Fig. 99.

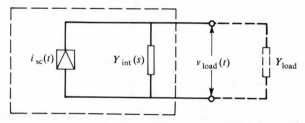

FIG. 99.   The dual of the Thévenin equivalent circuit. This is the Norton equivalent circuit.

We are now interested in the voltage between the points (a, b). In the $\mathscr{L}T$ representation, the solution we are looking for is

$$\{Y_{\text{int}}(s) + Y_L(s)\}V_{\text{load}}(s) = I_{\text{sc}}(s).$$

To connect this form with the result obtained in the development of Thevénin's theorem, we again write the equation for the current $I_N(s) = I_L(s)$ in the output loop:

$$\left\{\frac{1}{Y_{NN}} + Z_L(s)\right\}I_N(s) = \frac{\displaystyle\sum_{k=1}^{N} Y_{Nk}E_k}{Y_{NN}}.$$

The voltage across the load is

$$V_L(s) = Z_L(s)I_N(s)$$

or

$$I_N(s) = Y_L(s)V_L(s).$$

The open-circuit voltage and short-circuit current are as before, with

$$Y_{\text{int}}(s) = Y_{NN}(s) = \frac{I_{\text{sc}}(s)}{E_{\text{oc}}(s)}$$

and

$$I_{\text{sc}}(s) = \sum_{k=1}^{N} Y_{Nk}E_k(s).$$

Thus, our expression above can be written

$$I_N(s) + Y_{NN}Z_L I_N = I_{\text{sc}}$$

or

$$\{Y_{\text{int}}(s) + Y_L(s)\}V_N(s) = I_{\text{sc}}(s).$$

This proves our theorem and shows that the amplitude of the current supplied by the current generator is given by the short-circuit current.

NONFLAT NETWORKS

Maxwell's loop method was applied quite readily to the flat network. In this representation, once the circuit was laid out, the loop currents could be chosen in an unambiguous fashion, and the branch currents were obtained as the algebraic sum of the adjoining loop currents. This uniqueness of choice is lost when a nonflat network is encountered.

Although the dimensions of the problem increase, one can maintain a unique representation by setting the problem up in terms of Kirchoff's laws and the branch currents.

A nonflat network contains one or more branches that cross over other branches. This crossover cannot be removed by any flat representation of the circuit without introducing another crossover.

It is important to recognize that the problem is still *linear*. Therefore, all statements that were previously made regarding network theorems which rely upon the linearity of the problem are still true, i.e., Thévenin's and other theorem. Because of the lack of uniqueness of representation, the matrices encountered may on occasion be nonsymmetric.

ONE-LOOP CIRCUITS

In a previous section all possible combinations of the three passive elements were anticipated in the outline of the elementary transfer functions. The reader will recall that the transfer characteristics were catalogued in terms of the poles and zeros of the function. It was pointed out that all higher-order transfers are built up of products of the elementary high-pass and low-pass types. During this same discussion, functions with complex poles and zeros were handled somewhat separately, for convenience only.

Because the general characteristics and responses to several types of excitation have been noted, we can tabulate the results in a consistent form. Table 6 provides information concerning step response and sinusoidal response of many of the possible combinations of R, L, and C. These charts of the quadratic combinations could be extended. One could discuss the combinations with split resistance, split capacitance, and split inductance in all possible combinations, but this is unnecessary in view of the fundamental information that could be obtained.

One aspect of the quadratic LRC forms, which is apparent in the diagrams, is the variation of the position of the poles as L, R, and C are changed. The basic quadratic is

$$s^2 + 2as + \omega_0^2,$$

where

$$a = \frac{R}{2L}$$

and

$$\omega_0^2 = \frac{1}{LC}.$$

The roots have been examined time and time again.

$$s^2 + 2as + \omega_0^2 \doteq (s + a - \sqrt{a^2 - \omega_0^2})(s + a + \sqrt{a^2 - \omega_0^2}).$$

We notice in general that when $a \geqslant \omega_0$ (type I), the roots are on the real axis; as a decreases relative to ω_0, the roots move onto the circumference of a circle of radius ω_0.

Variations in L

L enters both the expression for a and the expression for ω_0. Because ω_0 varies as $1/\sqrt{L}$, an increase in L reduces a by a larger fraction than the respective reduction in ω_0. We now consider an overdamped LRC circuit. Initially, the poles are on the real axis. As L is increased, keeping R and C fixed, the poles move toward one another and then split and move on the circumference of a circle of radius $(1/RC)$ centered at $(-1/RC)$ in the complex s plane. The locus of all points in the s plane for fixed values of R and C is given by

$$\omega^2 + \left(\sigma + \frac{1}{RC}\right)^2 = \frac{1}{(RC)^2}.$$

The motion of the roots as L is increased is shown in Fig. 100.

Circuit	Class	Transfer Function	No. of Poles	No. of Zeros	s Plane	Step Response $e(t) = E_0 U(t)$	Sinusoidal Response $e(t) = E_0 e^{i\omega t} U(t)$
	Low-Pass Type I	$\dfrac{\alpha}{(s+\alpha)}$ $\alpha_C = \dfrac{1}{RC}$ $\alpha_L = \dfrac{R}{L}$	1	0		$v(t) = E_0(1 - e^{-\alpha t})U(t)$	
	High-Pass Type I	$\dfrac{s}{(s+\alpha)}$ $\alpha_C = \dfrac{1}{RC}$ $\alpha_L = \dfrac{R}{L}$	1	1		$v(t) = E_0 e^{-\alpha t} U(t)$	
	Compound Low-Pass Type I $\alpha < \beta$	$k\,\dfrac{(s+\beta)}{(s+\alpha)}$ $k_C = \dfrac{R_2}{R_1 + R_2}$ $\beta_C = \dfrac{1}{R_2 C}$ $\alpha_C = \dfrac{1}{(R_1 + R_2)C}$ $k_L = \dfrac{L_2}{L_1 + L_2}$ $\beta_L = \dfrac{R}{L_2}$ $\alpha_L = \dfrac{R}{(L_1 + L_2)}$	1	1		$v(t) = E_0\left\{1 - \left(\dfrac{\beta - \alpha}{\beta}\right)e^{-\alpha t}\right\}U(t)$	

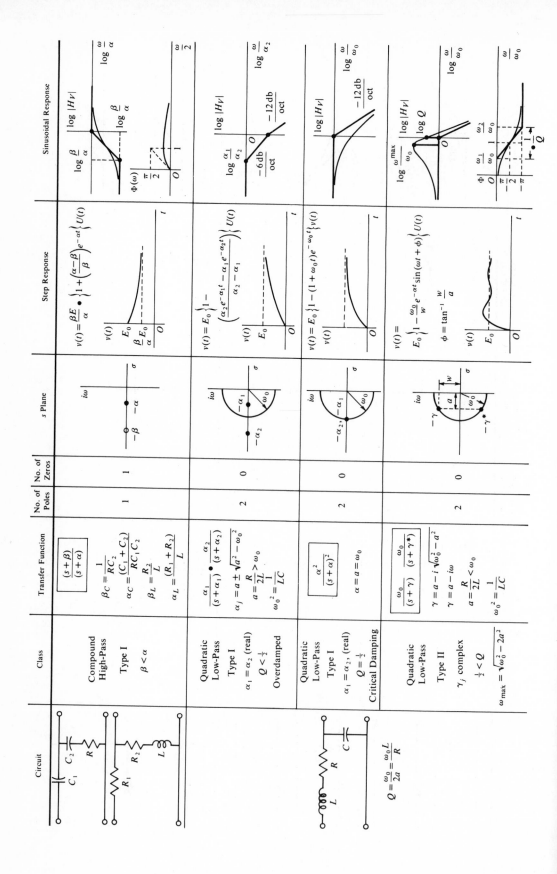

Circuit	Class	Transfer Function	No. of Poles	No. of Zeros	s Plane	Step Response	Sinusoidal Response
$Q = \dfrac{\omega_0 L}{R} = \dfrac{\omega_0 L}{R}$ $a = \dfrac{R}{2L}$ $w = \sqrt{\omega_0^2 - a^2}$ $\omega_0^2 = \dfrac{1}{LC}$	Quadratic High-Pass Type I $\alpha_1 < \alpha_2$ (real) $Q < \tfrac{1}{2}$ Overdamped	$\dfrac{s}{(s+\alpha_1)} \cdot \dfrac{s}{(s+\alpha_2)}$ $\alpha_j = a \pm \sqrt{a^2 - \omega_0^2}$	2	2		$v(t) = \dfrac{E_0}{(\alpha_2 - \alpha_1)} \left\{ -\alpha_1 e^{-\alpha_1 t} + \alpha_2 e^{-\alpha_2 t} \right\} U$	
	Quadratic High-Pass Type I $\alpha_1 = \alpha_2 = \omega_0$ $Q = \tfrac{1}{2}$ Critical Damping	$\dfrac{s^2}{(s+\omega_0)^2}$	2	2		$v(t) = E_0(1 - \omega_0 t)e^{-\omega_0 t} V(t)$	
	Quadratic High-Pass Type II γ complex $\tfrac{1}{2} < Q$	$\dfrac{s}{(s+\gamma)} \cdot \dfrac{s}{(s+\gamma^*)}$ $\gamma = a - iw$	2	2		$v(t) =$ $-E_0 \dfrac{\omega_0}{w} e^{-at} \sin(wt - \phi) U(t)$	

Circuit	Class	Transfer Function	No. of Poles	No. of Zeros	s Plane	Step Response	Sinusoidal Response
L R C $Q = \dfrac{\omega_0}{2a} = \dfrac{\omega_0 L}{R}$ $a = \dfrac{R}{2L}$ $\omega_0^2 = \dfrac{1}{LC}$ $w = \sqrt{\omega_0^2 - a^2}$ Half-Power Points ω_1, ω_2 $\dfrac{\omega_2 - \omega_1}{\omega_0} = \dfrac{1}{Q}$	Quadratic Resonance Type I $\alpha_1 < \tfrac{1}{2}$ Overdamped	$\dfrac{(\alpha_1 + \alpha_2)s}{(s+\alpha_1)(s+\alpha_2)} =$ $\dfrac{(\alpha_1+\alpha_2)s}{[s^2 + 2as + \omega_0^2]}$ $\alpha_j = a \pm \sqrt{a^2 - \omega_0^2}$	2	1		$v(t) = \dfrac{E_0 a}{\sqrt{a^2 - \omega_0^2}} \{e^{-\alpha_1 t} - e^{-\alpha_2 t}\} U(t)$ 	
	Quadratic Resonance Type I $\alpha_1 = \alpha_2 = \omega_0$ (real) $Q = \tfrac{1}{2}$ Critical Damping	$\boxed{\dfrac{2\omega_0 s}{(s+\omega_0)^2}}$	2	1		$v(t) = E_0 2\omega_0 t e^{-\omega_0 t} U(t)$ 	
	Quadratic Resonance Type II γ complex $\tfrac{1}{2} < Q$ Underdamped	$\dfrac{2as}{(s+\gamma)(s+\gamma^*)} =$ $\dfrac{2as}{[s^2 + 2as + \omega_0^2]}$ $\gamma = a - iw$ $\dfrac{\omega_2}{\omega_0} \rightarrow 1 + \dfrac{1}{2Q}$ $\dfrac{\omega_1}{\omega_0} \rightarrow 1 - \dfrac{1}{2Q}$	2	1		$v(t) = \dfrac{2aE_0}{w} e^{-at} \sin wt\, U(t)$ 	

Circuit	Class	Transfer Function	No. of Poles	No. of Zeros	s Plane	Step Response	Sinusoidal Response
	Quadratic Compound Low-Pass Type I $Q < \frac{1}{2}$ Overdamped	$H = 1 - H_L$ $H = \dfrac{2a(s + Q\omega_0)}{\lvert s^2 + 2as + \omega_0^2 \rvert}$	2	1		$v(t) = E_0 \left\{ 1 - \dfrac{2a}{(\alpha_2 - \alpha_1)}\left(\dfrac{(Q\omega_0 - \alpha_1)}{\alpha_1}e^{-\alpha_1 t} - \dfrac{(Q\omega_0 - \alpha_2)}{\alpha_2}e^{-\alpha_2 t}\right) \right\}$	
	Quadratic Compound Low-Pass Type I $Q = \frac{1}{2}$ Critical Damping	$H = 1 - H_L$	2	1		$v(t) = E_0\{1 - (1 - \omega_0 t)e^{-\omega_0 t}\}U(t)$	
	Quadratic Compound Low-Pass Type II $\frac{1}{2} < Q$ Underdamped	$H = 1 - H_L$	2	1		$v(t) = E_0\left\{1 + \dfrac{\omega_0}{w}e^{-\alpha t}\sin(wt - \phi)\right\}U(t)$	

Circuit	Class	Transfer Function	No. of Poles	No. of Zeros	s Plane	Step Response	Sinusoidal Response
	Quadratic Compound High-Pass Type I $Q < \frac{1}{2}$ Underdamped	$H = 1 - H_C$ $$H = \frac{s(s+2a)}{[s^2 + 2as + \omega_0^2]}$$	2	2		$\dfrac{E_0}{(\alpha_2 - \alpha_1)}\{\alpha_2 e^{-\alpha_1 t} - \alpha_1 e^{-\alpha_2 t}\}U(t)$	
	Quadratic Compound High-Pass Type I $Q = \frac{1}{2}$ Critical Damping	$H = 1 - H_C$	2	2		$v(t) = E_0\{1 + \omega_0 t\}e^{-\omega_0 t}U(t)$	
	Quadratic Compound High-Pass Type II $\frac{1}{2} < Q$ Underdamped	$H = 1 - H_C$	2	2		$v(t) = E_0 \dfrac{\omega_0}{w} e^{-\alpha t} \sin(wt + \phi)U(t)$	

Circuit	Class	Transfer Function	No. of Poles	No. of Zeros	s Plane	Step Response	Sinusoidal Response
	Quadratic Compound Inverse Resonance Type I $Q < \frac{1}{2}$ Overdamped	$H = 1 - H_R$ $$\boxed{H = \frac{(s^2 + \omega_0^2)}{|s^2 + 2as + \omega_0^2|}}$$	2	2		$v(t) = E_0\left\{1 - \frac{(\alpha_2 + \alpha_1)}{(\alpha_2 - \alpha_1)}\left(e^{-\alpha_1 t} - e^{-\alpha_2 t}\right)\right\}U(t)$ 	
	Quadratic Compound Inverse Resonance Type I $Q = \frac{1}{2}$ Critical Damping	$H = 1 - H_R$	2	2		$v(t) = E_0\{1 - 2\omega_0 t e^{-\omega_0 t}\}U(t)$ 	
	Quadratic Compound Inverse Resonance Type II $\frac{1}{2} < Q$ Underdamped	$H = 1 - H_R$	2	2		$v(t) = E_0\left\{1 - \frac{2a}{w}e^{-at}\sin wt\right\}U(t)$ 	

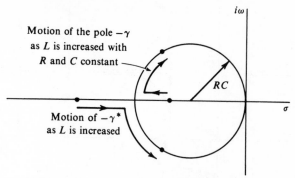

FIG. 100.   Diagram of the motion of the poles of an LRC circuit as L is increased while R and C are held constant.

Variations in R

If L and C are held constant while R is varied, the poles move along the real-negative axis or on a circle of radius ω_0 centered at the origin. Because only a is affected, an increase in R increases the damping, as shown in Fig. 101.

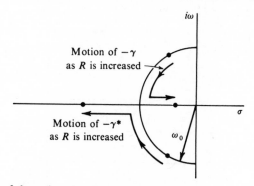

FIG. 101.   Behavior of the poles of an LRC circuit as R is increased while L and C are held constant.

Variations in C

The value of the capacitance C only affects the frequency ω_0. Thus the locus of points for fixed R/L is a vertical line of constant a or a motion along the real axis. See Fig. 102.

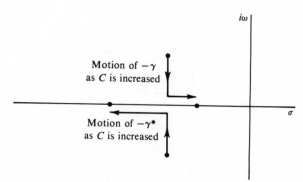

FIG. 102.   Behavior of the poles of an LRC circuit as C is increased while L and R are held constant.

THREE-PORT NETWORK THEORY

One of the most general problems encountered in linear circuit problems is the algebraic relations between the current and voltage relative to ground of three ports. See Fig. 103.

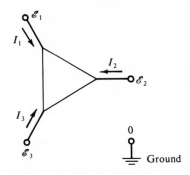

FIG. 103.   The three-port network. $\mathscr{E}_j$ is the potential of the terminal relative to the ground.

In the problem diagrammed in Fig. 103, the voltages $\mathscr{E}_j$ are given relative to the ground. If the elements in the box are linear, we can write the relations between the $\mathscr{E}_l(s)$ and the $I_m(s)$ as

$$\mathscr{E}_m(s) = \sum_{k=1}^{3} \mathscr{Z}_{mk}(s)I_k(s).$$

The fact that the sum of the voltage drops around the three terminals is zero and the fact that the total charge is conserved provide us with two useful constraints, which serve to reduce the number of dimensions to 2. In other words,

$$(\mathscr{E}_1 - \mathscr{E}_2) + (\mathscr{E}_2 - \mathscr{E}_3) + (\mathscr{E}_3 - \mathscr{E}_2) = 0$$

and

$$I_1(s) + I_2(s) + I_3(s) = 0.$$

To achieve the reduction, we work in terms of the voltage drops $(\mathscr{E}_1 - \mathscr{E}_3)$ and $(\mathscr{E}_2 - \mathscr{E}_3)$. Let

$$E_1(s) = (\mathscr{E}_1 - \mathscr{E}_3)$$

and

$$E_2(s) = (\mathscr{E}_2 - \mathscr{E}_3).$$

The current $I_3(s)$ is now $-(I_1(s) + I_2(s))$ See Fig. 104.

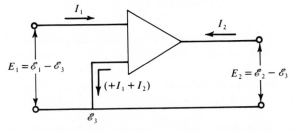

FIG. 104.   Reduction of a three-port network to a two-port network.

The relations between $E_m(s)$ and $I_j(s)$ are

$$E_1(s) = Z_{11}(s)I_1(s) + Z_{12}(s)I_2(s)$$

and

$$E_2(s) = Z_{21}(s)I_1(s) + Z_{22}(s)I_2(s).$$

These will be written in the matrix form:

$$\mathbf{E}(s) = \begin{bmatrix} E_1(s) \\ E_2(s) \end{bmatrix} = \mathbb{Z}(s) \cdot \mathbf{I}(s) = \begin{pmatrix} Z_{11}(s) & Z_{12}(s) \\ Z_{21}(s) & Z_{22}(s) \end{pmatrix} \begin{bmatrix} I_1(s) \\ I_2(s) \end{bmatrix}.$$

When $\mathbb{Z}$ has an inverse, we can write

$$\mathbb{Z}^{-1}(s) = \mathbb{Y}(s),$$

with

$$\mathbf{I}(s) = \mathbb{Y}(s) \cdot \mathbf{E}(s).$$

If the matrix $\mathbb{Z}$ does not exist (as in the case of a series impedance), one would initiate the analysis with $\mathbb{Y}(s)$. Ordinarily, if $\mathbb{Z}(s)$ does not exist, the magnitude of $\mathbb{Y}(s)$ is zero, and $\mathbb{Y}(s)$ is still a useful matrix. The reverse is, of course, also true.

FOUR-TERMINAL NETWORK THEORY

The Z Matrix or Impedance Matrix

The conventional four-terminal formalism is in reality a two-port theory. This particular representation is quite useful in many applications, although there is an implied constraint on the problem which, if ignored, may in some cases lead to nonsense.

The reduced three-port problem can be represented as the two-port problem. This is called a four-terminal network. See Fig. 105.

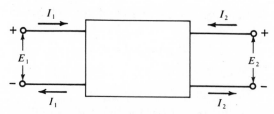

Fig. 105. The four-terminal network, a two-port device. This diagram illustrates the sign convention on E_m and I_n.

The current of the third port has been split proportionately in this application. The reader should notice carefully that applications of the methods that follow must maintain the loop-current invariant at either port as shown. In other words, in any connection, if I_1 flows into the first port, I_1 must flow out of the lower terminal of that port. Later cases will be shown in which this loop-current constraint is not satisfied.

The basic linear relationships are of the form

$$E_j(s) = \sum_{k=1}^{2} Z_{jk}(s)I_k(s)$$

or

$$\mathbf{E}(s) = \mathbb{Z}(s) \cdot \mathbf{I}(s).$$

This representation is particularly useful when two four-terminal networks are combined in a series input, series output configuration. This connection will be designated as the series-series connection (or Z connection). It is shown in Fig. 106.

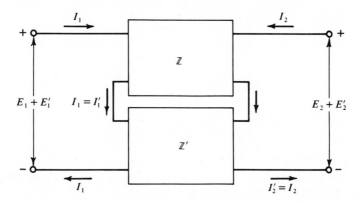

FIG. 106.   The series-series combination in terms of the $\mathbb{Z}$ matrices.

The combination in this manner is achieved by simply adding the $\mathbb{Z}$ matrices. The total voltage vector $\mathbf{E}_T$ is merely the sum of the voltage vectors $\mathbf{E}$ and $\mathbf{E}'$:

$$\mathbf{E}_T = \begin{bmatrix} E_1 + E_1' \\ E_2 + E_2' \end{bmatrix} = \mathbb{Z} \cdot \mathbf{I} + \mathbb{Z}' \cdot \mathbf{I}'.$$

Because the current vectors $\mathbf{I}$ and $\mathbf{I}'$ are equal,

$$\mathbf{E}_T = \{\mathbb{Z} + \mathbb{Z}'\} \cdot \mathbf{I} = \mathbb{Z}_T \cdot \mathbf{I},$$

and the equivalent $\mathbb{Z}_T$ matrix for the combination is the sum

$$\mathbb{Z}_T = \mathbb{Z} + \mathbb{Z}',$$

or

$$\mathbb{Z}_T = \begin{pmatrix} [Z_{11} + Z_{11}'] & [Z_{12} + Z_{12}'] \\ [Z_{21} + Z_{21}'] & [Z_{22} + Z_{22}'] \end{pmatrix}$$

See Fig. 107

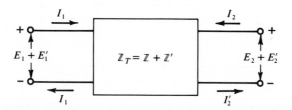

FIG. 107.   The equivalent four-terminal matrix for the series-series combination of $\mathbb{Z}$ and $\mathbb{Z}'$.

The Admittance Matrix

The admittance matrix, or inverse $\mathbb{Z}$ matrix, is obtained from the relationship

$$\mathbf{I}(s) = \mathbb{Y}(s) \cdot \mathbf{E} = \begin{pmatrix} Y_{11}(s) & Y_{12}(s) \\ Y_{21}(s) & Y_{22}(s) \end{pmatrix} \begin{bmatrix} E_1(s) \\ E_2(s) \end{bmatrix}.$$

The $\mathbb{Y}(s)$ matrix can be computed directly, or it can be obtained from the relationship

$$\mathbb{Y}(s) = \mathbb{Z}^{-1}(s),$$

where

$$Y_{lm} = \frac{(-1)^{l+m} \text{ minor } Z_{ml}}{|\mathbb{Z}|}.$$

Thus,

$$Y_{11} = \frac{Z_{22}}{|\mathbb{Z}|} \qquad Y_{12} = -\frac{Z_{12}}{|\mathbb{Z}|}$$

$$Y_{21} = \frac{-Z_{21}}{|\mathbb{Z}|} \qquad Y_{22} = \frac{Z_{11}}{|\mathbb{Z}|}.$$

The reader is reminded again that the inverse of the $\mathbb{Z}$ or $\mathbb{Y}$ matrix need not exist in problems involving idealized passive elements. In the event that the magnitude of one vanishes, the other will be undefined.

The admittance form is useful for combinations of two four-terminal networks when the voltage vector is the same for both. This is called a *parallel-parallel combination* in which the total current vector of the equivalent network is the sum of the two original current vectors. See Fig. 108. For this case

$$\mathbf{I}_{\text{total}} = \mathbf{I} + \mathbf{I}' = \mathbb{Y} \cdot \mathbf{E} + \mathbb{Y}' \cdot \mathbf{E}' = \{\mathbb{Y} + \mathbb{Y}'\} \cdot \mathbf{E}$$

or

$$\mathbf{I}_{\text{total}} = \mathbb{Y}_T \cdot \mathbf{E},$$

where

$$\mathbb{Y}_T = \mathbb{Y} + \mathbb{Y}'.$$

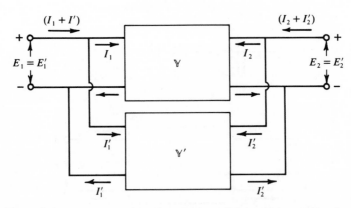

FIG. 108. The admittance connection for the parallel-parallel combination of the $\mathbb{Y}$ matrices.

The Cascade Matrix

To connect two four-terminal networks in cascade, it is necessary to construct hybrid vectors, i.e., a vector with a different set of units associated with each element. In turn, the matrix elements of the cascade matrix will have different units. Two networks are shown in a cascade connection in the diagram in Fig. 109. The common elements of the two networks in cascade are the intermediate voltages

$$E_2 = E_1'$$

and the intermediate currents

$$I_2 = -I_1'.$$

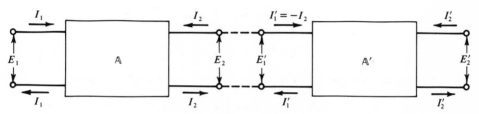

FIG. 109.   The combination of two four-terminal networks in cascade. The $\mathbb{A}$ matrix representation combines by an inner product.

The final vectors for the equivalent single network will have E_1 and I_1 as the input variables, with E_2' and I_2' as the output. To obtain equal intermediate vectors, we define the cascade vectors as

$$\xi_1(s) = \begin{bmatrix} E_1(s) \\ I_1(s) \end{bmatrix}$$

and

$$\xi_2(s) = \begin{bmatrix} E_2(s) \\ -I_2(s) \end{bmatrix}.$$

The variables are connected by the linear equations

$$E_1 = A_{11}E_2 - A_{12}I_2$$

and

$$I_1 = A_{12}E_2 - A_{22}I_2.$$

In matrix form,

$$\xi_1 = \begin{bmatrix} E_1 \\ I_1 \end{bmatrix} = A \cdot \xi_2 = \begin{pmatrix} A_{11} & A_{12} \\ A_{21} & A_{22} \end{pmatrix} \begin{bmatrix} E_2 \\ -I_2 \end{bmatrix}.$$

The A_{jk} can be related directly to the Z_{mn} or the Y_{mn}. This can be accomplished in several ways; a direct algebraic solution is, of course, always possible. It is perhaps instructive, on the other hand, to use a method employing projection operators. This is a quite general technique, which operates on the matrices and vectors as a whole without the ordinary algebraic tedium.

We define four projection operators $\mathbb{P}_k$:

$$\mathbb{P}_1 = \begin{pmatrix} 1 & 0 \\ 0 & 0 \end{pmatrix} ; \qquad \mathbb{P}_2 = \begin{pmatrix} 0 & 0 \\ 1 & 0 \end{pmatrix},$$

$$\mathbb{P}_3 = \begin{pmatrix} 0 & 1 \\ 0 & 0 \end{pmatrix} ; \qquad \mathbb{P}_4 = \begin{pmatrix} 0 & 0 \\ 0 & 1 \end{pmatrix}.$$

The $\xi_i(s)$ vectors can then be generated from the $\mathbf{E}$ and $\mathbf{I}$ vectors. For instance,

$$\xi_1 = \mathbb{P}_1 \cdot \mathbf{E} + \mathbb{P}_2 \cdot \mathbf{I}$$

and

$$\xi_2 = \mathbb{P}_3 \cdot \mathbf{E} - \mathbb{P}_4 \cdot \mathbf{I}.$$

The inverse relationships are

$$\mathbf{E} = \mathbb{P}_1 \cdot \xi_1 + \mathbb{P}_2 \cdot \xi_2$$

and

$$\mathbf{I} = \mathbb{P}_3 \cdot \xi_1 - \mathbb{P}_4 \cdot \xi_2.$$

The last pair of equations is obtained from the relations of the type

$$\mathbf{E} = \{ \mathbb{P}_1 \cdot \mathbb{P}_1 + \mathbb{P}_2 \cdot \mathbb{P}_3 \} \cdot \mathbf{E}$$

and

$$\mathbf{I} = \{ \mathbb{P}_3 \cdot \mathbb{P}_2 + \mathbb{P}_4 \cdot \mathbb{P}_4 \} \cdot \mathbf{I},$$

or

$$\mathbb{P}_1 \cdot \mathbb{P}_1 + \mathbb{P}_2 \cdot \mathbb{P}_3 = \mathbb{P}_3 \cdot \mathbb{P}_2 + \mathbb{P}_4 \cdot \mathbb{P}_4 = \mathbb{I}$$

Also,

$$\mathbb{P}_1 = \mathbb{P}_3 \cdot \mathbb{P}_2 \quad \text{and} \quad \mathbb{P}_4 = \mathbb{P}_2 \cdot \mathbb{P}_3.$$

The conversion of $\mathbb{Z}$ to $\mathbb{A}$ is obtained by substituting $\mathbf{E}(\xi_1, \xi_2)$ and $\mathbf{I}(\xi_1, \xi_2)$ into

$$\mathbf{E} = \mathbb{Z} \cdot \mathbf{I},$$

giving

$$\{ \mathbb{P}_1 - \mathbb{Z} \cdot \mathbb{P}_3 \} \cdot \xi_1 = -\{ \mathbb{P}_2 + \mathbb{Z} \cdot \mathbb{P}_4 \} \cdot \xi_2.$$

Writing this out, we find

$$\begin{pmatrix} 1 & -Z_{11} \\ 0 & -Z_{21} \end{pmatrix} \begin{bmatrix} E_1 \\ I_1 \end{bmatrix} = -\begin{pmatrix} 0 & Z_{12} \\ 1 & Z_{22} \end{pmatrix} \begin{bmatrix} E_2 \\ -I_2 \end{bmatrix}.$$

Inverting the left-hand matrix and multiplying from the left by this inverse, we get

$$\xi_1 = \mathbb{A} \cdot \xi_2 = \begin{pmatrix} \dfrac{Z_{11}}{Z_{21}} & \dfrac{|\mathbb{Z}|}{Z_{22}} \\[2mm] \dfrac{1}{Z_{21}} & \dfrac{Z_{22}}{Z_{21}} \end{pmatrix} \cdot \xi_2.$$

This equation defines the elements A_{lm} in terms of the elements of $\mathbb{Z}$. A similar manipulation of $\mathbf{I} = \mathbb{Y} \cdot \mathbf{E}$ provides the relations between the Y_{km} and the A_{jk}. A complete table of interrelationships between the various matrix elements will be given at the end of this section (Table 7).

When two four-terminal networks are cascaded, we use the following equations to obtain the overall matrix for the pair:

$$\xi_1' = A' \cdot \xi_2'$$

and

$$\xi_1 = A \cdot \xi_2.$$

In cascade $\xi_2 = \xi_1'$; then

$$\xi_1 = A \cdot \xi_1' = A \cdot A' \cdot \xi_2' = A_T \cdot \xi_2'.$$

The equivalent matrix of the cascaded pair is the inner product of the individual matrices:

$$A_T = A \cdot A'$$

or

$$A_{jk}^{(T)} = \sum_{m=1}^{2} A_{jm} A_{mk}'.$$

The Hybrid H Combination for Series-Parallel Connections

The next connection that is useful to us is the series input parallel output. See Fig. 110.

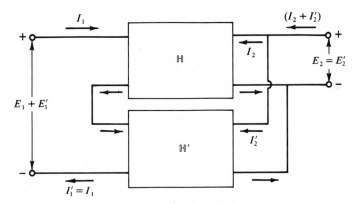

FIG. 110.   A diagram illustrating the hybrid H combination. This has a series connection at the input and a parallel connection at the output. Thus, it will be known as the series-parallel combination.

The common variables are $E_2 = E_2'$ and $I_1 = I_1'$. To use these in combination, we generate vectors σ and ρ where

$$\sigma = \begin{bmatrix} E_1 \\ I_2 \end{bmatrix}$$

and

$$\rho = \begin{bmatrix} I_1 \\ E_2 \end{bmatrix}.$$

The $\mathbb{H}(s)$ hybrid matrix is defined from the relation†

$$\sigma = \begin{bmatrix} E_1 \\ I_2 \end{bmatrix} = \mathbb{H} \cdot \rho = \begin{pmatrix} H_{11} & H_{12} \\ H_{21} & H_{22} \end{pmatrix} \begin{bmatrix} I_1 \\ E_2 \end{bmatrix}.$$

In order to relate the H_{lm} to the previous matrices, we note that

$$\sigma = \mathbb{P}_1 \cdot \mathbf{E} + \mathbb{P}_4 \cdot \mathbf{I}, \qquad \mathbf{E} = \mathbb{P}_1 \cdot \sigma + \mathbb{P}_4 \cdot \rho,$$

and

$$\rho = \mathbb{P}_1 \cdot \mathbf{I} + \mathbb{P}_4 \cdot \mathbf{E}. \qquad \mathbf{I} = \mathbb{P}_1 \cdot \rho + \mathbb{P}_4 \cdot \sigma.$$

Starting with $\mathbf{E} = \mathbb{Z} \cdot \mathbf{I}$, we obtain

$$[\mathbb{P}_1 - \mathbb{Z} \cdot \mathbb{P}_4] \cdot \sigma = [\mathbb{Z} \cdot \mathbb{P}_1 - \mathbb{P}_4] \cdot \rho,$$

giving

$$\sigma = \mathbb{H} \cdot \rho = \begin{pmatrix} \dfrac{|\mathbb{Z}|}{Z_{22}} & \dfrac{Z_{12}}{Z_{22}} \\[2mm] -\dfrac{Z_{21}}{Z_{22}} & \dfrac{1}{Z_{22}} \end{pmatrix} \cdot \rho.$$

Relations between the H_{lm} and the elements of other matrices can be readily obtained with the same technique. The problem shown in Fig. 110 represents the combination of

$$\sigma = \mathbb{H} \cdot \rho$$

and

$$\sigma' = \mathbb{H}' \cdot \rho';$$

with

$$\rho' = \rho.$$

Then

$$\sigma_{\text{total}} = \sigma + \sigma' = \{\mathbb{H} + \mathbb{H}'\} \cdot \rho$$

or

$$\sigma_T = \mathbb{H}_T \cdot \rho$$

This defines the $\mathbb{H}$ matrix for the combination as

$$\mathbb{H}_{\text{total}} = \mathbb{H} + \mathbb{H}' = \begin{pmatrix} [H_{11} + H'_{11}] & [H_{12} + H'_{12}] \\ [H_{21} + H'_{21}] & [H_{22} + H'_{22}] \end{pmatrix}.$$

The Parallel-Series Combination, The Hybrid $\mathbb{G}$

If we turn the preceding problem around, σ becomes the invariant vector. See Fig. 111.

---

† This is not to be confused with the notation $\mathbb{H}(s)$ for the generalized transfer matrix.

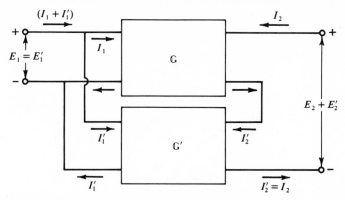

FIG. 111.   The hybrid $\mathbb{G}$ configuration, consisting of a parallel input connection and a series output connection. The $\mathbb{G}$ matrix is the inverse of the hybrid $\mathbb{H}$ matrix.

The elements of $\mathbb{G}$ are merely the inverse elements of $\mathbb{H}$:

$$\rho = \mathbb{H}^{-1} \cdot \sigma = \mathbb{G} \cdot \sigma.$$

Therefore,

$$\mathbb{G} = \mathbb{H}^{-1}$$

The combination of the two networks as shown is

$$\rho_{\text{total}} = \rho + \rho' = \{\mathbb{G} + \mathbb{G}'\} \cdot \sigma,$$

with

$$\mathbb{G}_{\text{total}} = \mathbb{G} + \mathbb{G}'.$$

The matrix elements for a specific four-terminal network in the laboratory must in many instances be measured experimentally. As an example, consider the elements of the $\mathbb{H}$ matrix. In order to obtain the matrix elements, *at least* four measurements must be made. For example

$$H_{11}(s) = \left[\frac{E_1}{I_1}\right]_{E_2=0} = \text{the input impedance with the output short-circuited;}$$

$$H_{12}(s) = \left[\frac{E_1}{E_2}\right]_{I_1=0} = \text{the inverse of the forward voltage transfer with the input open-circuited;}$$

$$H_{21}(s) = \left[\frac{I_2}{I_1}\right]_{E_2=0} = \text{the forward current transfer with the output shorted;}$$

$$H_{22}(s) = \left[\frac{I_2}{E_2}\right]_{I_1=0} = \text{the output admittance with the input open-circuited.}$$

These parameters are particularly useful for transistors when the forward current transfer is the important factor. The elements of $\mathbb{G} = \mathbb{H}^{-1}$ are useful when vacuum tubes are considered. Table 7, consisting of cross references, can be employed to convert a measured set of matrix elements to any representation desired (as long as it exists).

TABLE 7

MATRIX INTERRELATIONS

From \ To	Z	Y	H	G	A
Z	$\begin{matrix} Z_{11} & Z_{12} \\ Z_{21} & Z_{22} \end{matrix}$	$\begin{matrix} \dfrac{Y_{22}}{|Y|} & \dfrac{-Y_{12}}{|Y|} \\[2mm] \dfrac{-Y_{21}}{|Y|} & \dfrac{Y_{11}}{|Y|} \end{matrix}$	$\begin{matrix} \dfrac{|H|}{H_{22}} & \dfrac{H_{12}}{H_{22}} \\[2mm] \dfrac{-H_{21}}{H_{22}} & \dfrac{1}{H_{22}} \end{matrix}$	$\begin{matrix} \dfrac{1}{G_{11}} & \dfrac{-G_{12}}{G_{11}} \\[2mm] \dfrac{G_{21}}{G_{11}} & \dfrac{|G|}{G_{11}} \end{matrix}$	$\begin{matrix} \dfrac{A_{11}}{A_{21}} & \dfrac{|A|}{A_{21}} \\[2mm] \dfrac{1}{A_{21}} & \dfrac{A_{22}}{A_{21}} \end{matrix}$
Y	$\begin{matrix} \dfrac{Z_{22}}{|Z|} & \dfrac{-Z_{12}}{|Z|} \\[2mm] \dfrac{-Z_{21}}{|Z|} & \dfrac{Z_{11}}{|Z|} \end{matrix}$	$\begin{matrix} Y_{11} & Y_{12} \\ Y_{21} & Y_{22} \end{matrix}$	$\begin{matrix} \dfrac{1}{H_{11}} & \dfrac{-H_{12}}{H_{11}} \\[2mm] \dfrac{H_{21}}{H_{11}} & \dfrac{|H|}{H_{11}} \end{matrix}$	$\begin{matrix} \dfrac{|G|}{G_{22}} & \dfrac{G_{12}}{G_{22}} \\[2mm] \dfrac{-G_{21}}{G_{22}} & \dfrac{1}{G_{22}} \end{matrix}$	$\begin{matrix} \dfrac{A_{22}}{A_{12}} & \dfrac{-|A|}{A_{12}} \\[2mm] \dfrac{-1}{A_{12}} & \dfrac{A_{11}}{A_{12}} \end{matrix}$
H	$\begin{matrix} \dfrac{|Z|}{Z_{22}} & \dfrac{Z_{12}}{Z_{22}} \\[2mm] \dfrac{-Z_{21}}{Z_{22}} & \dfrac{1}{Z_{22}} \end{matrix}$	$\begin{matrix} \dfrac{1}{Y_{11}} & \dfrac{-Y_{12}}{Y_{11}} \\[2mm] \dfrac{Y_{21}}{Y_{11}} & \dfrac{|Y|}{Y_{11}} \end{matrix}$	$\begin{matrix} H_{11} & H_{12} \\ H_{21} & H_{22} \end{matrix}$	$\begin{matrix} \dfrac{G_{22}}{|G|} & \dfrac{-G_{12}}{|G|} \\[2mm] \dfrac{-G_{21}}{|G|} & \dfrac{G_{11}}{|G|} \end{matrix}$	$\begin{matrix} \dfrac{A_{12}}{A_{22}} & \dfrac{|A|}{A_{22}} \\[2mm] \dfrac{-1}{A_{22}} & \dfrac{A_{21}}{A_{22}} \end{matrix}$
G	$\begin{matrix} Z_{11} & \dfrac{-Z_{21}}{Z_{11}} \\[2mm] \dfrac{Z_{21}}{Z_{11}} & \dfrac{|Z|}{Z_{11}} \end{matrix}$	$\begin{matrix} \dfrac{|Y|}{Y_{22}} & \dfrac{Y_{12}}{Y_{22}} \\[2mm] \dfrac{-Y_{21}}{Y_{22}} & \dfrac{1}{Y_{22}} \end{matrix}$	$\begin{matrix} \dfrac{H_{22}}{|H|} & \dfrac{-H_{12}}{|H|} \\[2mm] \dfrac{-H_{21}}{|H|} & \dfrac{H_{11}}{|H|} \end{matrix}$	$\begin{matrix} G_{11} & G_{12} \\ G_{21} & G_{22} \end{matrix}$	$\begin{matrix} \dfrac{A_{21}}{A_{11}} & \dfrac{-|A|}{A_{11}} \\[2mm] \dfrac{1}{A_{11}} & \dfrac{A_{12}}{A_{11}} \end{matrix}$
A	$\begin{matrix} \dfrac{Z_{11}}{Z_{21}} & \dfrac{|Z|}{Z_{21}} \\[2mm] \dfrac{1}{Z_{21}} & \dfrac{Z_{22}}{Z_{21}} \end{matrix}$	$\begin{matrix} \dfrac{-Y_{22}}{Y_{21}} & \dfrac{-1}{Y_{21}} \\[2mm] \dfrac{-|Y|}{Y_{21}} & \dfrac{-Y_{11}}{Y_{21}} \end{matrix}$	$\begin{matrix} \dfrac{-|H|}{H_{21}} & \dfrac{-H_{11}}{H_{21}} \\[2mm] \dfrac{-H_{22}}{H_{21}} & \dfrac{-1}{H_{21}} \end{matrix}$	$\begin{matrix} \dfrac{1}{G_{21}} & \dfrac{G_{22}}{G_{21}} \\[2mm] \dfrac{G_{11}}{G_{21}} & \dfrac{|G|}{G_{21}} \end{matrix}$	$\begin{matrix} A_{11} & A_{12} \\ A_{21} & A_{22} \end{matrix}$

Terminated Networks

Many applications of the four-terminal representation involve a terminating load impedance $Z_L = Y_L^{-1}$ and an input generator impedance $Z_G = Y_G^{-1}$. See Fig. 112.

As a sample calculation we shall compute the input impedance in terms of the elements of $\mathbb{Z}(s)$ and the load termination $Z_L(s)$. Starting with

$$E_j = \sum_{l=1}^{2} Z_{jl} I_l,$$

we incorporate the termination condition $E_2 = -Z_L I_2$ to give

$$Z_{in}(s) = \frac{E_1}{I_1} = \frac{|\mathbb{Z}| + Z_{11} Z_L}{Z_{22} + Z_L}.$$

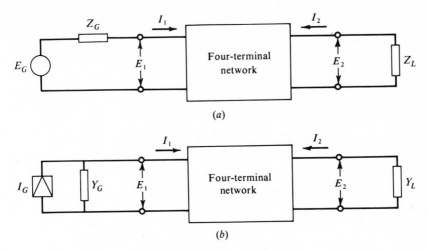

FIG. 112.   (a) A terminated voltage-excited four-terminal network. (b) A terminated current-excited four-terminal network.

Table 8 describes the input impedance $Z_{in}(s)$, the output impedance $Z_{out}(s)$, the forward voltage transfer $\{E_2/E_1\}$, and the forward current transfer $\{I_2/I_1\}$ in terms of Z_L, Z_G, and the various matrix elements.

TABLE 8

PROPERTIES OF THE TERMINATED FOUR-TERMINAL NETWORK

Property	Z	Y	H	G	A
Input Impedance, Z_1	$\dfrac{\lvert Z\rvert + Z_{11}Z_L}{Z_{22} + Z_L}$	$\dfrac{Y_{22} + Y_L}{\lvert Y\rvert + Y_{11}Y_L}$	$\dfrac{\lvert H\rvert + H_{11}Y_L}{H_{22} + Y_L}$	$\dfrac{G_{22} + Z_L}{\lvert G\rvert + G_{11}Z_L}$	$\dfrac{A_{11}Z_L + A_{12}}{A_{21}Z_L + A_{22}}$
Output Impedance, Z_o	$\dfrac{\lvert Z\rvert + Z_{22}Z_G}{Z_{11} + Z_G}$	$\dfrac{Y_{11} + Y_G}{\lvert Y\rvert + Y_{22}Y_G}$	$\dfrac{H_{11} + Z_G}{\lvert H\rvert + H_{22}Z_G}$	$\dfrac{\lvert G\rvert + G_{22}Y_G}{G_{11} + Y_G}$	$\dfrac{A_{22}Z_G + A_{12}}{A_{21}Z_G + A_{11}}$
Voltage Ampl., $H_v(s) = \dfrac{E_2}{E_1}$	$\dfrac{Z_{21}Z_L}{\lvert Z\rvert + Z_{11}Z_L}$	$\dfrac{-Y_{21}}{Y_{22} + Y_L}$	$\dfrac{-H_{21}Z_L}{H_{11} + \lvert H\rvert Z_L}$	$\dfrac{G_{21}Z_L}{G_{22} + Z_L}$	$\dfrac{Z_L}{A_{12} + A_{11}Z_L}$
Current Ampl., $H_I(s) = \dfrac{-I_2}{I_1}$	$\dfrac{Z_{21}}{Z_{22} + Z_L}$	$\dfrac{-Y_{21}Y_L}{\lvert Y\rvert + Y_{11}Y_L}$	$\dfrac{-H_{21}Y_L}{H_{22} + Y_L}$	$\dfrac{G_{21}}{\lvert G\rvert + G_{11}Z_L}$	$\dfrac{1}{A_{22} + A_{21}Z_L}$

The *characteristic impedance* Z_0 of a four-terminal passive network is defined in terms of two particular measurements of the input impedance. Experimentally this impedance is the square root of the input impedance measured with the output terminals open circuited (Z_{oc}) times the input impedance measured with the output terminals short circuited (Z_{sc}). In terms of the Z matrix elements.

$$Z_{oc} = Z_{oc}(s) = \lim_{Y_L \to 0} Z_{in}(s) = Z_{11}(s),$$

and

$$Z_{sc} = Z_{sc}(s) = \lim_{Z_L \to 0} Z_{in}(s) = \frac{|\mathbb{Z}|}{Z_{22}}.$$

The square of the characteristic impedance is

$$Z_0^2 = Z_{oc} \cdot Z_{sc} = (Z_{11}Z_{22} - Z_{12}Z_{21})\frac{Z_{11}}{Z_{22}} = \frac{Z_{11}}{Z_{22}}|\mathbb{Z}|.$$

The *image impedance* $Z_I(s)$ is the terminating impedance which reflects without distortion into the input. In other words, if a Z_I exists, and we set $Z_I = Z_L$; then Z_{in} is also equal to Z_I.

By setting $Z_L = Z_{in} = Z_I$ in the expression for Z_{in} we find that

$$Z_I^2 + (Z_{22} - Z_{11})Z_I - |\mathbb{Z}| = 0.$$

We designate the difference in the diagonal terms as 2Δ where

$$2\Delta = (Z_{11} - Z_{22}),$$

and

$$Z_I = \sqrt{|\mathbb{Z}|}\left\{\sqrt{1 + \frac{\Delta^2}{|\mathbb{Z}|}} + \frac{\Delta}{\sqrt{|\mathbb{Z}|}}\right\}.$$

In the special case of geometric symmetry, when $Z_{11} = Z_{22}$, $\Delta = 0$, and

$$Z_{image} = Z_0, \, (Z_{11} = Z_{22}).$$

A Series Impedance $Z_s(s)$.

This elementary arrangement is undefined in the $\mathbb{Z}$ representation because we view it as an idealized problem. In the unterminated form this network has an infinite impedance between the upper set of terminals and the lower set. Therefore, the unterminated input and output loop currents must be zero. Since the voltages are in no manner restricted the elements of the $\mathbb{Z}$ matrix must be arbitrarily large.

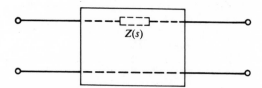

Fig. 113.   The series impedance. The $\mathbb{Z}$ matrix is not defined for the connection, whereas the $\mathbb{Y}$ matrix is defined.

The admittance matrix on the other hand generates the currents from the voltages. The $\mathbb{Y}$ matrix for this circuit is defined but has a magnitude equal to zero indicating the undefined nature of its inverse.

Let the single series term be Z_s; then

$$\mathbb{Y}(s) = \begin{pmatrix} \dfrac{1}{Z_s} & -\dfrac{1}{Z_s} \\[2ex] -\dfrac{1}{Z_s} & \dfrac{1}{Z_s} \end{pmatrix} = \frac{1}{Z_s(s)} \begin{pmatrix} 1 & -1 \\ -1 & 1 \end{pmatrix},$$

with

$$\mathbb{A}(s) = \begin{pmatrix} 1 & Z_s \\ 0 & 1 \end{pmatrix}$$

and

$$\mathbb{H}(s) = \begin{pmatrix} Z_s & 1 \\ -1 & 0 \end{pmatrix}; \qquad \mathbb{G} = \mathbb{H}^{-1} = \begin{pmatrix} 0 & -1 \\ 1 & Z_s \end{pmatrix}.$$

A Parallel Admittance $Y_P(s)$.

This is the dual of the series impedance. By dual arguments we recognize that the Y matrix does not exist; however, the Z matrix is well defined:

$$\mathbb{Z}(s) = \frac{1}{Y_p(s)} \begin{pmatrix} 1 & 1 \\ 1 & 1 \end{pmatrix}.$$

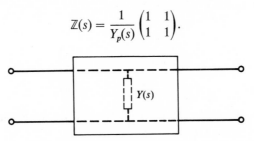

FIG. 114.   The parallel admittance has a defined $\mathbb{Z}$ matrix. The $\mathbb{Y}$ matrix for this connection is undefined.

The Γ Network.

This particular form will be useful to us on several occasions. It is the elementary building block of the phase-shifting network. Also, it is a form employed in many asymmetric filters.

Solving for the elements of $\mathbb{Z}(s)$, we obtain

$$\mathbb{Z}_\Gamma(s) = \begin{pmatrix} \dfrac{[1 + ZY]}{Y} & \dfrac{1}{Y} \\[2ex] \dfrac{1}{Y} & \dfrac{1}{Y} \end{pmatrix}.$$

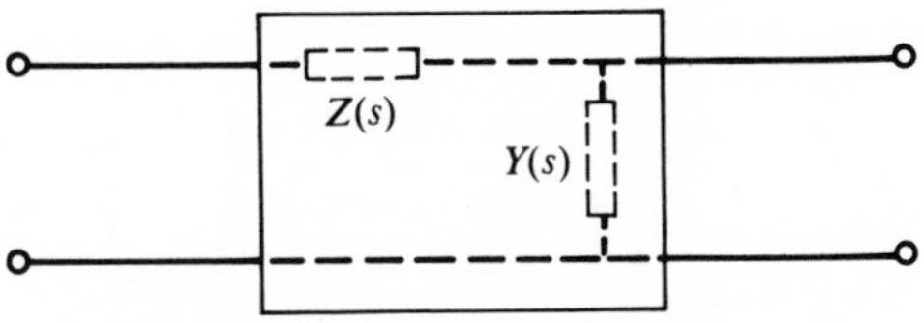

FIG. 115.   The Γ network.

The Γ Network.

This network has an admittance element at the input terminals. It is the dual of the Τ arrangement. One can see for the first time the geometric symmetry of the internal circuit appearing in the matrix. Both the Γ and Τ matrices are geometrically asymmetric. Consequently, the Z matrix has unequal diagonal elements. The 2×2 Z and Y matrices of four-terminal networks involving passive elements are always symmetric in that $Z_{jk} = Z_{kj}$, $(k \neq j)$. A geometrical symmetry, however, produces equal diagonal terms. We shall see examples of this in the geometrically symmetric T and π networks.

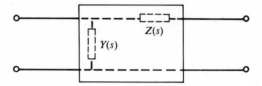

FIG. 116.   The Γ network.

The Z_Γ matrix of the Γ network is

$$\mathbb{Z}_\Gamma(s) = \begin{pmatrix} \dfrac{1}{Y} & \dfrac{1}{Y} \\[2mm] \dfrac{1}{Y} & \dfrac{[1+ZY]}{Y} \end{pmatrix}.$$

Because of the Γ is the mirror image of the Τ network, the elements could have been obtained by interchanging the indices.

The T Network

This basic network has geometric symmetry for reflections about the admittance element. The circuit can be viewed as a half-Τ and a half-Γ circuit hooked in cascade. By "half" we mean that the networks contain $Z/2$ and $Y/2$. The combination is illustrated in Fig. 117.

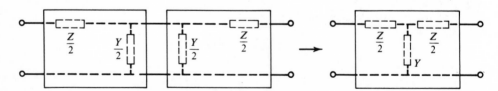

FIG. 117.   A Τ in cascade with a Γ forms a symmetric T network.

The Z matrix for the T network is

$$\mathbb{Z}^{(T)}(s) = \begin{pmatrix} \dfrac{[2+ZY]}{2Y} & \dfrac{1}{Y} \\[2mm] \dfrac{1}{Y} & \dfrac{[2+ZY]}{2Y} \end{pmatrix}.$$

Geometric symmetry is exhibited by the fact that $Z_{11} = Z_{22}$ and $Y_{11} = Y_{22}$. The magnitude of the $\mathbb{Z}$ matrix is used quite often. It is

$$|\mathbb{Z}^{(T)}(s)| = \frac{Z(s)[4 + Z(s)Y(s)]}{4Y(s)}.$$

The Pi Network

The dual of the T network is the π. It is formed by cascading a Γ with a T network and has geometric symmetry for reflections about the midpoint of the series Z element. See Fig. 118.

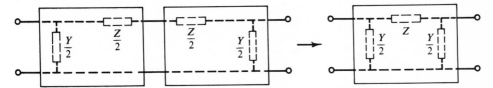

Fig. 118.   A T and Γ in cascade form a symmetric π network.

Because the π is the dual of the T, the associated admittance matrix has a form similar to that of the T. The $Z(s)$ and $Y(s)$ elements are merely interchanged, and the off-diagonal term-change sign to give

$$\mathbb{Y}^{(\pi)}(s) = \begin{pmatrix} \dfrac{[2 + ZY]}{2Z} & -\dfrac{1}{Z} \\[3mm] -\dfrac{1}{Z} & \dfrac{[2 + ZY]}{2Z} \end{pmatrix}.$$

The magnitude of the admittance for the π is

$$|\mathbb{Y}^{(\pi)}(s)| = \frac{Y(s)[4 + ZY]}{4Z}.$$

Once again we observe that the geometric symmetry gives symmetry along the diagonal of the matrix $Y_{11} = Y_{22}$ and $Z_{11}^{\pi} = Z_{22}^{\pi}$. As mentioned before, all passive networks have bilateral symmetry, which makes $Y_{12} = Y_{21}$ and $Z_{12} = Z_{21}$.

The Lattice Network or Bridge Network

The lattice section is formed with four branches. Because of the additional branch, this section has properties that cannot be attained from the flat networks. The two crossover arms Z' and Y form a nonflat network, as shown in Fig. 119. One can also observe that the lattice can be laid out to represent the general bridge structure. See Fig. 119a.

The notation chosen provides a relatively simple result in which the functions

$$P(s) = 1 + Z(s)Y(s)$$

and

$$P'(s) = 1 + Z'(s)Y'(s)$$

form the basic elements of the admittance matrix and the transfer functions.

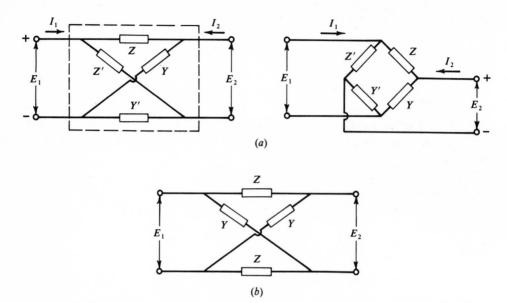

FIG. 119.   (a) The lattice network, or bridge network, shown in two different orientations.
(b) The lattice network in the antisymmetric arrangement $Z' = 1/Y$ and $Y' = 1/Z$.

The geometric symmetry evidenced by the equality of the diagonal elements of the $\mathbb{Z}$ matrix and $\mathbb{Y}$ matrix in the case of the T and π networks is not present here. The lattice is not geometrically symmetric.

The admittance elements can be found by direct loop analysis. The $\mathbb{Y}$ matrix for the lattice section shown in Fig. 119 is

$$\mathbb{Y}(s) = \frac{1}{Z'P + ZP'} \begin{pmatrix} (Z + Z')(Y + Y') & (P - P') \\ (P - P') & PP' \end{pmatrix}.$$

In its most general form, the magnitude of $\mathbb{Y}(s)$ does not exhibit any unique symmetries. One can observe, however, that the voltage transfer to an infinite load has the following characteristic functional form:

$$H_V(s) \xrightarrow[Y_L = 0]{} \frac{(P(s) - P'(s))}{PP'} = \frac{(ZY - Y'Z')}{(1 + ZY)(1 + Z'Y')}.$$

This function indicates several applications of the lattice section. One important application is the amplitude bridge. For this, we set $Z'Y' = R_1 G_2$; in other words, we make half the network a resistive attenuator. If the product $Z(s)\,Y(s)$ is now set to produce either the function $(s + a)^2/bs$ or $bs/(s + a)^2$, the voltage transfer $H_V(s)$ can be constructed to zero at $s = \pm ia$ by setting $R_1 G_2 = 2a/b$ in the first case or $G_1 R_2 = 2a/b$ in the second. The Wien bridge, which will be developed in detail, is an example of the first case.

A second application of this circuit arises when the elements are adjusted to provide some type of symmetry. A trivial application occurs if we set $Z' = Z$ and $Y' = Y$. This arrangement is always balanced and delivers a zero output voltage for all frequencies. A more useful symmetry is that provided by

$$Z' = \frac{1}{Y}$$

and

$$Y' = \frac{1}{Z}.$$

See Fig. 119b.
  In this case, $Z'Y' = 1/ZY$ and

$$\mathbb{Y}(s) \xrightarrow[\substack{Z'=1/Y \\ Y'=1/Z}]{} \frac{1}{2Z(1+ZY)} \left(\begin{array}{cc} (1+ZY)^2 & [(ZY)^2-1] \\ [(ZY)^2-1] & (1+ZY)^2 \end{array} \right),$$

with an image admittance Y_0 given by

$$|\mathbb{Y}(s)| = Y_0^2 = \frac{Y(s)}{Z(s)}.$$

This is quite an important result in that the image impedance of an antisymmetric lattice section can be a pure resistance for all frequencies if the ratio $Y(s)/Z(s)$ is not a function of s. This property will be used later to form a phase-shifting section of excellent quality.
  The cascade matrix for the symmetry shown above is

$$\mathbb{A}(s) \xrightarrow[\substack{Z'=1/Y \\ Y'=1/Z}]{} \frac{1}{(1-ZY)} \left(\begin{array}{cc} (1+ZY) & 2Z \\ 2Y & (1+ZY) \end{array} \right).$$

One difficulty that is encountered when a lattice section is employed lies in the fact that one cannot ground both sides of the four-terminal network. Such a common ground short-circuits one of the four elements of the network. When these circuits are employed, a transformer is often used to couple the network to another circuit that can be grounded.

The Circuit Elements of the Four-Terminal Network

When one regards the matrix elements of the T, Γ, T, π, and lattice networks, one notices the consistent appearance of the product $Z(s)Y(s)$. The frequency dependence of this product can be tabulated for all the most common combinations of L, R, and C. To generalize our results, we shall define a dimensionless parameter that is proportional to s. Then the various network combinations can be listed in terms of the functional form of $Z(x)Y(x)$.
  Define the quantity

$$x = \frac{s}{\omega_0}.$$

Tables 9a–e provide many of the possible functions of x that can be constructed from a $Z(x)Y(x)$ product.

$Z(s)\cdot Y(s)$	Circuit	$Z(s)$	$Y(s)$	ω_0	Z/Y
$x = \dfrac{s}{\omega_0}$		R	Cs	$\dfrac{1}{RC}$	$\dfrac{R^2}{x}$
		Ls	$G = \dfrac{1}{R}$	$\dfrac{1}{sL}$	$\dfrac{x}{G^2}$
$\dfrac{1}{x}$		$\dfrac{1}{Cs}$	$\dfrac{1}{R}$	$\dfrac{1}{RC}$	$\dfrac{R^2}{x}$
		$R = \dfrac{1}{G}$	$\dfrac{1}{Ls}$	$\dfrac{1}{GL}$	$\dfrac{x}{G^2}$
$(1+x)$		R	$\dfrac{1+RCs}{R}$	$\dfrac{1}{RC}$	$\dfrac{R^2}{1+x}$
		$\dfrac{1+GLs}{G}$	G	$\dfrac{1}{GL}$	$\dfrac{1+x}{G^2}$
$\dfrac{1}{(1+x)}$		$\dfrac{R}{1+RCs}$	$\dfrac{1}{R}$	$\dfrac{1}{RC}$	$\dfrac{R^2}{1+x}$
		$R = \dfrac{1}{G}$	$\dfrac{G}{1+GLs}$	$\dfrac{1}{GL}$	$\dfrac{1+x}{G^2}$

$Z(s)\cdot Y(s)$	Circuit	$Z(s)$	$Y(s)$	ω_0	Z/Y
$\dfrac{(1+x)}{x}$	(R series, C series, R shunt)	$\dfrac{(1+RCs)}{Cs}$	$\dfrac{1}{R}$	$\dfrac{1}{RC}$	$\dfrac{(1+x)}{x}R^2$
	(R series; R ∥ L shunt)	$R=\dfrac{1}{G}$	$\dfrac{(1+GLs)}{Ls}$	$\dfrac{1}{GL}$	$\dfrac{x}{(1+x)}\dfrac{1}{G^2}$
$\dfrac{x}{(1+x)}$	(R series, C shunt, R shunt)	R	$\dfrac{Cs}{1+RCs}$	$\dfrac{1}{RC}$	$\dfrac{(1+x)}{x}R^2$
	(R ∥ L series; R shunt)	$\dfrac{Ls}{1+GLs}$	G	$\dfrac{1}{GL}$	$\dfrac{x}{(1+x)}\dfrac{1}{G^2}$
x^2	(L series, C shunt)	Ls	Cs	$\dfrac{1}{\sqrt{LC}}$	$\dfrac{L}{C}$
$\dfrac{1}{x^2}$	(C series, L shunt)	$\dfrac{1}{Cs}$	$\dfrac{1}{Ls}$	$\dfrac{1}{\sqrt{LC}}$	$\dfrac{L}{C}$
Wien Type $\dfrac{(1+x)^2}{x}$	(R series, C series; R ∥ C shunt)	$\dfrac{1+RCs}{Cs}$	$\dfrac{1+RCs}{R}$	$\dfrac{1}{RC}$	$\dfrac{R^2}{x}$
	(R series, L series; R ∥ L shunt)	$\dfrac{1+GLs}{G}$	$\dfrac{1+GLs}{Ls}$	$\dfrac{1}{GL}$	$\dfrac{x}{G^2}$

$Z(s)\cdot Y(s)$	Circuit	Z	Y	ω_0	Z/Y
Wien Type					
$\dfrac{x}{(1+x)^2}$		$\dfrac{R}{1+RCs}$	$\dfrac{Cs}{1+RCs}$	$\dfrac{1}{RC}$	$\dfrac{R^2}{x}$
		$\dfrac{Ls}{1+GLs}$	$\dfrac{G}{1+GLs}$	$\dfrac{1}{GL}$	$\dfrac{x}{G^2}$
$x_1(1+x_2) \xrightarrow{\;x_1=x_2\;} x(1+x)$		$\dfrac{1+GLs}{G}$	Cs	$\omega_1 = \dfrac{1}{RC}$ $\omega_2 = \dfrac{1}{GL}$	$\dfrac{(1+x_2)}{x_1}R^2$
		Ls	$G(1+RCs)$	$\omega_1 = \dfrac{1}{GL}$ $\omega_2 = \dfrac{1}{RC}$	$\dfrac{x_1}{(1+x_2)}\dfrac{1}{G_2}$

	Circuit			ω	
$\dfrac{1}{x_1(1+x_2)} \xrightarrow{x_1=x_2} \dfrac{1}{x(1+x)}$		$\dfrac{1}{Cs}$	$\dfrac{1}{R(1+GLs)}$	$\omega_1 = \dfrac{1}{RC}$ $\quad\omega_2 = \dfrac{1}{GL}$	$\dfrac{(1+x_2)}{x_1}\,R^2$
		$\dfrac{R}{1+RCs}$	$\dfrac{1}{Ls}$	$\omega_1 = \dfrac{1}{GL}$ $\quad\omega_2 = \dfrac{1}{RC}$	$\dfrac{x_1}{(1+x_2)}\,\dfrac{1}{G^2}$
$(1+x_1)(1+x_2) \xrightarrow{x_1=x_2} (1+x)^2$		$R(1+GLs)$	$G(1+RCs)$	$\omega_1 = \dfrac{1}{RC}$ $\quad\omega_2 = \dfrac{1}{GL}$	$\dfrac{(1+x_2)}{(1+x_1)}\,R^2 \xrightarrow{x_1=x_2} R^2$
$\dfrac{1}{(1+x_1)(1+x_2)} \xrightarrow{x_1=x_2} \dfrac{1}{(1+x)^2}$		$\dfrac{R}{(1+RCs)}$	$\dfrac{G}{1+GLs}$	$\omega_1 = \dfrac{1}{GL}$ $\quad\omega_2 = \dfrac{1}{RC}$	$\dfrac{(1+x_1)}{(1+x_2)}\,R^2 \xrightarrow{x_1=x_2} R^2$

TABLE 9d

$Z(s)\cdot Y(s)$	Circuit	Z	Y	ω_0	Z/Y
$\dfrac{x_0^2}{1+x_1}\xrightarrow{x_0=x_1}\dfrac{x^2}{1+x}$		$\dfrac{Ls}{1+GLs}$	Cs	$\omega_0=\dfrac{1}{\sqrt{LC}}$ $\omega_1=\dfrac{1}{GL}$	$\dfrac{L/C}{(1+x_1)}$
		Ls	$\dfrac{Cs}{1+RCs}$	$\omega_0=\dfrac{1}{\sqrt{LC}}$ $\omega_1=\dfrac{1}{RC}$	$\dfrac{L}{C}$
$\dfrac{(1+x_1)}{x_0^2}\xrightarrow{x_0=x_1}\dfrac{(1+x)}{x^2}$		$\dfrac{1}{Cs}$	$\dfrac{1+GLs}{Ls}$	$\omega_0=\dfrac{1}{\sqrt{LC}}$ $\omega_1=\dfrac{1}{GL}$	$\dfrac{L}{C}\dfrac{1}{(1+x_1)}$
		$\dfrac{1+RCs}{Cs}$	$\dfrac{1}{Ls}$	$\omega_0=\dfrac{1}{\sqrt{LC}}$ $\omega_1=\dfrac{1}{RC}$	$\dfrac{L}{C}(1+x_1)$

	Circuit			ω	
$x_1\dfrac{(1+x_2)}{(1+x_1)} \xrightarrow{x_1=x_2} x$	(L∥R) — (R∥C) network	$\dfrac{Ls}{(1+GLs)}$	$G(1+RCs)$	$\omega_1=\dfrac{1}{GL}$; $\omega_2=\dfrac{1}{RC}$	$\dfrac{x_1R^2}{(1+x_1)(1+x_2)} \xrightarrow{x_1=x_2} \dfrac{xR^2}{(1+x)^2}$
	R–L series — R–C network	$R(1+GLs)$	$\dfrac{Cs}{1+RCs}$	$\omega_1=\dfrac{1}{RC}$; $\omega_2=\dfrac{1}{GL}$	$\dfrac{(1+x_1)(1+x_2)R^2}{x_1} \xrightarrow{x_1=x_2} \dfrac{(1+x)^2R^2}{x}$
$\dfrac{(1+x_1)}{x_1(1+x_2)} \xrightarrow{x_1=x_2} \dfrac{1}{x}$	(C∥R) — (R∥L) network	$\dfrac{R}{1+RCs}$	$\dfrac{1+GLs}{Ls}$	$\omega_1=\dfrac{1}{GL}$; $\omega_2=\dfrac{1}{RC}$	$\dfrac{x_1R^2}{(1+x_1)(1+x_2)} \xrightarrow{x_1=x_2} \dfrac{xR^2}{(1+x)^2}$
	R–C series — R–L network	$\dfrac{1+RCs}{Cs}$	$\dfrac{1}{R(1+GLs)}$	$\omega_1=\dfrac{1}{RC}$; $\omega_2=\dfrac{1}{GL}$	$\dfrac{(1+x_1)(1+x_2)R^2}{x_1} \xrightarrow{x_1=x_2} \dfrac{(1+x)^2R^2}{x}$

TABLE 9e

$Z(s)\cdot Y(s)$	Circuit	Z	Y	ω_0	Z/Y
$\dfrac{(1+x_1)(1+x_2)}{x_0^2} \xrightarrow{x_1=x_2} \dfrac{(1+x)^2}{x^2}$		$\dfrac{1+RCs}{Cs}$	$\dfrac{1+GLs}{Ls}$	$\omega_0 = \dfrac{1}{\sqrt{LC}}$ $\omega_1 = \dfrac{1}{GL}$ $\omega_2 = \dfrac{1}{RC}$	$\dfrac{L}{C}\dfrac{(1+x_2)}{(1+x_1)} \xrightarrow{x_1=x_2} \dfrac{L}{C}$
$\dfrac{x_0^2}{(1+x_1)(1+x_2)} \xrightarrow{x_1=x_2} \dfrac{x^2}{(1+x)^2}$		$\dfrac{Ls}{1+GLs}$	$\dfrac{Cs}{1+RCs}$	$\omega_0 = \dfrac{1}{\sqrt{LC}}$ $\omega_1 = \dfrac{1}{RC}$ $\omega_2 = \dfrac{1}{GL}$	$\dfrac{L}{C}\dfrac{(1+x_2)}{(1+x_1)} \xrightarrow{x_1=x_2} \dfrac{L}{C}$
$\sqrt{\dfrac{L_1 C_2}{L_2 C_1}}\,\dfrac{x_1 x_2}{(1+x_1^2)(1+x_2^2)} \xrightarrow{x_1=x_2} \dfrac{x^2}{(1+x^2)^2}$		$\dfrac{L_1 s}{1+L_1 C_1 s^2}$	$\dfrac{C_2 s}{1+L_2 C_2 s^2}$	$\omega_1 = \dfrac{1}{\sqrt{L_1 C_1}}$ $\omega_2 = \dfrac{1}{\sqrt{L_2 C_2}}$	$\sqrt{\dfrac{L_2 L_1}{C_1 C_2}}\,\dfrac{x_1(1+x_2^2)}{x_2(1+x_1^2)} \xrightarrow{x_1=x_2} \dfrac{L}{C}$

$$\frac{2\alpha x}{1+x^2} R^2$$

$$\omega_0 = \frac{1}{\sqrt{LC}}$$

$$\alpha = G\sqrt{\frac{L}{C}}$$

$$\frac{(LCs^2+GLs+1)}{Ls}$$

$$\frac{R(LCs^2+GLs+1)}{1+LCs^2}$$

$$\frac{(1+2\alpha x+x^2)^2}{2\alpha x(1+x^2)}$$

$$\frac{2\alpha_L x}{G^2} = \frac{Ls}{G}; \text{ if } \alpha_L = \alpha_C$$

$$\omega_0 = \frac{1}{\sqrt{LC}}$$

$$2\alpha_L = G\sqrt{\frac{L}{C}}$$

$$2\alpha_C = R\sqrt{\frac{C}{L}}$$

$$\frac{G(1+RCs)}{LCs^2+GLs+1}$$

$$\frac{Ls(1+RCs)}{LCs^2+RCs+1}$$

$$\frac{2\alpha_L x_0(1+x_1)^2}{(x_0^2+2\alpha_L x_0+1)(x_0^2+2\alpha_C x_0+1)} \xrightarrow[x_1=x_2=2x_0]{} \frac{2x(1+2x)^2}{(x^2+2x+1)^2}$$

$$X_1 = RCs; \quad X_2 = GLs$$

The reader should refer to the matrices for the T, Γ, T, π, and lattice networks. In the T, Γ, and antisymmetric lattice, the function $(1 + ZY)$ is a fundamental term. The T and π networks each contain the function $(2 + ZY)$, and the magnitude of the impedance matrices contains $(4 + ZY)$. Depending upon the application, the combination of the ZY product with the appropriate constant can produce various pole-zero configurations.

For instance, the voltage transfer to an infinite impedance is $1/A_{11}$, where A_{11} is the one-one component of the cascade matrix. To illustrate the use of the tables we compute $H_V(Y_L = 0)$ for various configurations. Consider

$$ZY = \frac{(1 + x)^2}{x}.$$

For the T connection,

$$H_V(x) \xrightarrow[Y_L=0]{} \frac{1}{1 + ZY} = \frac{x}{x^2 + 3x + 1}.$$

This is an overdamped resonant transfer.

For the Γ connection,

$$H_V(x) \xrightarrow[Y_L=0]{} 1.$$

This connection has a unit transfer because the open-circulated load does not bring the Z arm into the problem.

In the case of the T network,

$$H_V^{(T)}(x) \xrightarrow[Y_L=0]{} \frac{2}{(2 + ZY)} = \frac{2x}{(x^2 + 4x + 1)}.$$

which is again a resonant transfer, but is more highly damped than the T connection.

For the π network,

$$H_V^{(\pi)}(x) \xrightarrow[Y_L=0]{} \frac{2x}{(x^2 + 4x + 1)}.$$

The asymmetric lattice section has an unloaded transfer for this ZY combination of

$$H_V^{(L)}(x) \xrightarrow[Y_L=0]{} \frac{(1 - ZY)}{(1 + ZY)} = \frac{(x^2 + x + 1)}{(x^2 + 3x + 1)}$$

$$= \frac{(x + \frac{1}{2}[1 + i\sqrt{3}])(x + \frac{1}{2}[1 - i\sqrt{3}])}{(x + \frac{1}{2}[3 + \sqrt{5}])(x + \frac{1}{2}[3 - \sqrt{5}])}.$$

This function tends toward inverse resonant transfer. The transfer dips to the value $-\,^1/_3$ when $x = i$.

These brief examples serve to illustrate the manner in which the ZY products can be employed to manufacture different unloaded transfers. Another important property of these networks is the image impedance or admittance. With the same example product $(ZY = (1 + x)^2/x)$, we can compute the image impedances for the five elementary sections:

$$\{Z_0^{(1)}\}^2 = \frac{Z}{Y}(1 + ZY) = \frac{1 + 3 \times + x^2}{x^2} R^2,$$

$$\{Z_0^{(\Gamma)}\}^2 = \frac{Z}{Y}\frac{1}{(1 + ZY)} = \frac{R^2}{(1 + 3x + x^2)},$$

$$\{Z_0^{(T)}\}^2 = \frac{Z(4 + x)}{4Y} = \frac{R^2(x^2 + 6x + 1)}{4x^2},$$

$$\{Z_0^{(\pi)}\}^2 = \frac{4Z}{Y(4 + x)} = \frac{4R^2}{(x^2 + 6x + 1)},$$

and for the lattice with $Z' = 1/Y$ and $Y' = 1/Z$,

$$\{Z_0^{(L)}\}^2 = \frac{Z}{Y} = \frac{R^2}{x}.$$

The Limitations of the Four-Terminal Representation

The preceding formalism is extremely useful under the conditions stated at the beginning. The reader should be aware of some of the precautions that must be observed. Every combination for which the matrix method is used must conserve the input loop current and the output loop current. Such combinations must also avoid connecting series elements in parallel.

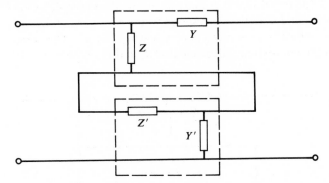

FIG. 120. An incorrect Z connection (series-series); the element Z' is short-circuited.

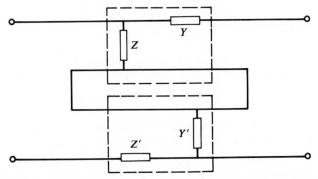

FIG. 121. A correct drawing of the series-series combination of a Γ and a T network. In this combination, Z' remains in the series leg.

To observe the types of pitfalls that can arise, regard first the series-series connection of a Γ and a T' network. If the series element in the primed network is connected in the Y branch, as shown in Figs. 120 and 121, it is shorted out and certainly does not give the same result as we obtain when the lower T' network is reversed in such a manner that Z' remains a series element.

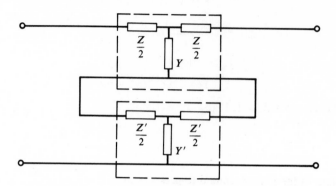

FIG. 122. An incorrect drawing of the series-series combination of two symmetric T networks by matrix addition. Notice that the $Z'/2$ elements are thrown in parallel by this connection.

In the second example in Fig. 122, two equal T networks are connected in a Z arrangement.† The first diagram in Fig. 122 throws the lower $Z'/2$ elements in parallel with one another and does not correspond to the addition $Z + Z'$.

The error shown is even more apparent when $Z \neq Z'$. The correct diagram for $Z + Z'$ makes the connection independent of I_1 and I_2, as shown in Fig. 123.

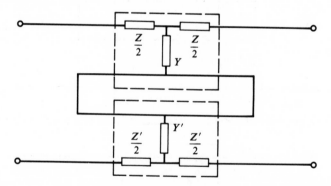

FIG. 123. A correct representation of the matrix addition of two symmetric T networks in a series-series combinations. Notice that this drawing maintains the $Z'/2$ elements in series with the $Z/2$ elements.

The second of the two connections illustrated has a total Z matrix of $Z + Z'$. One can demonstrate by direct computation that the first connection (improper) does not have the same Z matrix.

---

† By Z connection we mean a series-series connection. Thus, an A connection would be a cascade of two networks.

CHAPTER 4

SPECIAL CIRCUITS

THE DIFFERENTIATING CIRCUIT

An ideal differentiation has a transfer function with one zero at the origin:

$$H(s) = \tau s.$$
$$\text{diff}$$

Under these circumstances,

$$V(s) = \tau s E(s)$$

and

$$v(t) = \tau \frac{de(t)}{dt}.$$

(See Fig. 124.)

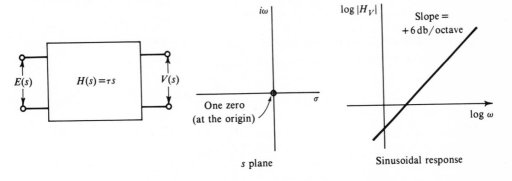

Fig. 124.   Characteristics of the ideal differentiating transfer function.

It is not possible to achieve a transfer function with a single zero at the origin with any combination of *real*-linear passive circuit elements.

One might conceive of the current through a series capacitor; however, a real capacitor has some stray conductance. Also, a series capacitor develops a voltage equal to $E(s)$. The current would provide a measure of the differentiation. To measure the current, one needs some series resistance. Thus, differentiation can be approximated by the high-pass circuit shown in Fig. 125.

179

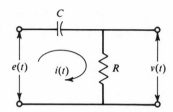

FIG. 125.   An approximate differentiating circuit. The operation is limited to frequencies less than $1/RC$.

In the interval to the left of $\omega = 1/RC$ [$\omega < 1/RC$], the circuit functions on a sinusoidal response characteristic, which has an asymptotic slope of $+6$db per octave (see Fig. 126). Any excitation that operates in the region $\omega \ll (1/RC)$ will then be subject to an approximate differentiation. Another way of saying this is to indicate that the first few important terms in the Fourier expansion of the excitation must fall in this interval.

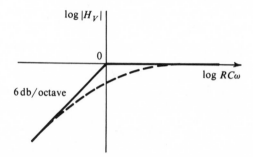

FIG. 126.   The magnitude of the frequency response of the RC differentiating circuit. The approximation is fair for frequencies less than $1/2RC$. The differentiating circuit is a high-pass circuit.

The complex frequency representation makes the condition even more obvious. The circuit shown in Fig. 127 has a response

$$V(s) = \frac{RCsE(s)}{(1 + RCs)} = \frac{s}{(s + a)}\,E(s),$$

where

$$a = \frac{1}{\tau} = \frac{1}{RC}.$$

If the characteristic period of the pulse is T (with a gate, for instance, this would be the width), our approximation is valid when $RC \ll T$ or when the important frequencies are much less than a. Under these conditions,

$$V(s) \xrightarrow[RC \ll T]{} RCs(1 - RCs + \cdots \text{h.t.})E_T(s) \simeq RCsE_T(s).†$$

The denominator of the exact expression has been expanded in a power series to achieve the approximation shown. There is invariably a correction term. In the series

---

† h.t. means higher order terms.

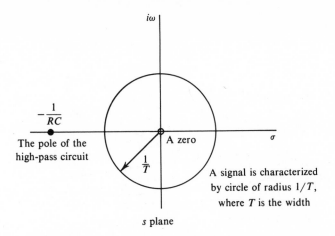

FIG. 127.   The pole-zero diagram of the real differentiating circuit. To obtain accuracy, the pole must be far removed from the circle characterizing the signal to be differentiated. If the mean-time width of the signal is T, the radius of the circle is $1/T$.

form, one can observe that the first correction to the approximation arises from the term $\tau^2 s^2$, which incorporates the second derivative of $e(\tau)$ times τ^2. The importance of having τ small is obvious if the series is to converge rapidly.

The dual of the RC circuit is also an approximate differentiating circuit (Fig. 128):

$$V(s) = \frac{sE(s)}{s + (R/L)} \underset{\substack{\omega \ll a \\ \tau \ll T}}{\longrightarrow} \tau s E(s),$$

where

$$a = \frac{R}{L} = \frac{1}{\tau},$$

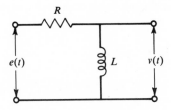

FIG. 128.   An RL differentiating circuit.

The effect of the differentiating circuit on a real pulse can be gauged by the response to an excitation of the form (see Fig. 129):

$$e(t) = E_0 e^{-\alpha t}(1 - e^{-\beta t}), \qquad (\alpha < \beta).$$

Then the approximation is relatively good if

$$\frac{1}{a} = \tau \ll T \sim \frac{1}{(\alpha + \beta)}.$$

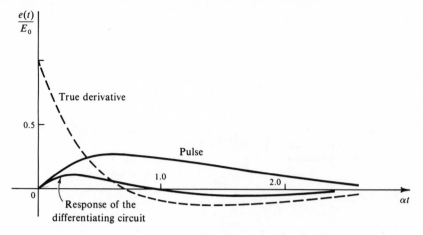

FIG. 129. Response of a poorly designed differentiating circuit to a pulse, $\mathscr{E}_0(e^{-at} - e^{-2at})$, when the time constant of the differentiating circuit is only $1/4a$. Notice that the deviation is large near the beginning of the pulse, indicating a poor high-frequency response.

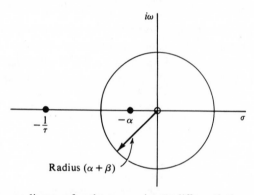

FIG. 130. The pole-zero diagram for the approximate differentiating circuit in the example, in which the radius of the pulse circle is only one-half the distance to the pole of the transfer function. This diagram has a poor high-frequency response.

THE INTEGRATING CIRCUIT

The transfer function for an ideal integrating circuit should have a single pole at the origin (see Fig. 131):

$$H_{int}(s) = \frac{1}{\tau s}.$$

Then

$$V(s) = \frac{E(s)}{\tau s}$$

and

$$v(t) = \int_0^t \frac{1}{\tau} e(t') \, dt'.$$

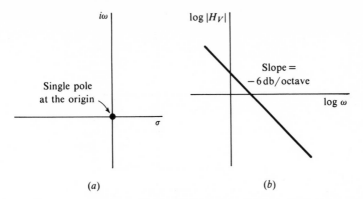

(a)   (b)

FIG. 131.   The pole-zero diagram and sinusoidal response for an ideal, integrating transfer function.

This device is the dual of the differentiator. As a result, the voltage across the capacitor in an RC network will integrate approximately if the RC time constant is long compared with the characteristic pulse period. This is to imply that if the pole of the nonideal network appears very close to the origin, the response will behave to a great extent as if the excitation were being integrated. See Fig. 132.

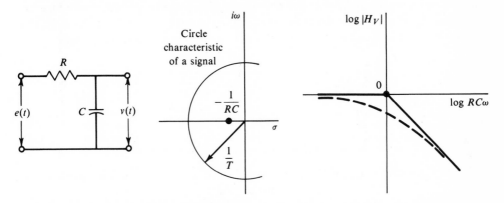

FIG. 132.   An approximate integrating circuit formed by an RC loop. The pole diagram indicates that the characteristic circle for a signal must have a radius much greater than the distance of the pole from the origin. The sinusoidal response at the right shows that this is a low-pass circuit. To achieve a good approximation of an integrating device, the frequencies involved must be greater than $1/RC$. This is equivalent to $T \ll RC$.

This is a low-pass device, and in this application the excitation must appear on the asymptote. In other words, the important Fourier components of the signal must be well above $a = 1/\tau = 1/RC$:

$$V(s) = \frac{a}{(s+a)} E_T(s) \xrightarrow[\substack{a \ll \omega \\ T \ll \tau}]{} \frac{1}{RCs}\left(1 - \frac{1}{RCs} + \cdots \text{h.t.}\right)E_T(s).$$

If the signal time is T, then $1/T$ must be much greater than $1/RC$. As in the differentiating circuit, there is an LR analogue to the RC circuit, which also integrates approximately. (See Fig. 133.) Here

$$a = \frac{1}{\tau} = \frac{R}{L}.$$

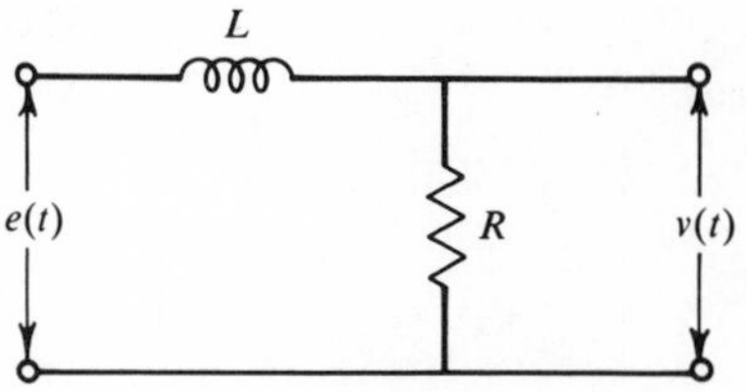

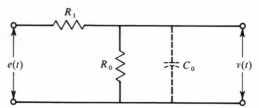

FIG. 133.   An LR integrating circuit.

THE ATTENUATOR AND ADDITION CIRCUITS

The Attenuator

An ordinary resistive voltage divider will serve as a device that provides division of an input signal by a constant factor. This is a useful concept until the times involved in the excitation become sufficiently short to be of the same order as the resistance times the distributed capacity of the real circuit. The wiring capacitance will integrate very fast signals. This statement becomes clearer if we consider the voltage divider shown in Fig. 134 along with the distributed capacitance C_0 of the real circuit.

FIG. 134. A resistive attenuator or voltage divider, shown with a distributed output capacitor C_0.

The transfer function of this circuit is (see Fig. 135)

$$H_{att}(s) = \frac{R_0}{(R_1 + R_0)} \left\{ \frac{1}{1 + [R_0 \parallel R_1]C_0 s} \right\}$$

and

$$H_{att}(s) = \frac{1}{R_1 C_0} \left\{ \frac{1}{s + a} \right\},$$

where

$$[R_0 \parallel R_1] = \frac{R_1 R_0}{(R_1 + R_0)}$$

(see Fig. 135) and

$$\tau = \frac{1}{a} = [R_0 \parallel R_1]C.$$

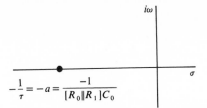

FIG. 135. The pole-zero diagram of a resistive voltage divider that has a distributed capacitance C_0 across the output. This circuit is a simple type I low-pass device that begins to cut off at frequencies greater than $1/[R_0//R_1]C_0$.

If τ is much smaller than the characteristic signal times T, the pole appears to be far from the origin and has little effect on the signal. When we regard times of the order of τ or less, a great deal of distortion is present. Consider now a case in which τ is a limitation. It turns out that the attenuator can be compensated by placing a capacitor C_1 in parallel with R_1. This is equivalent to placing a zero in the diagram. By adjusting C_1 to an appropriate value, the zero can be forced onto the pole, destroying the tendency to integrate.

The uncompensated response to a step function (see Fig. 136) is

$$V_U(s) = \frac{1}{R_1 C_0} \cdot \frac{1}{(s+a)} \frac{E_0}{s},$$

giving

$$v_U(t) = \frac{R_0 E_0}{(R_1 + R_0)} (1 - e^{-at})U(t).$$

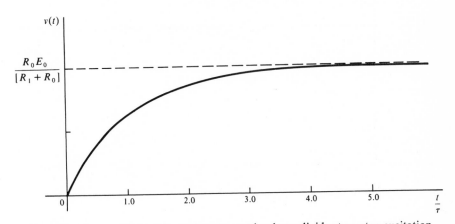

FIG. 136. The response of the uncompensated voltage divider to a step excitation.

The circuit with the compensating capacitor C_1 is shown in Fig. 137. The action of the compensating capacitor is quite simple. The value of C_1 is adjusted so that the voltage across C_1 builds up in relation to C_0 in the ratio $R_1/(R_0 + R_1)$.

The response of the compensated network to an excitation $e(t)$ is given by

$$V(s) = \frac{(1 + R_1 C_1 s)}{[1 + [R_0 \| R_1](C_1 + C_0)s]} \cdot \frac{R_0}{(R_1 + R_0)} E(s).$$

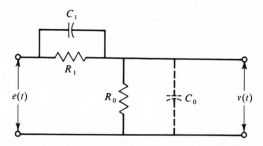

FIG. 137.   The voltage-divider network with a compensating capacitor C_1.

The zero can be set to be superimposed on the pole by adjusting C_1 to the value

$$C_1 = \frac{R_0}{R_1} C_0.$$

Then

$$V(s) = \frac{R_0}{(R_1 + R_0)} E(s).$$

The value of C_1 is quite critical. If C_1 is greater than $R_0 C_0/R_1$, the signal, overshoots, while a value of C_1 less than critical gives a response resembling the uncompensated case. See Fig. 138.

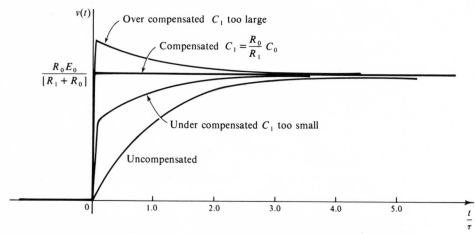

FIG. 138.   Response of a compensated voltage divider to a step excitation.

The Passive Addition Circuit

The voltage attenuator structure can be doubled to produce an approximate addition circuit. Because of the necessity to isolate one excitation from the other, the final circuit provides addition with a sizable attenuation of the signals. If signals with fast rise times are involved, the addition circuit can be compensated in the same manner as the voltage attenuator. The compensated circuit is shown in Fig. 139.

The signal e_1 is split between the number 2 input port and the output resistor R_0. R_0 is made small compared with R_2 (or R_1) to prevent excessive crossover of the signal.

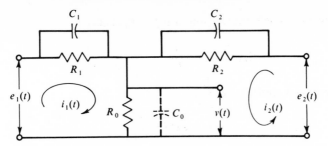

FIG. 139.   The passive addition circuit with a compensation for C_0.

In the same manner a fraction of $e_2(t)$ appears across R_0 in addition to $\{R_0/(R_0 + R_1)\}$ $e_1(t)$. Again, if $R_0 \ll R_1$, the interaction between input 1 and 2 is minimized.

Assuming signals $e_1(t)$ and $e_2(t)$ with transforms $E_1(s)$ and $E_2(s)$, the transform of the response is given by the relation

$$\left\{1 + \frac{R_0(1 + R_1C_1s)}{R_1(1 + R_0C_0)s} + \frac{R_0(1 + R_2C_2s)}{R_2(1 + R_0C_0s)}\right\}V(s)$$

$$= \frac{R_0(1 + R_1C_1s)}{R_1(1 + R_0C_0s)}E_1(s) + \frac{R_0(1 + R_2C_2s)}{R_2(1 + R_0C_0s)}E_2(s).$$

The circuit is compensated by setting

$$R_1C_1 = R_2C_2 = R_0C_0.$$

Then, to sum the signals, we set $R_1 = R_2 = R \gg R_0$ and

$$V(s) = \frac{R_0}{[R + 2R_0]}\{E_1(s) + E_2(s)\}.$$

THE PHASE-SHIFTING NETWORKS

It is often desirable to construct a circuit that shifts the phase of a sinusoid by a known amount. An elementary circuit that does this is the two-element T circuit (or the Γ circuit). Consider the network shown in Fig. 140. The cascade matrix for this section is

$$\mathbb{A}_\tau(s) = \begin{pmatrix} [1 + Z(s)Y(s)] & Z(s) \\ Y(s) & 1 \end{pmatrix}.$$

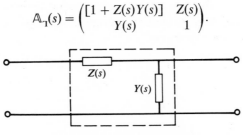

FIG. 140.   The T network.

This section would be employed as a voltage phase-shifting circuit because the series element $Z(s)$ is directly connected to a low-impedance generator, and one would assume that the output feeds a high impedance. We note that a Γ section fed by a low impedance would produce no phase change if the output terminals were open-circuited.

The forward voltage transfer into a high impedance is

$$H_V(s) \xrightarrow[Z_L \to \infty]{} \frac{1}{A_{11}} = \frac{1}{[1 + Z(s)Y(s)]}.$$

A conventional choice of Z and Y is

$$Z(s) = \frac{1}{Cs}$$

and

$$Y(s) = G.$$

Then

$$H_V \xrightarrow[Z_L \to \infty]{} \frac{s}{s + (1/RC)} = \frac{s}{(s + \omega_{RC})}.$$

See Fig. 141. The phase shift in this ideal case then becomes

$$\Phi(\omega) = \frac{\pi}{2} - \tan^{-1} \frac{\omega}{\omega_{RC}}.$$

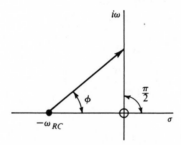

FIG. 141.   The pole-zero diagram of a simple high-pass, phase-shifting section.

When the network is tuned to the input frequency ω_s with $\omega_s = \omega_{RC}$, the phase shift is $(\pi/4)$. One must not be misled by the simplicity of this result, since loading of the output invariably reduces the total shift.

Ordinarily, and we shall see this in the section on oscillators, a number of these networks are cascaded to provide the appropriate change of phase. Two identical sections give a net cascade matrix of

$$A_T \cdot A_T = \begin{pmatrix} [1 + ZY]^2 + ZY & Z(2 + ZY) \\ Y(2 + ZY) & (1 + ZY) \end{pmatrix},$$

with

$$H_V(s) \xrightarrow[Z_L \to \infty]{} \frac{1}{[1 + 3ZY + (ZY)^2]}.$$

Again, if $Z = 1/Cs$ and $Y = G$, the forward voltage transfer is

$$H_V \xrightarrow[Z_L \to \infty]{} \frac{s^2}{[s^2 + 3\omega_{RC}s + \omega_{RC}^2]} = \frac{s^2}{(s + \frac{1}{2}[3 - \sqrt{5}]\omega_{RC})(s + \frac{1}{2}[3 + \sqrt{5}]\omega_{RC})}.$$

The phase change is now (see Fig. 142)

$$\Phi(\omega) = \pi - \tan^{-1}\frac{\omega}{\omega_1} - \tan^{-1}\frac{\omega}{\omega_2},$$

where

$$\omega_1 = \tfrac{1}{2}(3 - \sqrt{5})\omega_{RC},$$

$$\omega_2 = \tfrac{1}{2}(3 + \sqrt{5})\omega_{RC}.$$

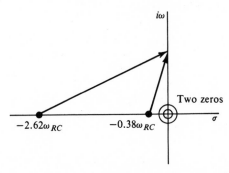

FIG. 142.   The pole-zero configuration for two high-pass T, phase-shifting sections connected in cascade.

Ordinarily, one might assume that large phase changes can be achieved by making ω_{RC} much larger than the operating frequency. The attenuation of the device will be very large if $\omega < \omega_{RC}$. In fact, at low frequencies, the gain will go like ω^2/ω_{RC}^2 if ω is small. Bringing the poles in close to the origin by making ω_{RC} smaller than the operating frequency provides a very small phase change but with a gain close to 1.

The best compromise is to set $\omega = \omega_{RC}$. Under these circumstances,

$$\Phi(\omega = \omega_{RC}) \xrightarrow[\substack{two\\sections}]{} \frac{\pi}{2}.$$

with an associated attenuation of ⅓.

Three sections are often employed in phase-shift oscillators to provide a phase shift near π. See Fig. 143.

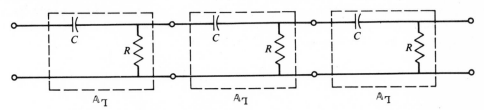

FIG. 143.   Three high-pass CR T-section connected in cascade to provide a phase shift greater than $\pi/2$.

The overall response of three identical sections is

$$\mathbb{A}^{(3)} = \mathbb{A}_T \cdot \mathbb{A}_T \cdot \mathbb{A}_T = \begin{pmatrix} [(1 + ZY)^3 + ZY(3 + 2ZY)] & Z(1 + ZY)(3 + ZY) \\ Y(1 + ZY)(3 + ZY) & [ZY(2 + ZY) + (1 + ZY)] \end{pmatrix}.$$

The open-circuit voltage transfer is

$$H_V \xrightarrow[Z_L \to \infty]{} \frac{1}{[1 + 6ZY + 5(ZY)^2 + (ZY)^3]}.$$

Letting $Z = 1/Cs$ and $Y = G$,

$$H_V \xrightarrow[Z_L \to \infty]{} \frac{s^3}{[s^3 + 6\omega_{RC}s^2 + 5\omega_{RC}^2 s + \omega_{RC}^3]} = \frac{s_3}{(s + 0.39\omega_{RC})(s + 0.67\omega_{RC})(s + 5.04\omega_{RC})}.$$

The total phase shift (see Fig. 144) is

$$\Phi(\omega) = \frac{3}{2}\pi - \tan^{-1}\frac{\omega}{\omega_1} - \tan^{-1}\frac{\omega}{\omega_2} - \tan^{-1}\frac{\omega}{\omega_3}.$$

At $\omega = \omega_{RC}$,

$$\Phi(\omega_{RC}) \simeq \tfrac{3}{4}\pi,$$

with an attenuation of $\dfrac{1}{\sqrt{41}}$

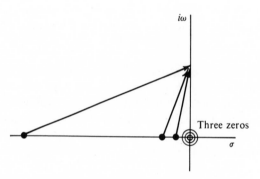

FIG. 144.   Rough sketch of the three poles and three zeros provided by the voltage transfer of three-pass T networks in cascade. The phase shift of this network to a high impedance is $3\pi/4$ at $\omega = \omega_{RC}$.

One can see immediately that each section operated at the design frequency ω_{RC} adds a phase shift of approximately $\pi/4$.

An equally suitable choice for phase-shifting a voltage wave form would have been an RL section with $Z(s) = R$ and $Y(s) = 1/Ls$. In this case, the characteristic frequency would have been $\omega_{LR} = R/L$. See Fig. 145.

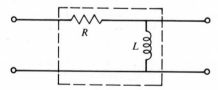

FIG. 145.   The RL phase-shifting section. This is arranged for voltage transfer.

When transistor oscillators are used, it is necessary to phase-shift a current excitation. The dual of the T network is suitable. This is the Γ network. See Fig. 146.

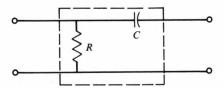

FIG. 146. The RC-current, phase-shifting section. This section is a Γ network and is arranged for optimum current transfer to a low impedance.

Because this represents a geometric reflection, the various cascades of this arrangement can be obtained from the voltage T sections by interchanging the diagonal sections. The $\mathbb{A}_\Gamma$ matrix is then

$$\mathbb{A}_\Gamma = \begin{pmatrix} 1 & Z \\ Y & (1+ZY) \end{pmatrix},$$

The same principle holds for 2, 3, and N sections. The attenuation and net phase shift of the current signals feeding a short circuit are then the same as those for the same number of sections for voltage excitations. There is a phase shift of approximately $(\pi/4)$ radians per section when the termination is a short circuit, and the attenuation is $\dfrac{1}{\sqrt{2}}, \dfrac{1}{3}$, and $\dfrac{1}{\sqrt{41}}$ for 1, 2, and 3 sections.

A phase-shifting section formed from a lattice or bridge network has some properties that are superior to the cascade of Γ or T sections. On the other hand, the lattice or bridge section possesses the inherent drawback that the output terminal cannot be grounded if the input is grounded.

The most useful symmetry for phase shifting is the antisymmetric arrangement with $Z' = 1/Y$ and $Y' = 1/Z$. To illustrate the properties of the network, this section can be terminated either in the image impedance or in an open circuit $Y_L = 0$. First regard an open-circuit termination. With the symmetry shown,

$$H_V(s) \xrightarrow[Y_L=0]{} \frac{(1-ZY)}{(1+ZY)}.$$

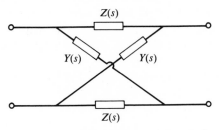

FIG. 147. The lattice phase-shifting section. The antisymmetric geometry is employed in this application.

Consider the case in which $Z = R$ and $Y = Cs$. Then

$$ZY = RCs = \frac{s}{\omega_0} = x$$

and

$$H_V(s) \xrightarrow[Y_L=0]{} \frac{(1-x)}{(1+x)} \xrightarrow[x \ll 1]{} e^{-2x}.$$

This transfer function has a zero on the positive-real axis at $+\omega_0$, and has a pole on the negative-real axis at $-\omega_0$. The fact that the zero and the pole are placed symmetrically about the origin of the s plane (i.e., the zero is a reflection of the pole about the imaginary axis) indicates that the magnitude of H_V is 1 for all frequencies. The only effect of the network is to cause a variation in the phase of the frequency components of a signal. The phase shift for one RC section with $ZY = x$ is

$$\Phi(\omega) = \pi - 2 \tan^{-1} \frac{\omega}{\omega_0} = \pi - 2 \tan^{-1} x \xrightarrow[\omega = \omega_0]{} \frac{\pi}{2}.$$

Thus, a sine wave of frequency ω_0 is shifted by $\pi/2$.

The characteristic impedance of this section is $\sqrt{Z/Y} = \sqrt{R/Cs}$. Because this function does not correspond to the s dependence of a real, passive element, it is not possible to terminate the section in a load that exhibits the impedance Z_0 for all frequencies. In narrow-band applications, however, one can design a network that provides $|Z_0|$ at the midband frequency.

Two antisymmetric lattice sections in cascade do not preserve the pole-zero symmetry of the unloaded voltage transfer. The cascade matrix for two sections is

$$\mathbb{A}^{(2)} = \mathbb{A} \cdot \mathbb{A} = \begin{pmatrix} \dfrac{(1 + 6ZY + (ZY)^2)}{(1 - ZY)^2} & \dfrac{4Z(1 + ZY)}{(1^1 - ZY)^2} \\[2ex] \dfrac{4Y(1 + ZY)}{(1 - ZY)^2} & \dfrac{(1 + 6ZY + (ZY)^2)}{(1 - ZY)^2} \end{pmatrix}.$$

The transfer to an open termination is

$$H_V^{(2)} \xrightarrow[Y_L = 0]{} \frac{(1 - ZY)^2}{(1 + 6ZY + (ZY)^2)} \xrightarrow[ZY = x]{} \frac{(1 - x)^2}{[1 + 6x + x^2]}.$$

When $ZY = x$, this transfer has two zeros at $+\omega_0$. The two poles, however, are now split and lie at $(-3 \pm 2\sqrt{2})\omega_0$. At the frequency $\omega_0(x \to i)$, the transfer is $-\frac{1}{3}$ and the net phase shift is π.

A consistent cascade can be produced if the image impedance is constructed to correspond to a possible network of passive elements. Since $Z_0 = \sqrt{Z/Y}$, it is clear that the choice $Z = Ls$ and $Y = Cs$ will give $ZY = x^2$, with $Z_0 = \sqrt{L/C}$. One section of this network has a transfer to its image impedance $(Z_L = Z_0)$ of

$$H_V \xrightarrow[Z_L = \sqrt{L/C}]{} \frac{(1 - x)}{(1 + x)},$$

where

$$x^2 = LCs^2$$

and

$$\omega_0^2 = \frac{1}{LC}.$$

Two sections in cascade, terminated in Z_0, have a voltage transfer

$$H_V^{(2)} \xrightarrow[Z_L = \sqrt{L/C}]{} \frac{(1 - x)^2}{(1 + x)^2}.$$

Thus, n sections in cascade terminating in $Z_0 = \sqrt{L/C}$ have a transfer

$$H_V^{(n)} \xrightarrow[Z_L = Z_0]{} \frac{(1-x)^n}{(1+x)^n}.$$

See Fig. 148.

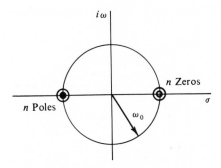

FIG. 148.   The pole-zero diagram for n, LC-lattice, phase-shifting sections terminated in the image impedance $\sqrt{L/C}$.

The magnitude of $H_V^{(n)}$ for all frequencies is 1, and the phase shift for n sections is

$$\Phi^{(n)}(\omega) \xrightarrow[Z_L = Z_0]{} n(\pi - 2\tan^{-1} x) \xrightarrow[\substack{x=1 \\ \omega = \omega_0}]{} \frac{n\pi}{2}.$$

This connection is an excellent phase shifter for a narrow-band signal if the output signal can be extracted without grounding the terminals.

On the other hand, this array has a high dispersion for wideband signals. In spite of the fact that the attenuation is zero, the variations in phase shift cause a large distortion in pulses. This can be demonstrated by computing the response of two sections terminated in Z_0 to a gate of width T. See Fig. 149.

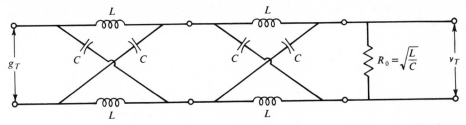

FIG. 149.   A two-section LC-lattice, phase-shifting network terminated in the image impedance.

We write $\mathscr{L}[g_T(t)]$ in terms of x:

$$G_T(x) = \frac{E_0}{\omega_0 x}(1 - e^{-\omega_0 T x}).$$

Then

$$V_T(x) = \frac{E_0(1-x)^2}{\omega_0 x(1+x)^2}(1 - e^{-\omega_0 T x}),$$

giving (see Fig. 150)

$$v_T(t) = E_0\{1 - 4\omega_0 t e^{-\omega_0 t}\}U(t) - E_0\{1 - 4\omega_0(t - T)e^{-\omega_0(t - T)}\}U(t - T).$$

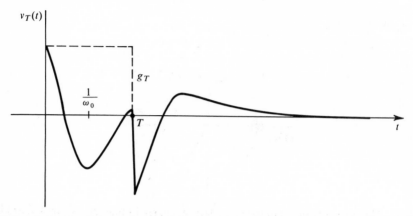

FIG. 150.   A sketch of the response of the LC lattice, phase-shifting network (two sections) to a gate excitation of width T. The excessive dispersion of this network is observed in the severe distortion of the output. Although attenuation is small, pulses having a wide-frequency spectrum are subject to a large phase distortion.

BRIDGE CIRCUITS

Amplitude Bridges

The lattice network has also been named the "bridge network" to signify the application of that particular circuit to amplitude bridges. If the primed arm $Z'(s) Y'(s)$ is constructed as a resistive attenuator $R_1 G_2$, a null bridge can be formed by making the ZY arm a resonant transfer section. The resonant function is a quadratic resonance in its most elementary form. However, it is fairly obvious that higher-order resonances can be employed. See Fig. 151.

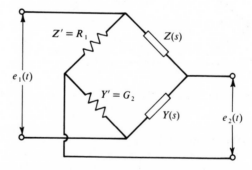

FIG. 151.   The amplitude bridge with one half connected as a resistive voltage divider.

The primed arm can be formed of more than just resistive elements; however, the resistive voltage divider is the most common.

In its most elementary form, then, the primed arm will consist of a resistive voltage divider with $Z'Y' = R_1G_2$, and the unprimed arm will be built to provide a resonant unloaded transfer:

$$H_V \xrightarrow[\substack{\text{unprimed} \\ \text{arm}}]{} \frac{f_0 2as}{s^2 + 2as + \omega_0^2}.$$

In general, the resonant transfer of the ZY section must have a peak amplitude less than 1. This condition is necessary to achieve a voltage match with the resistive arm. This match at resonance provides the null output of a balanced bridge.

The reader will recall that the elementary resonance is associated with a single LRC loop. Many complex networks exhibit a resonant transfer in the absence of one of the three basic passive elements. The Wien connection shown in Fig. 152 is a typical example.

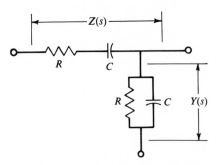

FIG. 152. The Wien ZY combination.

This ZY combination is listed in Tables 9a–e and has a transfer to an open circuit;

$$H_V \xrightarrow[\substack{Y_L = 0 \\ ZY = \frac{(1+x)^2}{x}}]{} \frac{x}{[x^2 + 3x + 1]},$$

where

$$x = RCs = \frac{s}{\omega_{RC}}$$

In the example given above, the function is an overdamped resonance having a Q value of $\frac{1}{3}$ and a net transfer at resonance of $\frac{1}{3}$. Thus, to form a null bridge, the voltage divider must be set to give $1/(1 + R_1G_2) = \frac{1}{3}$.

The most common bridges work on the following principle: The voltage difference between the two legs has a minimum at some frequency ω_0. This is defined as the *balance point*. The elementary forms are assumed to feed a high impedance; as a result, the net transfer can be represented as the difference between the open-circuit voltage transfers of the two arms.

If the two responses to an excitation $E(s)$ are

$$V(s) = \frac{f_0 2asE(s)}{[s^2 + 2as + \omega_0^2]}$$

and

$$V'(s) = \frac{E(s)}{(1 + R_1G_2)},$$

then the net response is

$$V_{\text{bridge}}(s) = V'(s) - V(s) = \left\{ \frac{s^2 + [1 - f_0(1 + R_1 G_2)]2as + \omega_0^2}{(1 + R_1 G_2)(s^2 + 2as + \omega_0^2)} \right\} E(s).$$

The null condition occurs if we set $f_0(1 + R_1 G_2) = 1$ (this is shown in Fig. 150):

$$V_{\text{bridge}}(s) \xrightarrow[f_0(1+R_1 G_2)=1]{} \frac{(s^2 + \omega_0^2)}{[s^2 + 2as + \omega_0^2]} \frac{E(s)}{(1 + R_1 G_2)}.$$

In this example, f_0 is the attenuation factor, and its relation to $R_1 G_2$ determines the degree to which the bridge is balanced. When $f_0(1 + R_1 G_2) = 1$, the bridge is perfectly balanced, and the frequency response becomes zero at $\omega = \omega_0$. If the bridge is not balanced, then $(1 + R_1 G_2) \neq 1/f_0$.

The degree of balance is designated by a *balance factor* δ/f_0, where

$$\frac{\delta}{f_0} = (1 + R_1 G_2) - \frac{1}{f_0}$$

or

$$(1 + R_1 G_2) = \frac{(1 + \delta)}{f_0}.$$

The transfer to the output terminals in terms of δ is

$$H_V(s) \xrightarrow[Y_L = 0]{} \frac{f_0[s^2 - 2a\,\delta s + \omega_0^2]}{(1 + \delta)[s^2 + 2as + \omega_0^2]}.$$

As the bridge is brought to balance, δ approaches zero from either polarity, and the zeros of $H_V(s)$ move on a circle of radius ω_0. At balance ($\delta = 0$), the zeros of $H_V(s)$ lie on the imaginary axis (in the s plane) at $\pm i\omega_0$. When R_1 is too large, the zeros lie in the right-hand plane, and δ is positive. If R_1 is too small relative to R_2, the zeros lie in the left-hand plane, and δ is negative.

The amplitude at the minimum of H_V is obtained from

$$H_V(i\omega) \xrightarrow[\omega = \omega_0]{} - \frac{\delta f_0}{(1 + \delta)}.$$

The phase at the minimum ($\omega = \omega_0$) is zero.

The argument has been quite restricted to this point. It is apparent from the general development of the lattice section that we have the formalism available to compute the bridge characteristics under the most general conditions. In other words, we can formally write down the transfer for a loaded voltage bridge, or as an alternative, we can construct a current bridge. It can be shown that the balance conditions are independent of the load. The general voltage transfer to a load admittance $Y_L(s)$ is

$$H_V(s) = + \frac{(P'(s) - P(s))}{PP' + Y_L(Z'P + ZP')},$$

where

$$P = (1 + Z(s)Y(s))$$

and

$$P' = (1 + Z'(s)Y'(s)).$$

If $Z'Y' = R_1 G_2$, representing the resistive voltage divider, and $ZY = M(x)/N(x)$, then the numerator of H_V has two zeros on the imaginary axis if

$$R_1 G_2 N(x) - M(x) = \pm(x^2 + a^2).$$

Multiple null points can be created by constructing

$$R_1 G_2 N(x) - M(x) = \prod_n (x^2 + a_n^2).$$

Several general conclusions can be drawn from the preceding development. First, the null condition is independent of the load $Y_L(s)$. By regarding the general $\mathbb{Y}$ matrix for the lattice, we notice that the current-transfer function has the same numerator. Thus, the current nulls (as one would expect) at the same point. The behavior of $H_V(s)$ away from the null points depends upon the loading or the use as a current bridge.

Secondly, we observe that it is not essential that the $Z'Y'$ arm consist of resistive elements only. The only condition necessary for a null is that the numerator $(Z'Y' - ZY)$ have roots on the imaginary axis of the s plane. As an example, a $Z'Y'$ product behaving as $2\alpha x$ will cause a null if $ZY = (x^2 + 2\alpha x + 1)$.

The Wien Bridge

A Wien Bridge is shown in Fig. 153. The transfer function of this bridge is given by

$$H_V \xrightarrow[Y_L=0]{} \frac{[s^2 - 3\delta\omega_{RC}s + \omega_{RC}^2]}{3(1+\delta)[s^2 + 3\omega_{RC}s + \omega_{RC}^2]} \xrightarrow[\substack{\text{balance} \\ \delta=0}]{} \frac{(s^2 + \omega_{RC}^2)}{3[s^2 + 3\omega_{RC}s + \omega_{RC}^2]}.$$

Here,

$$\omega_{RC} = \frac{1}{RC}$$

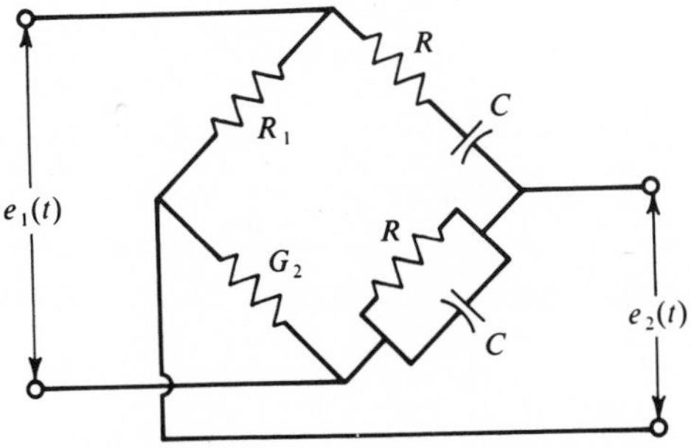

FIG. 153.   The Wien bridge.

The attenuation factor is $\frac{1}{3}$, and a balance is achieved when $R_1 G_2 = 2$. If $R_1 G_2$ is not set precisely at the balance point, the extent of imbalance is measured by δ, where $3\delta = (R_1 G_2 - 2)$. The phase shift as a function of frequency is given by

$$\Phi(\omega) = \tan^{-1} \frac{(x-1)}{\frac{3}{2}\delta} + \tan^{-1} \frac{2(x+1)}{3\delta} - \tan^{-1} \frac{2x}{(3+\sqrt{5})} - \tan^{-1} \frac{2x}{(3-\sqrt{5})}.$$

In this expression,

$$x = \frac{\omega}{\omega_{RC}} = RC\omega.$$

Near resonance, with $\delta \ll 1$,

$$\Phi \xrightarrow[\substack{\omega \sim \omega_{RC} \\ \delta \ll 1}]{} \tan^{-1}\frac{2(x-1)}{3\delta} - \tan^{-1}\frac{2x}{(3+\sqrt{5})} + 0.38.$$

The phase changes rapidly through π radians as ω moves through the null point or as x passes the value 1.

The Double Null Bridge

To illustrate the use of the general transfer function, a bridge with a double null can be developed. This can actually be done in a number of ways. Our method will use a resistive voltage divider $Z'Y' = R_1 G_2$ and an arm with a ZY product:

$$Z(x)Y(x) = \frac{(x+1)^4}{2x(x^2+1)}.$$

In this expression, $ZY = M(x)/N(x)$, with $M = (x+1)^4$ and $N(x) = 2x(x^2+1)$.

The difference term, $R_1 G_2 - ZY$, upon cross multiplication will behave as $\{x^4 + 6x^2 + 1\}$, if $R_1 G_2 = 2$. This particular function has four roots on the imaginary axis.

The particular form of ZY can be created by employing the circuit in Fig. 154. In this example,

$$Z(x)Y(x) = \frac{(x+1)^4}{2x(x^2+1)},$$

if

$$x = \sqrt{LCs} = \frac{s}{\omega_0}$$

and

$$\omega_0 = \frac{1}{\sqrt{LC}} = \frac{2}{GL}.$$

The complete bridge is illustrated in Fig. 155.

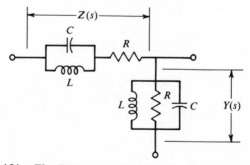

FIG. 154.   The ZY combination for the double-null bridge.

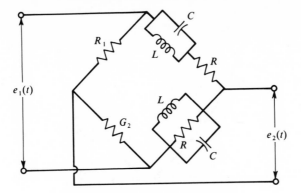

FIG. 155.   The double-null bridge.

The numerator of $H_V(s)$ is then

$$-P + P' = Z'Y' - ZY = R_1 G_2 - \frac{(x+1)^4}{2x(x^2+1)}.$$

The balance condition is achieved by setting $R_1 G_2 = 2$. Under these conditions, the overall voltage transfer is

$$H_V(x) \xrightarrow[\substack{R_1 G_2 = 2 \\ Y_L = 0}]{} \frac{[x^2 + 5.84][x^2 + 0.16]}{3(x + 0.20)(x + 5.04)(x^2 + 0.76x + 1)}.$$

This function has four zeros on the imaginary axis at $\pm(2.42\omega_0)i$ and $\pm i(0.40\omega_0)$. There are four poles, two on the real axis and two complex poles. The magnitude of the voltage transfer has the following point values (see Fig. 156):

$$|H_V(0)| = \tfrac{1}{3},$$
$$|H_V(0.4\omega_0 i)| = 0,$$
$$|H_V(i\omega_0)| = \tfrac{1}{3},$$
$$|H_V(2.42\omega_0 i)| = 0,$$
$$|H_V(i\infty)| = \tfrac{1}{3}.$$

See Fig. 157a and b.

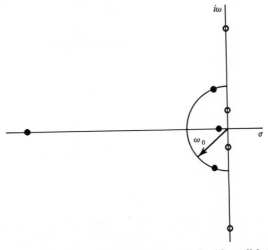

FIG. 156.   The pole-zero diagram for the double-null bridge.

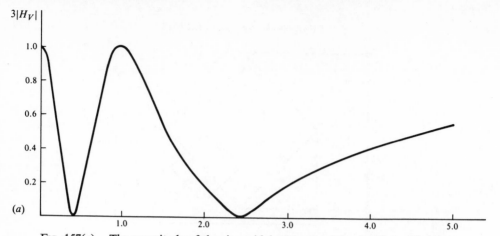

FIG. 157(a). The magnitude of the sinusoidal response of the double-null bridge.

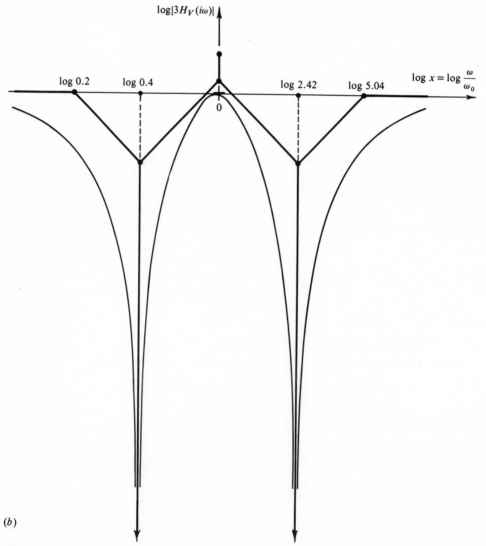

FIG. 157(b). The logarithm of the magnitude of the sinusoidal response of the double-null bridge.

Phase Bridges, The Bridged T and Twin T Networks

The preceding section illustrated a null circuit that operates on a potential-difference principle. Another type of null circuit can be constructed by splitting the signal, phase-shifting the two components, and recombining at the output. The concept of these bridges is not quite so simple as before, since the two sections tend to load one another. The possible forms, however, are easy to anticipate. For instance, the splitting of the signal can be achieved by a parallel-parallel connection (Y addition) of two four-terminal networks. As we shall see, these must provide a positive phase shift and a negative phase shift that add to a total of π radians when the split signals are recombined.

The first network that we shall consider is the bridged T shown in Fig. 158. The diagram indicates the two sections: An RC T-network which as a high-pass device gives a net positive-phase shift; the Lr series combination when loaded by the RC network gives an overall negative-phase shift to the signal. See Fig. 158a.

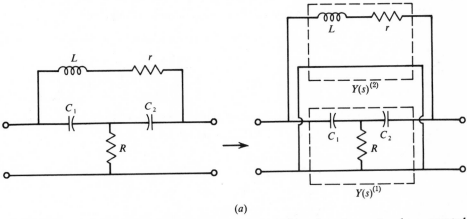

(a)

FIG. 158(a).   The bridged-T bridge with the decomposition into two networks connected in a parallel-parallel combination. Notice that $Y^{(1)}$ is a high-pass, while $Y^{(2)}$ is a low-pass device.

The admittance matrix for the RC network is

$$\mathbb{Y}^{(1)}(s) = \frac{x_1 x_2}{R(1 + x_1 + x_2)} \begin{pmatrix} \dfrac{(1 + x_2)}{x_2} & -1 \\ -1 & \dfrac{(1 + x_1)}{x_1} \end{pmatrix},$$

where

$$x_1 = RC_1 s$$

and

$$x_2 = RC_2 s.$$

The matrix for the Lr bridge is

$$\mathbb{Y}^{(2)}(s) = \frac{1}{r(1 + x_L)} \begin{pmatrix} 1 & -1 \\ -1 & 1 \end{pmatrix},$$

where

$$x_L = \frac{L}{r} s.$$

One can observe the phase-shifting properties by regarding the individual voltage transfers

$$H_V = -\frac{Y_{21}}{(Y_{22} + Y_{\text{load}})}.$$

The total $\mathbb{Y}(s)$ matrix for these two networks, connected as shown, is

$$\mathbb{Y}(s) = \mathbb{Y}^{(1)}(s) + \mathbb{Y}^{(2)}(s)$$

$$\mathbb{Y}(s) = \frac{1}{Rr(1 + x_1 + x_2)(1 + x_L)} \begin{pmatrix} \left\{ \begin{matrix} x_1(1 + x_2)r(1 + x_L) \\ + R(1 + x_1 + x_2) \end{matrix} \right\} & \left\{ \begin{matrix} -rx_1x_2(1 + x_L) \\ -R(1 + x_1 + x_2) \end{matrix} \right\} \\ \left\{ \begin{matrix} -rx_1x_2(1 + x_L) \\ -R(1 + x_1 + x_2) \end{matrix} \right\} & \left\{ \begin{matrix} x_2(1 + x_1)r(1 + x_L) \\ + R(1 + x_1 + x_2) \end{matrix} \right\} \end{pmatrix}.$$

The voltage transfer of the total network to an infinite load impedance is

$$H_v(s) \xrightarrow[Y_{\text{load}}=0]{} -\frac{Y_{21}}{Y_{22}} = \frac{s^3 + \dfrac{r}{L} s^2 + \dfrac{(C_1 + C_2)}{C_1 C_2 L} s + \dfrac{1}{RC_1 C_2 L}}{\left\{ s^3 + \left(\dfrac{r}{L} + RC_1 \right) s^2 + \left(\dfrac{rC_1 + R(C_1 + {}_2C)}{RC_1 C_1 L} \right) s + \dfrac{1}{RC_1 C_2 L} \right\}}.$$

This function will have two zeros on the imaginary axis if the numerator behaves as the product $(s^2 + \omega_0^2)(s + \omega_0/Q_0)$. Such roots are obtained if

$$\omega_0^2 = \frac{(C_1 + C_2)}{C_1 C_2 L},$$

$$\frac{\omega_0}{Q_0} = \frac{1}{R(C_1 + C_2)} = \frac{r}{L},$$

and

$$Q_0 = \sqrt{\frac{(C_1 + C_2)^2 R}{C_1 C_2 r}} \xrightarrow[C_1 = C_2]{} 2\sqrt{\frac{R}{r}}.$$

then, in this notation,

$$H_V(s) \xrightarrow[Y_{\text{load}}=0]{} \frac{\left\{ s^3 + \dfrac{\omega_0}{Q_0} s^2 + \omega_0^2 s + \dfrac{\omega_0^3}{Q_0} \right\}}{\left\{ s^3 + 3\dfrac{\omega_0}{Q_0} s^2 + \left(1 + \dfrac{2}{Q_0^2} \right) \omega_0^2 s + \dfrac{\omega_0^3}{Q_0} \right\}} = \frac{(s^2 + \omega_0^2)}{\left[s^2 + 2\dfrac{\omega_0}{Q_0} s + \omega_0^2 \right]}.$$

The voltage transfer to an infinite load has two zeros at $\pm i\omega_0$, one zero at $(-\omega_0/Q_0)$, two complex poles on a circle of radians ω_0, and one real pole inside this circle. The denominator factors such that the real zero and real pole are superimposed. Thus, in the final form.

$$H_V(s) \xrightarrow[Y_{\text{load}}=0]{} \frac{(s + i\omega_0)(s - i\omega_0)}{\left[s^2 + 2\dfrac{\omega_0}{Q_0} s + \omega_0^2 \right]}.$$

See Fig. 158b.

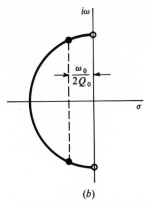

(b)

FIG. 158(b). The pole-zero diagram for the bridged *T*.

Q_0 can be made quite large by making one capacitor small. This causes L to be large, however, when ω_0 is fixed. The frequency response $H_V(i\omega)$ is the familiar form found in most texts and is shown in Figs. 156 and 157:

$$H_V(i\omega) = \frac{1}{\left[1 - \dfrac{2i\omega_0\omega}{Q_0(\omega^2 - \omega_0^2)}\right]}.$$

In many applications the requirements on L in the bridged T network are excessive. It is reasonable to expect that we can construct two T networks in a parallel configuration; one that advances the signal by $\pi/2$, and another that retards the signal by an amount $\pi/2$. A high-pass RC T-network and a low-pass $C'r$, T-network will serve this purpose. Such a connection is known as a *twin T-bridge*. The twin T is shown in Fig. 158c.

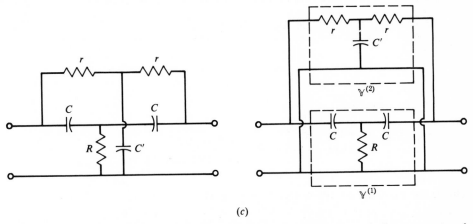

(c)

FIG. 158(c). The twin-T bridge with its representation as a high-pass and a low-pass network in a parallel-parallel connection.

The $\mathbb{Y}$ matrix for the unprimed network is

$$\mathbb{Y}^{(1)}(s) = \frac{x}{R(1 + 2x)}\begin{pmatrix} (1 + x) & -x \\ -x & (1 + x) \end{pmatrix},$$

where

$$x = RCs.$$

This network is a high-pass device and contributes a positive-phase shift to a sinusoid.

The $\mathbb{Y}$ matrix for the primed network is characteristic of a low-pass device, contributing a negative-phase shift to a sinusoidal excitation.

$$\mathbb{Y}^{(2)}(s) = \frac{1}{r(2 + x')}\begin{pmatrix} (1 + x') & -1 \\ -1 & (1 + x') \end{pmatrix},$$

where

$$x' = rC's.$$

The total $\mathbb{Y}$ matrix is the sum of the two, giving

$$\mathbb{Y} = \mathbb{Y}^{(1)} + \mathbb{Y}^{(2)} = \frac{1}{rR(1 + 2x)(2 + x')}$$

$$\times \begin{pmatrix} \left\{ \begin{matrix} r(2 + x')x(1 + x) \\ + R(1 + 2x)(1 + x') \end{matrix} \right\} & \left\{ \begin{matrix} -r(2 + x')x^2 \\ -R(1 + 2x) \end{matrix} \right\} \\ \left\{ \begin{matrix} -r(2 + x')x^2 \\ -R(1 + 2x) \end{matrix} \right\} & \left\{ \begin{matrix} r(2 + x')x(1 + x) \\ + R(1 + 2x)(1 + x') \end{matrix} \right\} \end{pmatrix}.$$

The voltage transfer to an infinite load is

$$H_V(s) \xrightarrow[Y_L = 0]{} \frac{rx^2(2 + x') + R(1 + 2x)}{rx(1 + x)(2 + x') + R(1 + 2x)(1 + x')}$$

This transfer will have two zeros on the imaginary axis if we set

$$\tfrac{1}{2}(2 + x') = (1 + 2x)$$

or

$$\frac{1}{2RC} = \frac{2}{rC'}.$$

Then

$$H_V(s) \xrightarrow[\substack{Y_L = 0 \\ 2x = \frac{1}{2}x'}]{} \frac{(x^2 + (R/2r))}{\{x^2 + (1 + (2R/r))x + (R/2r)\}}.$$

Under these conditions, the bridge nulls at $\pm i(1/C\sqrt{2rR}) = \pm i\omega_0$. The twin T-figure of merit is a quantity k, where

$$k = \frac{r}{2R} = \frac{2C}{C'},$$

with

$$\omega_0^2 = \frac{1}{2rRC^2} = \frac{2}{r^2CC'}.$$

In this notation,

$$H_V(s) \xrightarrow[\substack{Y_L=0 \\ 4x=x'}]{} \frac{(s^2 + \omega_0^2)}{\left\{s^2 + 2\dfrac{(1+k)}{\sqrt{k}}\omega_0 s + \omega_0^2\right\}},$$

(see Fig. 158d) or in the standard form along the imaginary axis,

$$H_V(i\omega) \xrightarrow[\substack{Y_L=0 \\ 4x=x'}]{} \frac{1}{\left\{1 - 2i\dfrac{(1+k)}{\sqrt{k}}\dfrac{\omega_0\omega}{(\omega^2 - \omega_0^2)}\right\}}$$

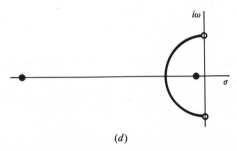

(d)

FIG. 158(d). The pole-zero diagram for the twin-T bridge with $k = 4$.

Although the denominators of the transfer function of the twin T and bridged T networks have the same form, the bridged T can have far better selectivity than the twin T. The poles of the twin T network always lie on the real axis. In the high k and low k limits, these poles are approximately at

$$-\frac{2(1+k)}{\sqrt{k}}\omega_0 \quad \text{and} \quad -\frac{1}{2}\frac{\sqrt{k}}{(1+k)}\omega_0$$

The bridged T can be made to have a larger Q_0 value, giving complex poles. These enhance the sharpness of the null.

From the type of analysis presented, we would guess that the twin T (as well as the bridged T) has a dual. Strict duality is achieved if we form a set of LR π-networks connected in a series-series or Z connection. The twin π-bridge is shown in Fig. 158e.

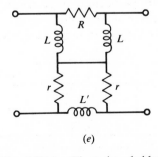

(e)

FIG. 158(e). The twin-π bridge.

The individual $\mathbb{Z}$ matrices are

$$\mathbb{Z}^{(1)} = \frac{Rx}{(1 + 2x)}\begin{pmatrix} (1 + x) & x \\ x & (1 + x) \end{pmatrix}$$

and

$$\mathbb{Z}^{(2)} = \frac{r}{(2 + x')}\begin{pmatrix} (1 + x') & 1 \\ 1 & (1 + x') \end{pmatrix},$$

where

$$x = \frac{Ls}{R},$$

and

$$x' = \frac{L's}{r}.$$

The analogy is apparent in that we add $\mathbb{Z}^{(1)}$ and $\mathbb{Z}^{(2)}$. Then the current transfer has the same form as that for the twin T-network.

Before closing this section we should also note that an LR combination can be constructed as a twin T and that an RC combination can also be employed in a twin π-network.

The twin T, as we have derived its characteristics, in some sense acts as an interferometer. One should be able to achieve a higher degree of selectivity (or resolution in optical language) by constructing sections that provide higher-order phase shifts. This is accomplished with three or more sections in each Y branch.

THE IDEAL TRANSFORMER

The transformer is formed by constructing two sets of current coils that possess a mutual coupling. Ordinarily, this is done by winding a primary set of turns N_1 and a secondary set of turns N_2 on the same magnetic core. To idealize the problem, we assume that core eddy currents and hysteresis losses can be neglected. These quantities produce heat losses and could be approximated to some extent by associating an effective resistance with the inductances.

If the core is ferromagnetic, we shall at first assume that the field versus current relations are linear. This is to say that we assume the relative permeability of the core to be linear.

The preceding remarks are particularly important when power transformers are involved. Many circuits, however, employ nonmagnetic transformers for which the coupling occurs through air (or a vacuum); in these cases our idealization is good.

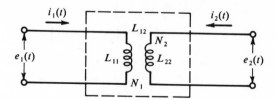

FIG. 159.   The transformer as a four-terminal network.

The emf are given in terms of the time rates of change of the currents by the fourth Maxwell equation. The emf and the current changes are related to one another by geometrical factors called the *inductance* (both self and mutual). Thus, we can write the voltage drop e_j across a set of terminals as the negative of the emf developed. If the number of turns on the primary is N_1 and the number of secondary turns is N_2 (ϕ_j is the flux linking the jth coil):

$$e_1(t) = N_1 \frac{d\phi_1}{dt} = \frac{N_1^2}{\mathcal{R}_{11}} \frac{di_1}{dt} + \frac{N_1 N_2}{\mathcal{R}_{12}} \frac{di_2}{dt},$$

$$e_1(t) = L_{11} \frac{di_1}{dt} + L_{12} \frac{di_2}{dt};$$

and†

$$e_2(t) = N_2 \frac{d\phi_2}{dt} = \frac{N_2 N_2}{\mathcal{R}_{21}} \frac{di_1}{dt} + \frac{N_2^2}{\mathcal{R}_{22}} \frac{di_2}{dt},$$

$$e_2(t) = L_{21} \frac{di_1}{dt} + L_{22} \frac{di_2}{dt}.$$

This is a general case in which $\mathcal{R}_{jk}$ is the reluctance of the jk coupling. $\mathcal{R}_{jk}$ is related to the geometry of the coils and the magnetic permeability of the medium supporting the magnetic fields. Under any circumstance, the off-diagonal, mutual-inductance elements are related to the product of the self-inductance terms through a constant called the *coupling constant* k. This occurs because $\mathcal{R}_{12} = \mathcal{R}_{21}$ and

$$L_{21} = L_{12},$$

with††

$$\frac{L_{12} L_{21}}{L_{11} L_{22}} = \frac{L_{21}^2}{L_{11} L_{12}} = k^2 = \frac{\mathcal{R}_{11} \mathcal{R}_{22}}{\mathcal{R}_{12}^2}.$$

When magnetic cores are used, as is done in the case of power transformers and pulse transformers, the magnetic fields are confined essentially to the core volume. When this is the case, the geometry of $\mathcal{R}_{11}$ and $\mathcal{R}_{22}$ become the same, and

$$\frac{L_{11}}{L_{22}} = \frac{N_1^2 \mathcal{R}_{22}}{N_2^2 \mathcal{R}_{11}} \sim \frac{N_1^2}{N_2^2}, \qquad \text{(magnetic core)}.$$

In all instances

$$|\mathbb{L}| = L_{11} L_{22} - L_{12} L_{21} = L_{11} L_{22}(1 - k^2).$$

The equations relating the terminal voltages and currents of the four-terminal transformer are best represented as a matrix. In the $\mathcal{L}T$ representation, the $\mathbb{Z}$ matrix is

$$\mathbb{Z} \cdot \mathbf{I} = \begin{pmatrix} L_{11}s & L_{12}s \\ L_{21}s & L_{22}s \end{pmatrix} \begin{bmatrix} I_1 \\ I_2 \end{bmatrix} = \begin{bmatrix} E_1 \\ E_2 \end{bmatrix} + \begin{bmatrix} L_{11}i_1(0+) + L_{12}i_2(0+) \\ L_{21}i_1(0+) + L_{22}i_2(0+) \end{bmatrix}.$$

---

† The L_{12} and L_{21} here are to be contrasted with the L_{jk} in the representation of Maxwell loop currents. In practice, because the primary and secondary are isolated, the L_{12} and L_{21} can be used in the same fashion except that they then refer to mutual inductance.

†† The parameter k can take either a positive or negative sign, depending upon the helicity of the winding of N_2 relative to N_1.

When the transformer is terminated in a pure resistance R_L, the transfers and impedances take on the following forms:

$$Z_{in}(s) = \frac{|\mathbb{L}|}{L_{22}} \frac{s}{[s + (R_L/L_{22})]} \cdot \left(s + \frac{L_{11}R_L}{|\mathbb{L}|}\right) = \frac{(1-k^2)L_{11}s(s + a'_{L2})}{(s + a_{L2})},$$

$$Z_{out}(s) = \frac{|\mathbb{L}|}{L_{11}} \frac{s}{[s + (R_G/L_{11})]} \left(s + \frac{L_{22}R_G}{|\mathbb{L}|}\right) = \frac{(1-k^2)L_{22}s(s + a'_{G1})}{(s + a_{G2})},$$

and

$$H_V(s) = \frac{L_{21}R_L}{|\mathbb{L}|[s + (L_{11}R_L/|\mathbb{L}|)]} = \frac{kR_L}{(1-k^2)\sqrt{L_{11}L_{22}}(s + a'_{L2})},$$

$$H_I(s) = \frac{L_{21}s}{L_{22}[s + (R_L/L_{22})]} = k\sqrt{\frac{L_{11}}{L_{22}}} \frac{s}{(s + a_{L2})}.$$

The characteristic frequencies are

$$a_{L2} = \frac{R_L}{L_{22}}; \qquad\qquad a_{G1} = \frac{R_G}{L_{11}}.$$

$$a'_{L2} = \frac{L_{11}R_L}{|\mathbb{L}|} = \frac{a_{L2}}{(1-k^2)}; \qquad a'_{G1} = \frac{L_{22}R_G}{|\mathbb{L}|} = \frac{a_{G2}}{(1-k^2)}.$$

The frequency-dependent forms of the input impedance $Z_{in}(s)$ have two equivalent circuits. We mention both because both are encountered in the literature. See Fig. 160.

$$L_a = L_{11}, \qquad\qquad L_\alpha = \frac{|\mathbb{L}|}{L_{22}} = L_{11}(1-k^2);$$

$$L_b = \frac{L_{11}|\mathbb{L}|}{L_{12}L_{21}} = \frac{(1-k^2)}{k^2}L_{11}, \qquad L_\beta = \frac{L_{21}L_{12}}{L_{22}} = k^2L_{11};$$

$$R_b = \frac{L_{11}^2 R_L}{L_{12}L_{21}} = \frac{L_{11}R_L}{k^2 L_{22}}, \qquad\qquad R_\beta = \frac{L_{12}L_{21}}{L_{22}^2}R_L = k^2\frac{L_{11}}{L_{22}}R_L.$$

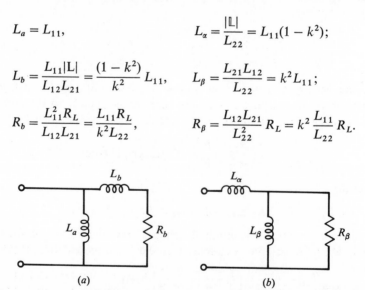

(a)   (b)

FIG. 160.   (a) A type I equivalent for the primary of a transformer. (b) The type II equivalent for the primary of a transformer.

The customary conditions for a transformer apply when the frequency components lie between the extremes a_{L2} and a'_{L2}, and when the coupling is close to 1.

The approximations given below hold for $a_{L2} \ll \omega \ll a'_{L2}$, and $k \sim 1$:

$$Z_{in} \to \left(\frac{N_1}{N_2}\right)^2 R_L,$$

$$Z_{out} \to \left(\frac{N_2}{N_1}\right)^2 R_G,$$

$$H_V \to +\frac{N_2}{N_1},$$

and

$$H_I \to +\frac{N_1}{N_2}.$$

Before proceeding, we should mention the effects of capacitance between turns in the primary and the secondary. Surprisingly, this capacitance affects both low-frequency and high-frequency responses. The first approximation that one might make would be to consider only nearest-neighbor interactions, which effectively produce single-shunt capacitances between each pair of turns. If the capacitance between pairs of turns is C_{pair}, the net effect on the transformer is a total shunt capacity across the input of $C_1 = C_{pair}/N_1$ and across the output of $C_2 = C_{pair}/N_2$. See Fig. 161.

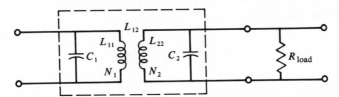

FIG. 161.   The transformer with distributed capacity between turns, shown as lumped capacitance at the input and output.

The cascade matrix for the transformer and its distributed capacity is

$$\mathbb{A} = \begin{pmatrix} 1 & 0 \\ C_1 s & 1 \end{pmatrix} \begin{pmatrix} \dfrac{L_{11}}{L_{21}} & \dfrac{|\mathbb{L}|s}{L_{21}} \\ \dfrac{1}{L_{21}s} & \dfrac{L_{22}}{L_{21}} \end{pmatrix} \begin{pmatrix} 1 & 0 \\ C_2 s & 1 \end{pmatrix},$$

and

$$\mathbb{A} = \begin{pmatrix} \dfrac{L_{11}}{L_{21}\omega_{22}^2}(s^2 + \omega_{22}^2) & \dfrac{|\mathbb{L}|s}{L_{21}} \\ \dfrac{|\mathbb{L}|C_1C_2}{L_{21}S}[s^4 + (\omega_{11}'^2 + \omega_{22}'^2)s^2 + \omega_{11}'^2\omega_{22}^2] & \dfrac{L_{22}}{L_{21}\omega_{11}^2}(s^2 + \omega_{11}^2) \end{pmatrix}.$$

In the preceding matrix,

$$\omega_{11}^2 = \frac{1}{(1-k^2)L_{11}C_1} = \frac{L_{22}}{|\mathbb{L}|C_1}; \qquad \omega_{11}'^2 = \frac{1}{L_{11}C_1} = (1-k^2)\omega_{11}^2;$$

$$\omega_{22}^2 = \frac{1}{(1-k^2)L_{22}C_2} = \frac{L_{11}}{|\mathbb{L}|C_2}; \qquad \omega_{22}'^2 = \frac{1}{L_{22}C_2} = (1-k^2)\omega_{22}^2.$$

In the case of an ideal transformer for which $k \sim 1$ (power transformers and pulse transformers):

$$A \xrightarrow[k \sim 1]{} \begin{pmatrix} \dfrac{L_{11}}{L_{21}} & 0 \\[2ex] \dfrac{(s^2 + \omega_0^2)}{L_{21} s \omega_0^2} & \dfrac{L_{22}}{L_{21}} \end{pmatrix},$$

where

$$\omega_0^2 = \left(\frac{1}{L_{11}C_1 + L_{22}C_2} \right).$$

The input impedance and power transfer illustrate vividly the effect of the distributed capacity in producing high- and low-frequency cutoffs. We terminate the transformer in G_L. The ideal case will be used because of the relative simplicity of the expressions.

$$Z_{in}(s) \xrightarrow[k \sim 1]{} \frac{L_{11}\omega_0^2 s}{[s^2 + G_L L_{22}\omega_0^2 s + \omega_0^2]}.$$

If the impedance is to be flat and resistive over a wide range of frequencies, this function must be highly overdamped. In other words,

$$4 \left\{ \frac{C_1 L_{11}}{L_{22}^2} + \frac{C_2}{L_{22}} \right\} \ll G_L^2.$$

Then the roots of Z_{in} are at

$$-\left(\frac{L_{22}G_L}{L_{11}C_1 + L_{22}C_2} \right) \quad \text{and} \quad -\left(\frac{R_L}{L_{22}} \right).$$

See Fig. 162.

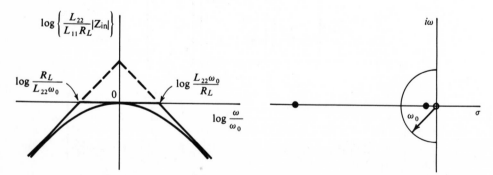

FIG. 162.   The logarithm of the response to a sinusoid and the overdamped resonant pole-zero diagram for a transformer with distributed capacity between the turns.

Thus, keeping $R_L \ll \frac{1}{4}(\omega_0 L_{22})$ maintains a flat midband region and a large bandwidth. This, of course, is equivalent to a statement that C_1 and C_2 should be kept small.

Others transfers are readily calculated. One example calculation, which is quite important in power transformers, is that of the power-transfer function as a function of frequency:

$$H_P(s) = H_V(s)H_I(s) = \frac{L_{22}}{L_{11}} G_L Z_{\text{in}}(s).$$

The loss in power at the half-power points (the poles in this case) occurs because of the relative change in phase between voltage and current. The capacitive distortion has been included to first approximation as a pure shunt capacitance; thus, the voltage-transfer function is relatively flat over a frequency range much wider than that for $Z_{\text{in}}(s)$.

Therefore, for pure voltage transfers, this effect of distributed capacity is not a serious problem.

THE DOUBLE-TUNED CIRCUIT

There are several versions of the double-tuned circuit. Each consists, however, of a primary LRC circuit coupled inductively to a secondary LRC circuit. The differences between the various arrangements of this general circuit lie in the method by which the signal is coupled into the primary and by the element across which the output voltage is measured. All versions have the same set of poles in the complex plane. The various methods of extracting the voltage change the structure of the zeros of the voltage-transfer function.

We consider first the circuit shown in Fig. 163. This can be represented as a cascade of the three four-terminal sections shown in Fig. 164.

We can write the overall $\mathbb{A}$ matrix as

$$\mathbb{A}(s) = \mathbb{A}_1 \cdot \mathbb{A}_L \cdot \mathbb{A}_2 = \begin{pmatrix} 1 & \dfrac{1 + R_1 C_1 s}{C_1 s} \\ 0 & 1 \end{pmatrix} \begin{pmatrix} \dfrac{L_{11}}{L_{21}} & \dfrac{|\mathbb{L}|s}{L_{21}} \\ \dfrac{1}{L_{21}s} & \dfrac{L_{22}}{L_{21}} \end{pmatrix} \begin{pmatrix} \dfrac{1 + R_2 C_2 s}{R_2 C_2 s} & \dfrac{1}{C_2 s} \\ \dfrac{1}{R_2} & 1 \end{pmatrix}.$$

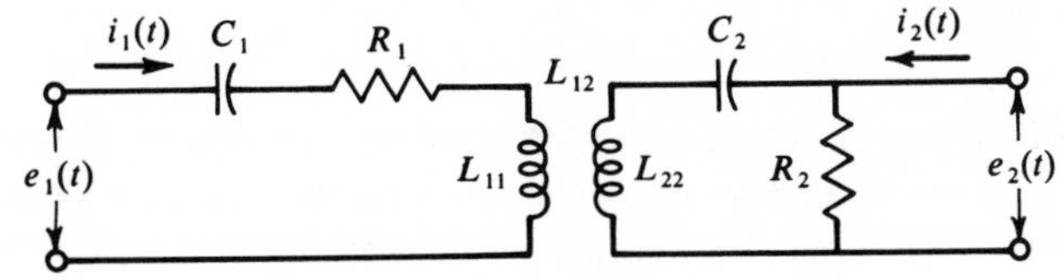

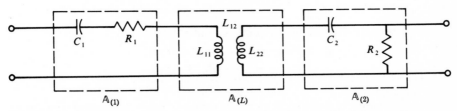

FIG. 163.   A double-tuned circuit.

FIG. 164.   The double-tuned circuit represented as the cascade of three units.

Finally,

$$A(s) = \frac{|\mathbb{L}|}{R_2 L_{21} s^3} \times$$

$$\begin{pmatrix} [s^4 + As^3 + Bs^2 + Cs + D] & R_2[s^4 + 2v^2 a_1 s^3 + v^2(\omega_1^2 + \omega_2^2)s^2 + 2v^2 a_1 \omega_2^2 s + D] \\ \dfrac{L_{22}s}{|\mathbb{L}|}[s^2 - 2a_2 s + \omega_2^2] & \dfrac{L_{22}R_2 s}{|\mathbb{L}|}[s^2 + \omega_2^2] \end{pmatrix},$$

where

$$2a_j = \frac{R_j}{L_{jj}} = \text{the damping in the primary or secondary circuit}$$

$$\omega_j^2 = \frac{1}{C_j L_{jj}} = \text{characteristic frequency of the } j\text{th circuit}$$

$$v^2 = \frac{1}{(1 - k^2)}, \text{ where } |\mathbb{L}| = L_{11}L_{22}(1 - k^2)$$

Then, with

$$A = v^2(2a_1 + 2a_2),$$

$$B = v^2(\omega_1^2 + \omega_2^2 + 4a_1 a_2),$$

$$C = v^2(2a_1\omega_2^2 + 2a_2\omega_1^2),$$

$$D = v^2\omega_1^2\omega_2^2,$$

the open-circuit voltage transfer function for this circuit is

$$H_V(s) \xrightarrow[Z_L \to \infty]{} \frac{kR_2 s^3}{\sqrt{L_{11}L_{22}}\left(s^4 + \dfrac{A}{v^2}s^3 + \dfrac{B}{v^2}s^2 + \dfrac{C}{v^2}s + \dfrac{D}{v} - k^2 s^4\right)}.$$

This can be factored initially to give

$$H_V(s) \xrightarrow[Z_L \to \infty]{} \frac{kR_2 s^3}{\sqrt{L_{11}L_{22}}\{(s^2 + 2a_1 s + \omega_1^2)(s^2 + 2a_2 s + \omega_2^2) - k^2 s^4\}}.$$

When the coupling is weak, $k \ll 1$, this expression can be approximated quite easily. To see this, consider the special case when the resonant frequencies of the primary and secondary circuit are the same and when the damping is the same. Then,

$$H_V(s) \xrightarrow[Z_L \to \infty]{} \frac{kR_2 s^3}{\sqrt{L_{11}L_{22}}([1 - |k|]s^2 + 2as + \omega_0^2)([1 + |k|]s^2 + 2as + \omega_0^2)}.$$

Finally, we obtain the approximate roots for this expression as†

$$\gamma_1 = \frac{a}{(1 + |k|)} - iW_0(1 - |k|)$$

---

† The magnitude of k is used because k can be positive or negative, depending upon this circulation of the secondary winding relative to the primary. This changes the sign of H_V.

and

$$\gamma_2 = \frac{a}{(1 - |k|)} - iW_0(1 + |k|),$$

where

$$W_0 = \sqrt{\omega_0^2 - a^2},$$

Then

$$H_V(s) \longrightarrow \frac{kR_2s^3}{(1 - k^2)\sqrt{L_{11}L_{22}}(s + \gamma_1)(s + \gamma_1^*)(s + \gamma_2)(s + \gamma_2^*)}.$$

These results can be written in terms of the midband frequency ω_0 and Q values of the resonant circuits, where

$$Q_0 = \frac{\omega_0}{2a}.$$

Then, for high Q_0 circuits,

$$\gamma_j \simeq \omega_0\left\{\frac{1}{2(1 \pm |k|)Q_0} - i\left(1 \mp \frac{|k|}{2}\right)\right\};$$

or more accurately,

$$\gamma_j = \frac{\omega_0}{(1 \pm |k|)}\left\{\frac{1}{2Q_0} - i\sqrt{(1 \pm |k|) - \frac{1}{4Q_0^2}}\right\}.$$

The effect of the coupling is quite apparent in this special case. Starting with two equal resonance functions, $\{2as/(s^2 + 2as + \omega_0^2)\}$, the coupling introduces a splitting of the poles. The final split pair are separated by $2|k|a$ along the real axis and approximately $|k|\omega_0$ along the imaginary axis. See Fig. 165.

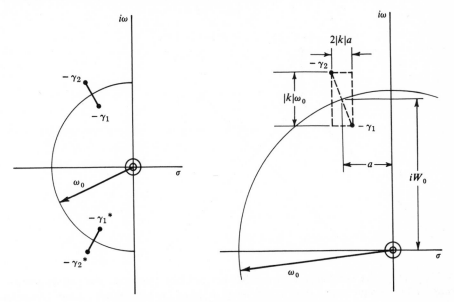

FIG. 165. Pole-zero diagrams of the double-tuned circuit, with both sections initially tuned to the same frequency. The splitting is shown.

The voltage-transfer function can be writtten as a function of s times two new resonant functions. Define

$$\mathscr{R}_1(s) = \dfrac{\dfrac{2as}{(1 + |k|)}}{\left[s^2 + \dfrac{2a}{(1 + |k|)}s + \dfrac{\omega_2^0}{(1 + |k|)} \right]}$$

and

$$\mathscr{R}_2(s) = \dfrac{\dfrac{2as}{(1 - |k|)}}{\left[s^2 + \dfrac{2a}{(1 - |k|)} s + \dfrac{\omega_0^2}{(1 - |k|)} \right]}.$$

Then

$$H_V \xrightarrow[Z_L \to \infty]{} \left(\dfrac{k\sqrt{L_{11}L_{22}}s}{(1 - k^2)R_1} \right) \mathscr{R}_1(s) \cdot \mathscr{R}_2(s).$$

The sinusoidal response is then quite simple. It is the sum of two high-Q resonance functions in the log plot modulated by the high-pass multiplier $(kQ_0/a\omega_0)s$. The Q values of the two functions are slightly different because of the shift of the damping

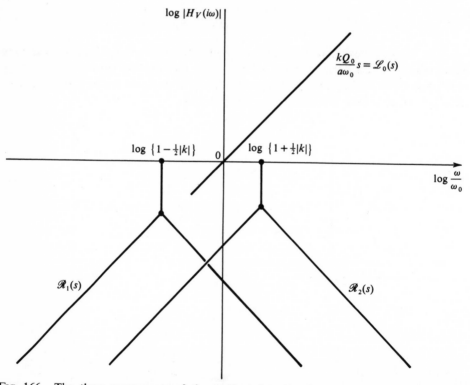

FIG. 166. The three components of the product function that make the voltage-transfer function of the double-tuned circuit. The magnitude of the asymptotes of the sinusoidal response is shown for the three components. $H(s) = \mathscr{L}_0(s)\mathscr{R}_1(s)\mathscr{R}_2(s)$. These are to be added (in logarithmic form) to produce the final response.

terms and the midband frequencies:

$$Q_1 \simeq Q_0(1 + \tfrac{1}{2}|k|)$$

and

$$Q_2 \simeq Q_0(1 - \tfrac{1}{2}|k|).$$

See Fig. 166. Summing the two, we obtain the diagram in Fig. 167.

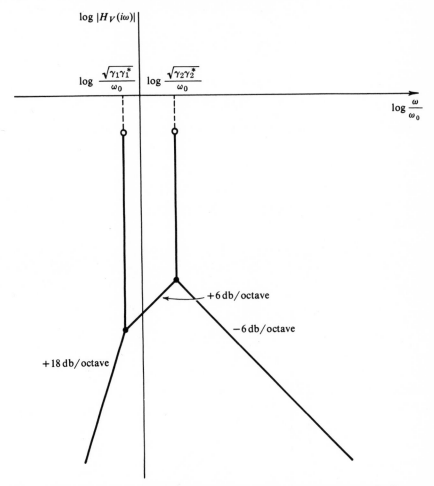

FIG. 167.   The resultant sum of the logarithms of the three separate asymptotic diagrams for the voltage-transfer function of the double-tuned circuit. This is a diagram for $Q_0 = 10$ and $k = \tfrac{1}{2}$.

The peaks of the two maxima occur at

$$|H_V(i\sqrt{\gamma_j\gamma_j^*})| = \frac{|k|Q_0}{[1 \mp |k| + 4k^2Q_0]^{\frac{1}{2}}} \xrightarrow[|k| \ll 1]{} \frac{|k|Q_0}{[1 + 4k^2Q_0^2]^{\frac{1}{2}}}\left(1 \pm \frac{|k|}{2[1 + 4k^2Q_0^2]^{\frac{1}{2}}}\right).$$

The maxima have essentially the same value. To illustrate the calculation, we take a special case in which $Q_0 = 10$, $k = 1/2$. This is somewhat unrealistic, since k is large and the exact expressions for all quantities must be used. On the other hand, it illustrates how well the asymptotic representation holds in the log plot (i.e., sinusoidal response).

Then, with $Q_0 = 10$ and $k = 1/2$,

$$\gamma_1 = \omega_0(\tfrac{1}{10} - i\sqrt{2}),$$

$$\gamma_2 = \omega_0(\tfrac{1}{30} - i\sqrt{\tfrac{2}{3}}),$$

$$\gamma_1\gamma_1^* = 2\omega_0^2, \qquad (\gamma_1 + \gamma_1^*) = 2a_1 = \frac{\omega_0}{5},$$

$$\gamma_2\gamma_2^* = \frac{2}{3}\omega_0^2, \qquad (\gamma_2 + \gamma_2^*) = 2a_2 = \frac{\omega_0}{15},$$

$$Q_1 = 5\sqrt{2},$$

$$Q_2 = 15\sqrt{\tfrac{2}{3}}.$$

Figure 168 shows the net asymptotic plot and the function $\log |H_V|$.

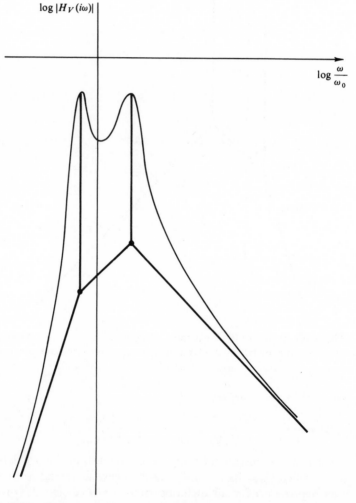

FIG. 168.   Relation between the true sinusoidal-response function and the asymptotic construction in the case of the double-tuned circuit.

There are several variations of this circuit. As we have performed the calculation. the voltage response was taken across the resistance in the secondary circuit. Thus, the secondary loop current is given by the $H_V(s)$ just calculated. In many applications, the output voltage is taken across C_2. This response can be obtained by dividing the previous H_V by $R_2 C_2 s$, giving

$$H_V^{(C_2)} \xrightarrow[Z_L \to \infty]{} \frac{ks^2}{(1 - k^2)C_2\sqrt{L_{11}L_{22}}(s + \gamma_1)(s + \gamma_1^*)(s + \gamma_2)(s + \gamma_2^*)},$$

or in terms of the resonance functions $\mathscr{R}_1(s)$ and $\mathscr{R}_2(s)$,

$$H_V^{(C_2)} \xrightarrow[Z_L \to \infty]{} \left\{ \frac{k\sqrt{L_{11}L_{22}}}{R_1 R_2 C_2} \right\} \cdot \mathscr{R}_1(s) \cdot \mathscr{R}_2(s).$$

These functions are symmetric about ω_0 for small k. As k becomes large (i.e., greater than 0.1), the splitting of ω_1 and ω_2 about ω_0 becomes asymmetric. See Fig. 169.

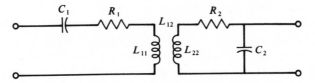

FIG. 169. A double-tuned circuit with the response taken across the capacitor C_2. This gives a symmetric voltage-transfer function in the logarithmic plot; i.e., $H_V \to R_1(s)R_2(s)$.

Various special cases of the double-tuned circuit shed some light on the limits of design. Consider first the high-Q case when $R_1 = R_2 = 0$. Then the symmetric response $H_V{}^{C_2}(s)$ becomes

$$H_V^{(C_2)} \xrightarrow[R_j = 0]{} \frac{ks^2}{C_2\sqrt{L_{11}L_{22}}\{(s^2 + \omega_1^2)(s^2 + \omega_2^2) - k^2 s^4\}}.$$

When the uncoupled frequencies are the same ($\omega_1 = \omega_2 = \omega_0$),

$$H_V^{(C_2)} \xrightarrow[\substack{R_j = 0 \\ Q_j \to \infty}]{} \frac{ks^2}{C_2\sqrt{L_{11}L_{22}}(1 - k^2)\left[s^2 + \dfrac{\omega_0^2}{(1 + |k|)} \right]\left[s^2 + \dfrac{\omega_0^2}{(1 - |k|)} \right]}.$$

Another circuit that is used quite often in tuned amplifiers is the double-tuned circuit consisting of two tank circuits inductively coupled. This is shown in Fig. 170.

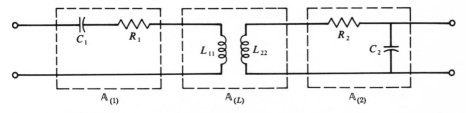

FIG. 170. Representation of a double-tuned circuit (with output across C_2) as a cascade of three four-terminal networks.

The cascade matrix for this circuit will be employed to compute the response of a tuned amplifier. Thus, we note its general form:

$$A(s) = \frac{|\mathbb{L}|}{L_{21}s} \times$$

$$\begin{pmatrix} C_2[s^3 + As^2 + (B - v^2\omega_1^2)s + 2v^2a_1\omega_2^2] & [s^2 + As + 4\gamma^2a_1a_2] \\ C_1C_2[s^4 + As^3 + Bs^2 + Cs + D] & C_1[s^3 + As^2 + (B - v^2\omega_2^2)s + 2v^2a_2\omega_1^2] \end{pmatrix}.$$

This particular form loses the symmetry of the earlier circuit when it is considered alone. One expects this because the voltage transfer does not include C_1 in the response.

FILTER NETWORKS

Ideal Filters

When the word "filter" is introduced, we are specifically talking of the sinusoidal response. In other words, the traditional idea of filtering is to remove or to pass preferentially, as the case may be, certain frequencies relative to another group of frequencies. Many of the circuits that we have already discussed are filters in one sense or another. For instance, the names "high pass" and "low pass" refer specifically to the sinusoidal response.

Therefore, it is not unreasonable to establish the characteristics of ideal filters in the Fourier representation. In general the $\mathscr{F}T$ of the response $V(\omega)$ is related to the $\mathscr{F}T$ of the excitation $E(\omega)$ according to

$$V(\omega) = H(\omega)E(\omega),$$

where $H(\omega)$ is the transfer function in the $\mathscr{F}T$ representation. Because $e(t) = \mathscr{F}^{-1}[E(\omega)]$ is real, $E^*(\omega) = E(-\omega)$. The same argument holds for $V(\omega)$:

$$V^*(\omega) = V(-\omega).$$

If these two statements regarding the real nature of $e(t)$ and $v(t)$ are true, the same statement must hold for $H(\omega)$:

$$H^*(\omega) = H(-\omega).$$

As a result, the amplitude of $H(\omega)$ is a symmetric function while the phase of $H(\omega)$ is an odd function. Writing

$$H(\omega) = \rho(\omega)e^{i\Phi(\omega)},$$

then

$$\rho(\omega) = +\rho(-\omega),$$

while

$$\Phi(\omega) = -\Phi(-\omega).$$

With these general properties of $H(\omega)$ in mind, we can regard several ideal cases of the transfer function.

The Delay Function

This was discussed in general when the shifting theorem was developed. Let

$$H = H_0 e^{-i\omega T},$$

where $H_0 = $ a constant for all ω: then

$$V(\omega) = H_0 e^{-i\omega T} E(\omega)$$

and

$$v(t) = \mathscr{F}^{-1}[V(\omega)] = H_0 e(t - T).$$

This is the transfer function for an ideal, lossless transmission line.

The Ideal Low-Pass Filter

This is a case for which the phase variation is zero (no delay) and the amplitude $\rho(\omega)$ is a step function. See Fig. 171. Let

$$\rho(\omega) = H_0, \qquad \text{for } |\omega| < \omega_0;$$

and

$$\rho(\omega) = 0, \qquad \text{for } \omega_0 < |\omega|;$$

with

$$\Phi(\omega) = 0, \qquad \text{for all } \omega.$$

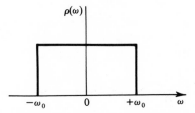

FIG. 171.   The amplitude of the ideal low-pass filter as a function of the frequency.

In this example, the response to a very short pulse (or in the limit a delta function) is

$$v_\delta(t) = \frac{H_0 E_0}{2\pi} \int_{-\omega_0}^{\omega_0} e^{i\omega t}\, d\omega = \frac{H_0 E_0 \omega_0}{\pi} j_0(\omega_0 t),$$

where

$$j_0(\omega_0 t) = \frac{\sin \omega_0 t}{\omega_0 t}.$$

See Fig. 172.

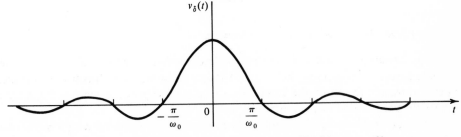

FIG. 172.   The delta-function response of an ideal low-pass filter.

This result is quite nonphysical because we have introduced a device with no delay; but more important, we have employed a nonphysical function that does not possess derivatives at ω_0 to any order.

It is somewhat more instructive to subject this transfer function to a step excitation:

$$U(\omega) = \frac{E_0}{\sqrt{2\pi i\omega}}.$$

The response to the step excitation has a nonphysical component in the negative-time interval, but the basic features of the response are present for positive t:

$$v_U(t) = \frac{H_0 E_0}{2\pi} \int_{-\omega_0}^{\omega_0} \frac{\sin \omega t}{\omega} \, d\omega.$$

The rise time can be obtained from the derivative $v_U(t)$ devaluate at $t = 0$:

$$\left[\frac{dv_U}{dt}\right]_{t=0} = \frac{H_0 E_0 \omega_0}{\pi},$$

giving

$$\tau_{\text{rise}} \simeq \frac{\pi}{2\omega_0}.$$

See Fig. 173.

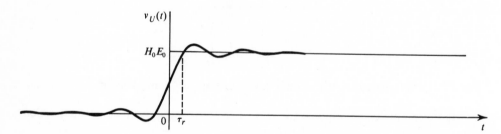

FIG. 173.   Response of the ideal low-pass filter to a step excitation.

The rise time is inversely proportional to the bandwidth ω_0. As one attempts to limit the frequency spectrum to a narrow interval, the front edge tends to spread out in time. This is a familiar example of the classical uncertainty principle of the conjugate variables of time and frequency:

$$\Delta t \, \Delta \omega \geqslant 1.$$

Amplitude Distortion, Symmetric Echos

Any deviation from flatness in the amplitude of $H(\omega)$ for the ideal low-pass filter leads to further distortion of the signal. If the appropriate delay function is included in the expression for $H(\omega)$, the amplitude distortion can produce echos if the delay is longer than the period of the amplitude distortion.

Consider a low-pass filter with an ideal linear phase response with a modulated amplitude. Let (see Fig. 174)

$$\rho(\omega) = H_0\left(1 + a \cos\frac{\pi\omega}{\omega_0}\right), \qquad |\omega| < \omega_0;$$

and with

$$\rho(\omega) = 0; \qquad \text{for } \omega_0 < |\omega|.$$

Then, if

$$\Phi(\omega) = -\omega T,$$

$$v(t) = \frac{a}{2} v_0(t - [T - \tau]) + v_0(t - T) + \frac{a}{2} v_0(t - [T + \tau]),$$

where

$$v_0(t - T) = \frac{H_0}{\sqrt{2\pi}} \int_{-\omega_0}^{\omega_0} E(\omega)e^{i\omega(t-T)}\,d\omega$$

and

$$\tau = \frac{\pi}{\omega_0}.$$

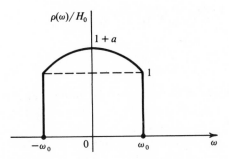

Fig. 174. The amplitude of a low-pass filter characteristic with amplitude distortion.

We see that the distortion caused by the modulation of the amplitude produces two symmetric echos, which are replicas of v_0 except that they are scaled by the factor $a/2$. When the width of the initial signal is small compared with τ, the distortion in the reception appears in terms of two separate echos. See Fig. 175.

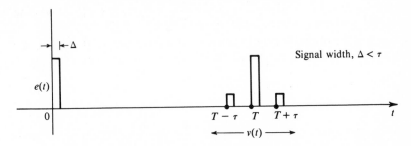

Fig. 175. The symmetric echos produced by amplitude distortion.

A signal that has a width greater than τ will appear as a distorted response because the echos now superimpose upon the main signal at T. The distortion is symmetric about T. See Fig. 176.

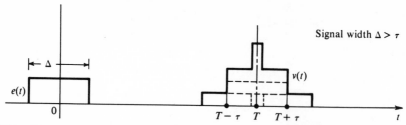

FIG. 176.   Symmetric echos produced by amplitude distortion appear as a distortion of the response when the width of the signal is greater than τ.

Phase Distortion, Antisymmetric Echos

The effect of deviations of the phase from linearity is to introduce echos again. However, in this case, the echos are antisymmetric. To clearly illustrate the effect, we take an $H(\omega)$ with no amplitude distortion but with a phase varying as

$$\Phi(\omega) = -\omega T + b \sin \omega \tau,$$

with

$$\rho(\omega) = H_0, \qquad \text{for } |\omega| < \omega_0,$$

and

$$\rho = 0, \qquad \text{for } \omega_0 < |\omega|.$$

The reader will notice that since $\Phi(\omega)$ must be an odd function, we can distort only with odd functions of ω. The response to an excitation $e(t) = \mathscr{F}^{-1}[E(\omega)]$ is

$$v(t) = \frac{H_0}{\sqrt{2\pi}} \int_{-\omega_0}^{\omega_0} E(\omega)e^{i\omega(t-T)}e^{ib \sin \omega \tau} \, d\omega.$$

We employ the two first-order terms in the expansion of $\exp(ib \sin \omega\tau)$ in terms of the Bessel functions $J_i(x)$:

$$e^{ib \sin \omega} \simeq J_0(b) + J_1(b)\{e^{i\omega\tau} - e^{-i\omega\tau}\} + \cdots \text{h.t.}$$

Substituting this form into the integral expression for $v(t)$, we obtain

$$v(t) = \frac{J_1(b)}{J_0(b)} v_0(t - [T - \tau]) + v_0(t - T) - \frac{J_1(b)}{J_0(b)} v_0(t - [T + \tau]) + \text{higher terms.}$$

Once again the results appear as echos or as a distortion of the signal, depending upon whether τ is greater than or less than the width of the signal. See Fig. 177.

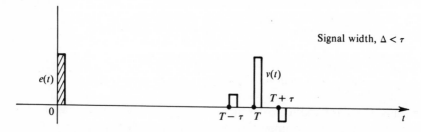

FIG. 177.   Antisymmetric echos produced by phase distortion.

It is now possible to see that the presence of both amplitude and phase distortion will produce at least eight echos. First we shall have a symmetric set and an antisymmetric set. Further, the interaction of the phase and amplitude distortions will produce at least four more first-order echos. See Fig. 178a.

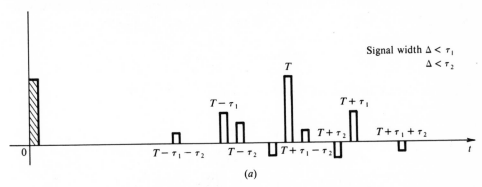

(a)

FIG. 178(a).   A few components of the response spectrum when both phase distortion and amplitude distortion are present.

Maximal Flatness

Various examples of pole configurations in low-pass transfers have given us some idea of the extent of the flatness of the response. For instance, it is now apparent that a highly overdamped transfer with the poles far apart on the negative-real axis results in a frequency response of poor quality. An underdamped low-pass transfer has a high overshoot near cutoff for Q values greater than 1 (poles within 30 deg of the imaginary axis). When the low-pass transfers have more than two poles, it is in no manner clear how one can gauge the quality of the response without calculating it in detail.

We shall concern ourselves then, with the problem of determining the positions of the poles in a low-pass transfer which provide optimal or maximal flatness. Later in this section we shall construct a conformal transformation that will allow the same techniques to be applied to a band-pass transfer.

The most elementary low-pass transfer can be written as

$$H(s) = \frac{\omega_0}{s + \omega_0} = \frac{1}{1 + z}$$

where $z = s/\omega_0$.

The magnitude of this function along the imaginary axis is

$$|H(i\omega)| = |H(iy)| = \frac{1}{\sqrt{1 + y^2}}.$$

Here,

$$y = \frac{\omega}{\omega_0}.$$

If n equivalent functions are cascaded without loading,

$$|H^{(n)}(iy)| = \frac{1}{\{1 + y^2\}^{n/2}}.$$

This function is not maximally flat. We demonstrate this fact by expanding the function in a Taylor's series about $y = 0$. One can observe immediately that the coefficients of all terms above the first order are nonvanishing, indicating the presence of the second and higher derivatives at $y = 0$.

Maximal flatness can be achieved from the Butterworth function,[†] which has the property that the first $2n - 1$ derivatives vanish at $y = 0$. This function is

$$|H_B^{(n)}(iy)| = \frac{1}{\{1 + y^{2n}\}^{\frac{1}{2}}}.$$

A plot of several Butterworth functions is indicated in Fig. 178b.

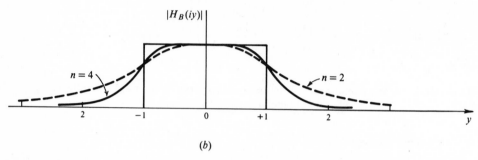

(b)

FIG. 178(b). The sinusoidal response of maximally flat functions in the two cases $n = 2$ and $n = 4$.

The deviation of the phase response from linearity is also important. Ideally, one would hope to achieve a linear-phase response with the same function. Unfortunately, both amplitude and phase distortions cannot be minimized simultaneously, although the Butterworth function for small n does give a reasonable minimization of the phase distortion. In any final design, however, it may be necessary to construct minor compromises.

The fact that real sections load one another works in our favor. As we have seen, a straight cascade of elementary, unloaded low-pass devices would not possibly fit the Butterworth criterion.

Our assumed form for $|H_B(iy)|$ does not locate the pole arrangements for various numbers of poles. One aspect is obvious: In lowest order, we must have at least two complex poles to achieve flatness. Let us consider the case, then, of $H^{(2)}$:

$$H^{(2)}(z) = \frac{1}{(z + \beta)(z + \beta^*)}.$$

We can find the magnitude of this complex function by multiplying by its mirror image in the complex plane, $H^{(2)}(-z)$. Then

$$|H^{(2)}(z)|^2 = \frac{1}{(z + \beta)(z + \beta^*)(-z + \beta)(-z + \beta^*)}$$

$$= \frac{1}{(\beta^2 - z^2)(\beta^{*2} - z^2)}.$$

† S. Butterworth, *Wireless Engineering*, **7** (1930), 536.

This function can now be constrained to be the square of the Butterworth function:

$$|H^{(2)}(iy)|^2 = \frac{1}{(\beta^2 + y^2)(\beta^{*2} + y^2)} = |H_B^{(2)}|^2 = \frac{1}{[1 + y^4]}.$$

Solving this equation for β, we obtain four poles (see Fig. 178c):

$$\beta = \pm \frac{1}{\sqrt{2}} \pm \frac{i}{\sqrt{2}}.$$

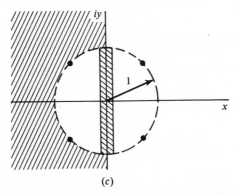

(c)

FIG. 178(c).   The pole locations in the z plane for a maximally flat, low-pass transfer function in the case $n = 2$. The poles in the right-hand side are omitted because they have been introduced solely for purposes of convenience in computing the square of the magnitude.

The poles in the right half-plane correspond to the mirror image, and therefore can be omitted, giving a solution of

$$\beta = -\frac{1}{\sqrt{2}} \pm \frac{i}{\sqrt{2}}.$$

Translating these results to the s plane is accomplished by multiplying the roots by ω_0. Thus, a two-pole problem is maximally flat if the poles make angles of $\pm \pi/4$ with respect to the real axis. A transfer having three poles represents a problem with two complex roots and one real root. Again we assume roots β, β^*, and a real root α. The square of the magnitude is used to compute $|H_B^{(3)}|^2$, giving

$$(\alpha + y^2)(\beta^2 + y^2)(\beta^{*2} + y^2) = 1 + y^6.$$

The roots of the resulting polynomial are

$$\alpha = \pm 1,$$

and

$$\beta = \pm \frac{1}{2} \pm i \frac{\sqrt{3}}{2}.$$

Splitting off the mirror terms, we obtain the roots $-\omega_0$ and $\{-1/2\} \pm i(\sqrt{3}/2)\}\omega_0$ (Fig. 178d). In general, the roots are obtained by splitting the unit circle in the z plane symmetrically relative to the imaginary axis. The roots then lie on the unit circle at positions given by $(-1)^{2n}$, with the mirror terms extracted at the conclusion.

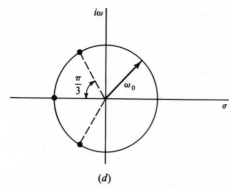

(d)

FIG. 178(d).   Location of the poles for a maximally flat function with $n = 3$.

A band-pass transfer can be handled in much the same manner by transforming $H(s)$ to $H(z)$ such that $H(z)$ is again a low-pass function. Consider a two-pole resonance function and its transformation to a low-pass function. We begin with

$$H(s) = \frac{2as}{\{s^2 + 2as + \omega_0^2\}} = \frac{1}{1 + \{(s/2a) + (\omega_0^2/2as)\}}.$$

Define the transformation

$$z = \frac{s}{2a} + \frac{\omega_0^2}{2as}.$$

Then

$$H(s) \to H(z) = \frac{1}{1 + z}.$$

This z-plane transformation takes the $i\omega$ axis to the iy axis. The origin in the s plane transforms to infinity, as does the infinite circle in the s plane. The point $\omega = \omega_0$ in the s plane transforms to the origin in the z plane. Thus, the band pass is converted to a low-pass z-plane transfer. All the flatness criteria in the z plane remain the same.

One must recognize, however, that the first flatness condition that corresponds (as before) to two complex poles in the z plane becomes two complex poles near $i\omega_0$ in the s plane. Consequently, our solutions for n poles in the z plane will give $2n$ poles in the s plane.

The first two-pole z-plane problem was maximally flat when $\beta = -1\sqrt{2} \pm i\sqrt{2}$. Converting directly to the s plane, we obtain from

$$z = \frac{s}{2a} + \frac{\omega_0^2}{2as}$$

the conversions

$$y = \frac{\omega[\sigma^2 + \omega^2 - \omega_0^2]}{2a[\sigma^2 + \omega^2]} \xrightarrow[\substack{\text{narrow band} \\ \sigma \ll \omega_0 \\ |\omega - \omega_0| \ll \omega_0}]{} \frac{(\omega - \omega_0)}{a}$$

and

$$x = \frac{\sigma[\sigma^2 + \omega^2 + \omega_0^2]}{2a[\sigma^2 + \omega^2]} \xrightarrow[\substack{\text{narrow band} \\ \sigma \ll \omega_0 \\ |\omega - \omega_0| \ll \omega_0}]{} \frac{\sigma}{a}.$$

Thus, the four poles in the s plane corresponding to a maximally flat band-pass transfer are approximately given by (Fig. 178e)

$$\gamma_1 = \frac{a}{\sqrt{2}} - i\left(\omega_0 - \frac{a}{\sqrt{2}}\right), \qquad \text{with } \gamma_1^*;$$

and

$$\gamma_2 = \frac{a}{\sqrt{2}} - i\left(\omega_0 + \frac{a}{\sqrt{2}}\right), \qquad \text{with } \gamma_2^*.$$

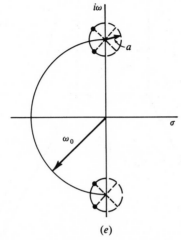

(e)

FIG. 178(e).   The four poles for the narrow-band, maximally flat, band-pass–transfer function ($n = 2$ in the z plane).

The log plot of the asymptotes is shown in Fig. 178f.

In the narrow-band case, the Q values are quite high. With our approximation, they are infinitesimally different:

$$Q_1 = \frac{\sqrt{\gamma_1 \gamma_1^*}}{2a} \simeq Q_0 - \frac{1}{2\sqrt{2}} + \frac{1}{8Q_0} \to Q_0,$$

$$Q_2 = \frac{\sqrt{\gamma_2 \gamma_2^*}}{2a} \simeq Q_0 + \frac{1}{2\sqrt{2}} + \frac{1}{8Q_0} \to Q_0,$$

where

$$Q_0 = \frac{\omega_0}{2a}.$$

If our band-pass problem involves a wideband transfer, then the conversion to the s plane must be done more carefully. With

$$z = \left(\frac{s}{2a} + \frac{\omega_0^2}{2as}\right),$$

we solve for s, giving

$$s - az \pm \sqrt{a^2 z^2 - \omega_0^2}.$$

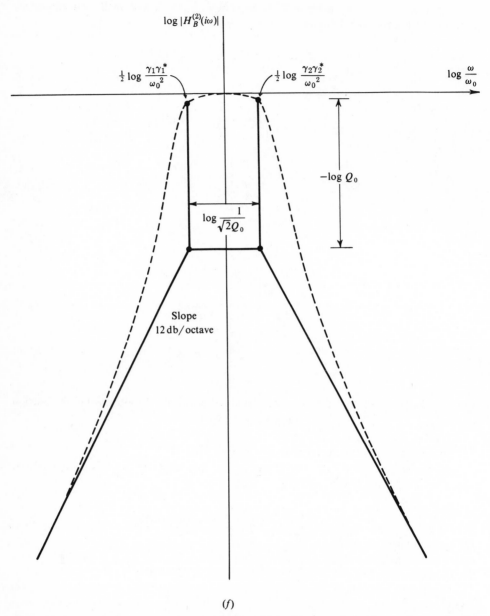

(f)

FIG. 178(f).   The asymptotic plot of the sinusoidal response of the four-pole, maximally flat, band-pass characteristic.

A pair of conjugate roots in the z plane produces two pairs of conjugate roots in the s plane. A single real root in the z plane gives one conjugate pair in the s plane. As before, if one-half the roots in the s plane is odd, there will be one real root in the Z plane.

The other problem, which must be considered for optimum response, is the dispersion of the function. Ideally, we should want a linear-phase response. As we observed in the preceding section, when the transfer function has a linear phase (i.e.,

$\phi \to \omega T$), there is no phase distortion in the output, since every Fourier component is shifted in time by the same amount.

A linear-phase response corresponds to a band-pass function $d\phi/d\omega$, which is maximally flat in the interval of the bandwidth. We can approach the problem in a similar manner by converting our s plane representation to the z plane again. Consider two sections:

$$H^{(2)}(z) = \frac{1}{(z+\beta)(z+\beta^*)};$$

here, $\beta = \zeta + i\xi$. The phase can be obtained from

$$[\Phi(iy)]_{x=0} = \frac{1}{2}\arg\frac{H^{(2)}(z)}{H^{(2)}(-z)} = \tan^{-1}\left\{\frac{y+\zeta}{\xi}\right\} + \tan^{-1}\left\{\frac{y-\zeta}{\xi}\right\}.$$

The band-pass function is now equated to

$$\frac{d\Phi(iy)}{dy} = \frac{1}{1+y^4}.$$

Equating the coefficient of y^2 in $d\Phi/dy$ to zero gives

$$\xi^2 = 3\zeta^2$$

or

$$\xi = \pm\sqrt{3}\zeta.$$

Thus, the pole location is somewhat altered for linear-phase response. The equality to the Butterworth function requires that $\xi^2 + \zeta^2 = 1$. If we extend the bandwidth for the phase-response computation, the bandwidth in the z plane is $4\zeta^2$. The phase bandwidth can be set near 1 if three sections are taken.

Symmetric Filters

Introduction

In previous sections we have discussed in sufficient detail the general properties of two-element high-pass and low-pass filters. These were the *RC*, *RL*, and *LRC* networks connected in either the Γ or ˥ configuration. The reader will recall that the type of connection employed depends upon whether one is concerned with voltage response or current response. The phase-shifting network consisted of several sections of two element filters.

The symmetric filters have an advantage in design in that the matrices for relatively complicated structures maintain certain well-defined characteristics. The two geometric symmetries are the T symmetry and the π symmetry. Either of these symmetries can be transformed to the other by a very simple operation, known in more general cases as the *wye-delta transformation.*

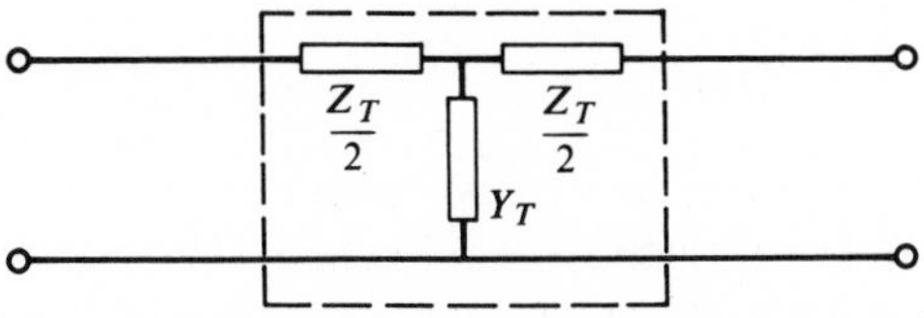

FIG. 179. The symmetric T-filter section.

The T section has a $\mathbb{Z}$ matrix:

$$\mathbb{Z}^{(T)}_{(s)} = \frac{1}{2Y_T}\begin{pmatrix} [2 + Z_T Y_T] & 2 \\ 2 & [2 + Z_T Y_T] \end{pmatrix},$$

and the π-section admittance matrix is

$$\mathbb{Y}^{(\pi)}_{(s)} = \frac{1}{2Z_\pi}\begin{pmatrix} [2 + Z_\pi Y_\pi] & -2 \\ 2 & [2 + Z_\pi Y_\pi] \end{pmatrix}.$$

See Fig. 180.

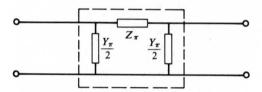

FIG. 180.   The symmetric π-filter section.

The relations between the T elements and the π elements can be obtained by inverting, say, $\mathbb{Y}^{(\pi)}$, and equating like terms in the two matrices. Setting

$$[\mathbb{Y}^{(\pi)}]^{-1} = \mathbb{Z}^{(T)},$$

we get

$$Y_\pi = \frac{4Y_T}{4 + Z_T Y_T}$$

and

$$Z_\pi = \frac{Z_T(4 + Z_T Y_T)}{4}.$$

In an earlier section it was demonstrated that the characteristic impedance of a symmetric four-terminal network is

$$Z_0(s) = \sqrt{|\mathbb{Z}|}.$$

For the symmetric sections, the characteristic impedance (or admittance in the case of the π) is

$$Z_0(s) = \sqrt{Z_{11}^2 - Z_{12}^2} = Z_{oc} \cdot Z_{sc}$$

or

$$Y_0(s) = \sqrt{Y_{11}^2 - Y_{12}^2} = Y_{oc} \cdot Y_{sc}.$$

The subscript "sc" refers to a measurement of the input impedance (or admittance) with the output terminals short-circuited. The subscript "oc" refers to a measurement with the output terminals open-circuited. We remind the reader that the input impedance is Z_0 when the network is terminated in Z_0.

Transformations

The general transformation problem with the symmetric sections concerns the transformation that operates upon $\mathbb{Z}$ in such a manner that Z_0 or $|\mathbb{Z}|$ is invariant under the transformation. Also, the geometric symmetry must be retained.

The transformation that maintains the magnitude of $\mathbb{Z}$ invariant and maintains the diagonal symmetry $(Z_{11} = Z_{22})$ is called an $\mathbb{M}$ *transformation*. The resultant filter section is known as an *m-derived filter*.

Because the magnitude of $\mathbb{Z}$ is kept invariant, the magnitude of the transformation matrix is $+1$.

We write $\mathbb{M}$ as†

$$\mathbb{M} = \begin{pmatrix} a & b \\ c & d \end{pmatrix},$$

with

$$|\mathbb{M}| = ad - cb = +1.$$

Since $\mathbb{Z}$ is a second-order tensor, it transforms as

$$\mathbb{Z}^{(M)} = \tilde{\mathbb{M}} \cdot \mathbb{Z} \cdot \mathbb{M}$$

or

$$Z_{jk}^{(M)} = \sum_{l=1}^{2} \sum_{m=1}^{2} \tilde{M}_{jl} Z_{lm} M_{mk} = \sum_{l=1}^{2} \sum_{m=1}^{2} M_{lj} Z_{lm} M_{mk}.$$

Operating on $\mathbb{Z}$ with $\tilde{\mathbb{M}}$ and $\mathbb{M}$, we obtain

$$\mathbb{Z}^{(M)}(s) = \begin{pmatrix} [(a^2 + c^2)Z_{11} + 2acZ_{12}] & [(ab + cd)Z_{11} + (ad + bc)Z_{12}] \\ [(ab + cd)Z_{11} + (ad + bc)Z_{12}] & [(b^2 + d^2)Z_{11} + 2bdZ_{12}] \end{pmatrix}.$$

Using the symmetry which requires that $Z_{11}^{(M)} = Z_{22}^{(M)}$, we find that $a = d$ and $c = b$. Finally, we get

$$\mathbb{M} = \begin{pmatrix} \sqrt{1 + b^2} & b \\ b & \sqrt{1 + b^2} \end{pmatrix} = \tilde{\mathbb{M}}.$$

We have used the fact that $a^2 - b^2 = 1$ to obtain the matrix given above. The most useful parameter is not b but rather a parameter m, which scales the components of the T directly.

If we set $(a - b)^2 = m$, then

$$\mathbb{M} = \begin{vmatrix} \dfrac{(1 + m)}{2\sqrt{m}} & \dfrac{(1 - m)}{2\sqrt{m}} \\ \dfrac{(1 - m)}{2\sqrt{m}} & \dfrac{(1 + m)}{2\sqrt{m}} \end{vmatrix}$$

Note the fact that $\mathbb{M} = \tilde{\mathbb{M}}$.

---

† This transformation is different from the unitary transformation that keeps the magnitude invariant, but retains the invariance of the trace rather than the geometric symmetry. The unitary transformation is designed specifically to preserve the roots of the characteristic polynomial. The $\mathbb{M}$ transformation has a different purpose.

With the transformation M represented in terms of the parameter m,

$$\mathbb{Z}^{(M)} = \tilde{\mathsf{M}} \cdot \mathbb{Z} \cdot \mathsf{M} = \begin{pmatrix} \dfrac{\left(1 + \left[\dfrac{1 + m^2}{4}\right]ZY\right)}{mY} & \dfrac{\left(1 + \left[\dfrac{1 - m^2}{4}\right]ZY\right)}{mY} \\[4mm] \dfrac{\left(1 + \left[\dfrac{1 - m^2}{4}\right]ZY\right)}{mY} & \dfrac{\left(1 + \left[\dfrac{1 + m^2}{4}\right]ZY\right)}{mY} \end{pmatrix}.$$

The elements (assuming a T section) of the m-*derived* section may be labeled Z' and Y'. Thus,

$$Z_{11}^{(MT)} = \frac{1}{Y'} + \frac{Z'}{2} = \frac{1 + \left[\dfrac{1 + m^2}{4}\right]ZY}{mY}$$

and

$$Z_{12}^{(MT)} = \frac{1}{Y'} = \frac{1}{mY} + \frac{\left[\dfrac{1 - m^2}{4}\right]Z}{m},$$

giving

$$\frac{Z'}{2} = m\frac{Z}{2}$$

and

$$\frac{1}{Y'} = \frac{1}{mY} + \left[\frac{1 - m^2}{4m}\right]Z.$$

The transformation can then be diagrammed (see Fig. 181).

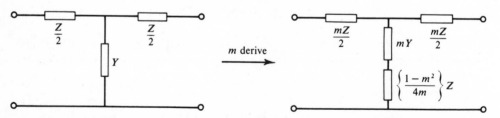

FIG. 181.   The relation between the symmetric T-section and its m-derived form.

The π section is most conveniently transformed in the admittance form because the $\mathbb{Z}$ matrix is a relatively complex representation for this geometry. We note that the transforming matrix is M^{-1}. If

$$\mathbb{Z}^{(M)} = \tilde{\mathsf{M}} \cdot \mathbb{Z} \cdot \mathsf{M},$$

then

$$\mathbb{Y}^{(M)} = [\tilde{\mathsf{M}} \cdot \mathbb{Z} \cdot \mathsf{M}]^{-1}.$$

and†

$$\mathbb{Y}^{(M)} = \frac{1}{|Z|} \begin{pmatrix} \sum\limits_{l,m} M_{2l}Z_{lm}M_{m2} & -\sum\limits_{l,m} M_{1l}Z_{lm}M_{m2} \\ -\sum\limits_{l,m} M_{2l}Z_{lm}M_{m1} & \sum\limits_{l,m} M_{1l}Z_{lm}M_{m1} \end{pmatrix}.$$

We notice now that this is equivalent to the product

$$\mathbb{Y}^{(M)} = \mathbb{M}^{-1} \cdot \mathbb{Y} \cdot \mathbb{M}^{-1}.$$

This is easily seen because $\tilde{\mathbb{M}} = \mathbb{M}$ and $\tilde{\mathbb{M}}^{-1} = \mathbb{M}^{-1}$. Thus, $\mathbb{M}^{-1}$ differs from M only in the sign of the off-diagonal element. Then

$$\mathbb{M}^{-1} = \begin{pmatrix} \dfrac{(1+m)}{2\sqrt{m}} & \dfrac{(m-1)}{2\sqrt{m}} \\ \dfrac{(m-1)}{2\sqrt{m}} & \dfrac{(1+m)}{2\sqrt{m}} \end{pmatrix}.$$

Finally,

$$\mathbb{Y}^{(M)} = \begin{pmatrix} \dfrac{[2+Z'Y']}{2Z'} & -\dfrac{1}{Z'} \\ -\dfrac{1}{Z'} & \dfrac{[2+Z'Y']}{2Z'} \end{pmatrix}.$$

and

$$\mathbb{Y}^{(M)} = \frac{1}{mZ} \begin{pmatrix} \left[1+\left(\dfrac{1+m^2}{4}\right)ZY\right] & -\left[1+\left(\dfrac{1-m^2}{4}\right)ZY\right] \\ -\left[1+\left(\dfrac{1-m^2}{4}\right)ZY\right] & \left[1+\left(\dfrac{1+m^2}{4}\right)ZY\right] \end{pmatrix}.$$

In this case, the image admittance is the same for $\mathbb{Y}$ and $\mathbb{Y}^{(M)}$, with

$$Y_0 = \sqrt{|\mathbb{Y}|} = \sqrt{\frac{Y}{Z} + \frac{Y^2}{4}}.$$

The m-derived components are related to the original π components by

$$Y' = mY$$

and

$$\frac{1}{Z'} = \frac{1}{mZ} + \left(\frac{1-m^2}{4}\right)Y.$$

The diagrams of the two sections are shown in Fig. 182.

---

† The repeated subscripts in the matrix elements indicate a sum over the range of l and the range of m; i.e.,

$$M_{2l}Z_{lm}M_{m2} = M_{21}Z_{11}M_{12} + M_{21}Z_{12}M_{22} + M_{22}Z_{21}M_{12} + M_{22}Z_{22}M_{22}.$$

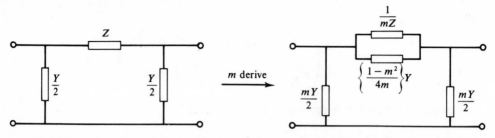

FIG. 182.   The relation between the elementary symmetric π and its m-derived form.

The duality of the T and π geometries is quite apparent when their transformation properties are developed.

Up to this point, two-terminal elements $Z(s)$ and $Y(s)$ have been completely general. They can be networks of any degree of complication or simplicity. Certain forms of $Z(s)$ and $Y(s)$ are known to have unique application.

A class of sections known as *constant k* sections have an image impedance that is resistive (or real) over a wide range of frequencies. In practice, we should like to develop a Z_0 that is independent of frequency. However, because of the square root, this is not possible except in approximation.

Consider the T section; the image impedance is

$$Z_0(s) = \sqrt{\frac{Z(s)}{Y(s)} + \frac{Z^2(s)}{4}}.$$

The resonant frequency of this section can be defined as

$$\omega_0 = \frac{s}{\sqrt{Z(s)Y(s)}} \qquad \text{(low pass),}$$

or

$$\omega_0 = \frac{\sqrt{Z(s)Y(s)}}{s} \qquad \text{(high pass).}$$

This is the form of ω_0 for elementary filters, say, containing only L and C. For elementary forms of Z and Y, ω_0 is independent of s. Substituting the *low-pass form* into $Z_0(s)$, we find that

$$Z_0(s) = \frac{Z(s)}{2s} \sqrt{s^2 + 4\omega_0^2} \qquad \text{(low pass).}$$

Thus, if ω_0 is independent of s, $Z_0(s)$ cannot be made completely s-independent because of the term $\sqrt{s^2 + 4\omega_0^2}$. A reasonable approximation for $Z_0(s)$ is obtained by making $Z(s)/Y(s)$ real and approximating Z_0 by $\sqrt{Z/Y}$. The approximation fails as $s \to \omega_0$. In other words, if

$$Z_0 = k = \sqrt{\frac{Z(s)}{Y(s)}} = \text{a real number,}$$

then

$$\omega_0 = \frac{s}{\sqrt{ZY}} = \frac{s}{kY(s)} \qquad \text{(low-pass section),}$$

and

$$Z_0 = k\sqrt{1 + \frac{ZY}{4}} = k\sqrt{1 + \frac{s^2}{4\omega_0^2}} \xrightarrow[\omega \ll \omega_0]{} k.$$

One can see that it is impossible to have Z a function of s and Y a function of s and still obtain a Z_0 completely independent of s.

The m-derived transformation is useful in that it allows us to set Z_0 and then to determine various configurations that match Z_0. Unfortunately, the cutoff frequencies ω_0 vary from one m-derived section to another. As a result, one value of m may give optimum flatness in the delay function of Z while a quite different value of m may give the smallest amplitude distortion. Because of the approximation, one must trade amplitude distortion of the section against phase distortion.

Before considering specific sections we can perceive some general characteristics of the transfer functions of sections. Some of these have been anticipated in the discussion of Z_0 and ω_0.

The voltage-transfer function of a single T section is

$$H_V^{(T)} = \frac{Z_{12}(s)Z_L}{|Z| + Z_{11}(s)Z_L}.$$

If one terminates in $Z_L = \sqrt{Z/Y}$, we obtain

$$H_V^{(T)}(s) = \frac{1}{[1 + x(s) + \frac{1}{2}x^2(s) + \frac{1}{4}x^3(s)]},$$

where

$$x^2(s) = Z(s)Y(s) = \frac{s^2}{\omega_0^2} \text{ (if low pass)} = \frac{\omega_0^2}{s^2} \text{ (if high pass)}.$$

The particular form of $ZY = x^2$, which we choose earlier, now begins to have meaning. We see that, regardless of the properties of $Z_L = \sqrt{Z/Y}$, this choice of $x^2(s)$ gives an excellent approximation to the shifting exponential

$$H_V^{(T)}(s) \xrightarrow[|s| \ll \omega_0/2]{} e^{-x} = e^{-(s/\omega_0)} \qquad \text{(low pass)}.$$

The voltage-transfer function of the π filter can be handled in much the same manner:

$$H_V^{(\pi)}(s) = \frac{-Y_{21}(s)}{Y_{22}(s) + Y_2}.$$

If we approximate the image admittance by $Y_0 = \sqrt{Y(s)/Z(s)}$, then

$$H_V^{(\pi)}(s) = \frac{1}{[1 + x(s) + \frac{1}{2}x^2(s)]},$$

where, again,

$$x^2(s) = Z(s)Y(s) = \frac{s^2}{\omega_0^2} \text{ (low pass)}$$

$$= \frac{\omega_0^2}{s^2} \text{ (high pass)}.$$

This function also approximates the shifting function for $|s| \ll \omega_0$

$$H_V^{(\pi)}(s) \xrightarrow[|s| \ll \omega_0]{} e^{-x} = e^{-s/\omega_0} \qquad \text{(low pass)}.$$

"Constant k" Sections

THE CONSTANT k, T SECTION

In order to make Z_0 as frequency-independent as possible over a wide range, we approximate Z_0 by

$$\sqrt{\frac{Z(s)}{Y(s)}} = k = \text{a real positive number.}$$

This, of course, will allow one to employ a resistive termination. Such a termination is desirable for several reasons, one of which is that the power transfer is maximized (since the voltage and current will be in phase).

The development in the preceding section demonstrated the voltage transfers for the T and the π sections when the product $Z(s)Y(s)$ is proportional to s^2 (this corresponds to a low-pass device). For a high-pass section, ZY varies as $\{1/s^2\}$. For the constant k,T section terminated in k,

$$H_V^{(T)} = \frac{4}{(x + \gamma)(x + \gamma^*)(x + \alpha)},$$

where, in general (see Fig. 183),

$$\gamma = 0.3522 - i1.723 \simeq \tfrac{9}{25} - i\sqrt{3},$$

$$\gamma\gamma^* \cong \tfrac{25}{8},$$

and

$$\alpha = 1.2956 \simeq \tfrac{32}{25},$$

$$\gamma\gamma^*\alpha = 4.$$

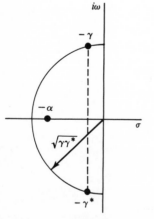

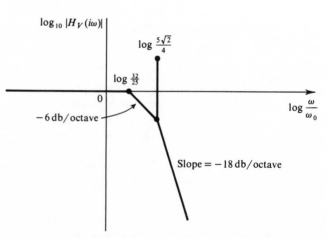

FIG. 183. The pole diagram for the voltage transfer to a load resistance equal to $k(\sqrt{Z/Y})$ of a low-pass LC T-section.

FIG. 184. The asymptotes of the magnitude of the sinusoidal response of the voltage transfer function of an elementary, terminated, low-pass T section.

Putting $H_V^{(T)}$ in the normal form

$$H_V^{(T)}(s) = \left\{ \frac{\gamma\gamma^*}{x^2 + (\gamma + \gamma^*)x + \gamma\gamma^*} \right\} \left(\frac{\alpha}{x + \alpha} \right).$$

This form clearly exhibits $H_V^{(T)}$ as the product of a quadratic low-pass (type II) function cutting off at $\{5/\sqrt{8}\}\omega_0$, and a low-pass (type I) function, cutting off at approximately $(4/3)\omega_0$.

The input impedance for the real circuit terminated in $Z_L = \sqrt{Z/Y} = k$ is

$$\frac{Z_{in}^{(T)}(s)}{k} = \frac{[1 + x(s) + \frac{1}{2}x^2 + \frac{1}{4}x^3]}{[1 + x + \frac{1}{2}x^2]}.$$

The numerator of $Z_{in}^{(T)}(s)$ [as well as the denominator of $H_V^{(T)}(s)$] contains the polynomial characteristic of all T sections that have ZY proportional to x^2. By choosing $Z(s) = Ls$ and $Y(s) = Cs$, we form the most elementary type of low-pass filter, satisfying the condition that the filter be "constant k" and that ZY be proportional to s^2.

$$Z(s) = Ls,$$

$$Y(s) = Cs,$$

$$ZY = LCs^2 = \frac{s^2}{\omega_0^2},$$

and

$$k = \sqrt{\frac{Z}{Y}} = \sqrt{\frac{L}{C}}.$$

See Figs. 185 and 186.

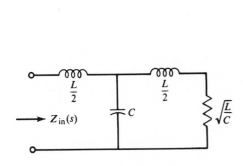

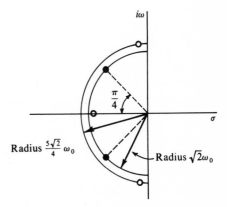

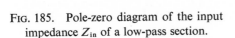

FIG. 185. Pole-zero diagram of the input impedance Z_{in} of a low-pass section.

FIG. 186. LC T-section terminated in a resistive load equal to k.

The input impedance has three zeros at the positions of the poles of $H_V^{(T)}$. It has two poles at $x = (-1 \pm i)$. See Fig. 187.

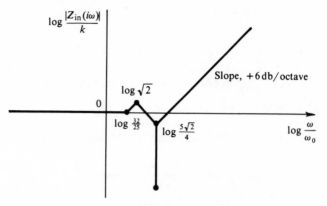

Fig. 187.   The asymptotes of the magnitude of the input impedance of an elementary, terminated, low-pass T filter.

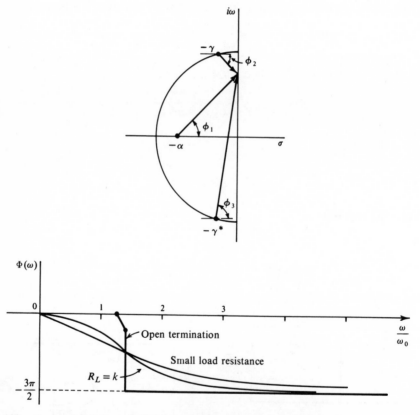

Fig. 188.   A sketch of the pole-zero contribution to the phase shift of the voltage-transfer function. In the second diagram, the phase shift as a function of frequency is indicated for various terminations of the low-pass T section.

The characteristic points closest to the origin are the poles on the circle of radius $\sqrt{2}\omega_0$. At this frequency, the input impedance begins to drop at 12 db per octave (the Q value is $\sqrt{2}/2$). At $\omega = (32/25)\omega_0$, the $Z_{in}(i\omega)$ function has a slope of only

6 db per octave. Then, at $\omega = (5\sqrt{2}/4)\omega_0$, the system recovers and rises at 6 db per octave, accompanied by an undershoot commensurate with the Q value of 2.5.

The voltage-transfer function, on the other hand, has a type I cutoff at $(32/25)\omega_0$. Then, at $(5\sqrt{2}/4)\omega_0$, the function cuts off at 18 db per octave, with an overshoot given by $Q = 2.5$. The phase varies from zero at small ω to $-(3\pi/2)$ at $\omega_0 \ll \omega$. A phase diagram is shown in Fig. 188.

As we have shown earlier, when the section is a low-pass section, the time delay can be obtained as the ratio of the last two coefficients of the polynomial of the denominator, or by approximating $H_V^{(T)}(s)$ as an exponential function. For this section,

$$\tau_d \simeq \sqrt{LC} = \frac{1}{\omega_0}.$$

The relationship between high-frequency distortion and time delay can be appreciated by computing the response across the termination of a low-pass T section (terminated in k) to a square-gate excitation:

$$\mathscr{L}[g_T(t)] = \frac{1}{s}\{1 - e^{-sT}\}.$$

$$v(t) = \mathscr{L}^{-1}\left[\frac{4}{(x+\gamma)(x+\gamma^*)(x+\alpha)} \cdot \frac{1}{x\omega_0}(1 - e^{-\omega_0 Tx})\right],$$

or

$$v(t) = \left\{1 - \frac{\alpha\sqrt{\gamma\gamma*}\,e^{-\frac{1}{2}(\gamma+\gamma^*)(\omega_0)t}\cos\left(\sqrt{\frac{i}{2}}(\gamma-\gamma^*)\omega_0 t + \phi\right)}{[4 - \frac{1}{8}(\gamma+\gamma^*)^3 + (\frac{1}{2}(\gamma-\gamma^*))^4]^{1/2}} - \frac{4e^{-\alpha\omega_0 t}}{[\alpha(\alpha-2a)+\gamma\gamma^*]}\right\}U(t)$$

$$-\left\{1 - \frac{4\sqrt{\alpha}e^{-a(t-T)\omega_0}\cos([\gamma\gamma^* - a^2]^{1/2}\omega_0(t-T)+\phi)}{[4 - \frac{1}{8}a^3 + (\gamma\gamma^* - a^2)^4]^{1/2}}\right.$$

$$\left. - \frac{4e^{-\alpha\omega_0(t-T)}}{[\alpha(\alpha-2a)+\gamma\gamma^*]}\right\}U(t-T).$$

When T (the width of the gate) is of the order of $1/\omega_0$ (the delay), the pulse is badly distorted. See Fig. 189.

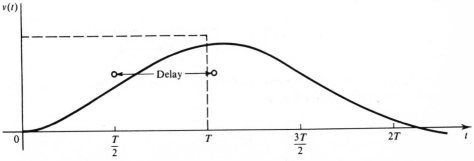

FIG. 189.   The response of a low-pass constant k T-section to a gate of width T. This is an example when the period of the gate is approximately twice $1/\omega_0$; i.e., $1/\omega_0 = 8T/5\pi$.

When T is somewhat longer than $1/\omega_0$, the distortion is less severe. See Fig. 190.

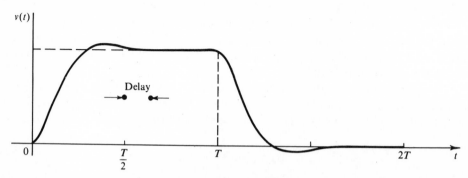

FIG. 190.   Response of a terminated constant k, low-pass T section to a gate whose duration T is much greater than $1/\omega_0$. In the case, $1/\omega_0 = (2/5\pi)T$.

The high-pass elementary T section is obtained by taking $k = \sqrt{Z/Y}$, and

$$x^2(s) = Z(s)Y(s) = \frac{\omega_0^2}{s^2}.$$

To accomplish this, we employ the dual parameters of the low-pass section:

$$Z(s) = \frac{1}{Cs}$$

and

$$Y(s) = \frac{1}{Ls}.$$

These relations then give

$$k = \sqrt{\frac{L}{C}} = R_0$$

and

$$x^2 = \frac{1}{LCs^2} = \frac{\omega_0^2}{s^2} \qquad \text{(high-pass form)}$$

The voltage-transfer function has the same x representation as that of the low-pass. The fact that x is now proportional to the inverse of s gives inverse roots for the high-pass filter:

$$H_V^{(T)}(x) = \frac{\alpha\gamma\gamma*}{(x + \gamma)(x + \gamma*)(x + \alpha)} = \frac{s^3}{\left(s + \dfrac{\omega_0}{\alpha}\right)\left(s + \dfrac{\omega_0}{\gamma}\right)\left(s + \dfrac{\omega_0}{\gamma*}\right)}.$$

Thus, the complex poles lie on a circle of radius $(\sqrt{1/\gamma\gamma*})\omega_0$. The damping factors are scaled now. The roots are (see Fig. 191)

$$s_1 = -\frac{\omega_0}{\alpha} = -\frac{25}{32}\omega_0,$$

$$s_2 = -\frac{\gamma*}{\gamma\gamma*}\omega_0 = -\frac{8}{25}\left(\frac{9}{25} + i\sqrt{3}\right)\omega_0,$$

and

$$s_3 = -\frac{\gamma}{\gamma\gamma*}\,\omega_0 = -\frac{8}{25}\left(\frac{9}{25} - i\sqrt{3}\right)\omega_0,$$

with

$$s_2 s_3 = \frac{1}{\gamma\gamma*}\,w_0^2 = \frac{8}{25}\,\omega_0^2.$$

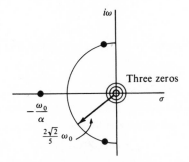

FIG. 191.   The pole-zero diagram of the high-pass T section terminated in a load resistance
equal to $\sqrt{L/C}$.

The relative position of the poles is now somewhat more spread out.
    The concept of a delay has no meaning, since

$$H_V^{(T)}(s) \xrightarrow[|x|\ll 1]{} e^{-x} = e^{-\omega_0/s} \qquad \text{(high pass).}$$

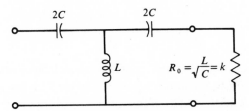

FIG. 192.   The terminated high-pass T section.

This function is not a shifting function. The input impedance again has the same form
as the low-pass case in the $x(s)$ variable, but

$$\frac{Z_{\text{in}}^{(T)}(s)}{k} = \frac{\left(s + \dfrac{\omega_0}{\alpha}\right)\left(s + \dfrac{\omega_0}{\gamma}\right)\left(s + \dfrac{\omega_0}{\gamma*}\right)}{s\left(s + \dfrac{\omega_0}{\beta}\right)\left(s + \dfrac{\omega_0}{\beta*}\right)},$$

where

$$\beta = (1 - i).$$

    The pole-zero diagram (see Fig. 193) is different in that the high-pass filter has a
pole at the origin, which gives a very high input impedance at low frequencies (i.e.,
$\omega \ll \omega_0$). At high frequencies ($\omega_0 \ll \omega$), Z_{in} is essentially constant and equal to k or R_0.

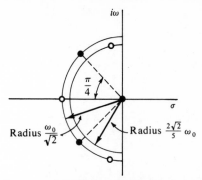

FIG. 193.   The pole-zero diagram of the input-impedance function $Z_{in}(s)$ for the high-pass, terminated T section.

THE "CONSTANT k," π-SECTION

The general forms of the voltage transfer and input impedance for one terminated section have already been exhibited as functions of

$$x(s) = Z(s)Y(s).$$

In the low-pass construction (elementary),†

$$Z(s) = Ls,$$

$$Y(s) = Cs,$$

and

$$x^2 = LCs^2 = \frac{s^2}{\omega_0^2}.$$

Then

$$H_V^{(\pi)}(s) = \frac{1}{[1 + x + \tfrac{1}{2}x^2]} \xrightarrow[|x| \ll 1]{} e^{-x} = e^{-s/\omega_0}.$$

The delay time is then $1/\omega_0$.

This transfer has only two poles, which lie on a circle of radius $\sqrt{2}\omega_0$ and make angles of $(\pi/4)$ relative to the negative-real axis in the s plane. See Figs. 194 and 195. The Q value is $\sqrt{2}/2$ or 0.707. Therefore, there is one break frequency at $\sqrt{2}\omega_0$ in the

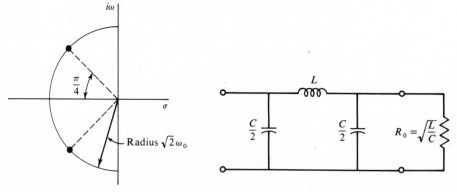

FIG. 194.   The pole-zero diagram for a low-pass, elementary π section terminated in $R_0 = \sqrt{L/C}$.

FIG. 195.   The elementary low-pass π section terminated in R_0.

---

† In more complicated sections, $Z(s)$ can vary as $L(s+w)$ while $Y(s)$ varies as $C(s+w)$. The section is constant k, but the roots are different and the attenuation is higher.

sinusoidal response, and there is no overshoot because the Q is less than 1. This is a very regular transfer function and has maximal flatness.

When we compute the input impedance for the π section, we find that the pole-zero distribution is inverted relative to that of the low-pass T section. See Fig. 196.

$$\frac{Z_{in}^{(\pi)}(s)}{k} = 2\left\{\frac{(x + \beta)(x + \beta^*)}{(x + \alpha)(x + \gamma)(x + \gamma^*)}\right\}.$$

Here (see Fig. 196),

$$\beta = (1 - i),$$

$$\gamma = \tfrac{9}{25} - i\sqrt{3},$$

and

$$\alpha = \tfrac{32}{25}.$$

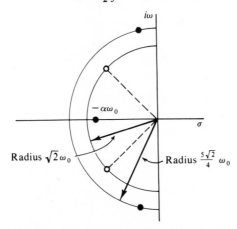

FIG. 196.   The pole-zero diagram of the input-impedance function $Z_W(s)$ for a low-pass, terminated π section.

It is again instructive to observe the response at the termination when this section is subjected to a square gate of width T (see Fig. 197):

$$v(t) = \mathscr{L}^{-1}\left[H_V^{(\pi)}(s) \cdot \frac{E_0}{s} \cdot (1 - e^{-sT})\right],$$

$$v(t) = E_0\left\{1 - \sqrt{2}e^{-\omega_0 t}\cos\left(\omega_0 t - \frac{\pi}{4}\right)\right\}U(t)$$

$$\quad - E_0\left\{1 - \sqrt{2}\,e^{-\omega_0(t-T)}\cos\left(\omega(t - T) - \frac{\pi}{4}\right)\right\}U(t - T).$$

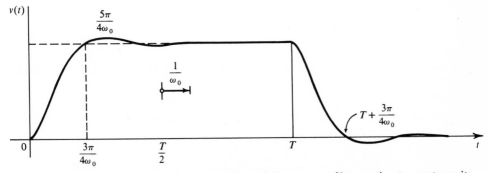

FIG. 197.   Response of an elementary, terminated, low-pass, π-filter section to a gate excitation of duration T.

The high-pass π filter is obtained by setting

$$Z(s) = \frac{1}{Cs}$$

and

$$Y(s) = \frac{1}{Ls}$$

See Fig. 198.

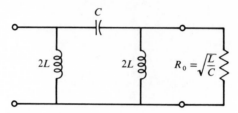

FIG. 198.   The elementary high-pass π section terminated in $k = R_0 = \sqrt{L/C}$.

Again,

$$x^2(s) = \frac{1}{LCs^2} = \frac{\omega_0^2}{s^2}.$$

The cutoff frequency now occurs at $\omega_0/\sqrt{2}$ because of the inversion. See Fig. 199.

$$H_V^{(\pi)}(s) = \frac{1}{\left[1 + x + \dfrac{1}{2}x^2\right]} = \frac{s^2}{\left(s + \dfrac{\omega_0}{\beta}\right)\left(s + \dfrac{\omega_0}{\beta^*}\right)}.$$

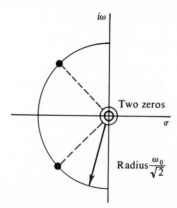

FIG. 199.   The pole-zero diagram of the voltage-transfer function of a terminated elementary, high-pass π filter.

The Q value is again equal to $\sqrt{2}/2$. This filter has a zero delay. A gate excitation of width T exhibits this nicely:

$$v(t) = \mathcal{L}^{-1}\left[H_V^{(\pi)}(\text{high pass})\frac{E_0}{s}(1 - e^{-sT})\right],$$

$$v(t) = E_0\sqrt{2}\, e^{-(\omega_0/2)t}\, \cos\!\left(\frac{\omega_0}{2}\, t + \frac{\pi}{4}\right) U(t)$$

$$- E_0\sqrt{2}\, e^{-(\omega_0/2)(t-T)}\, \cos\!\left(\frac{\omega_0}{2}(t - T) + \frac{\pi}{4}\right) U(t - T).$$

See Fig. 200.

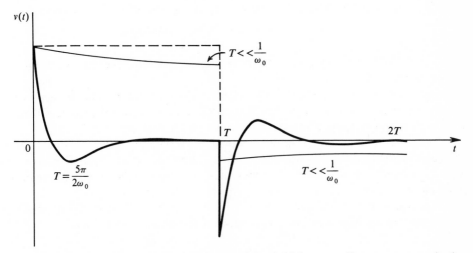

FIG. 200.   The response of an elementary, terminated, high-pass π filter to a gate excitation of duration T.

The low-pass π section has a phase shift of $(-\pi/4)$, indicating a delay. The high-pass section has an advance shown by a shift $(+\pi/4)$.

The " m-derived " Sections of "Constant k" Filters

The general method of transforming a filter matrix to an m-derived form was discussed on page 231. Because m-deriving retains the magnitude of $\mathbb{Z}$ or $\mathbb{Y}$ invariant, a constant k section transforms into a section of the same k. In spite of the fact that we are limiting our arguments to constant k sections, the methods are still quite general.

The m-derived, elementary, low-pass T section is shown in Fig. 201.

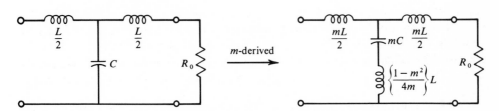

FIG. 201.   The m-derived, low-pass, T-filter section.

The forward-voltage transfer of the m-derived section $\left(\text{terminated in } \sqrt{\dfrac{Z}{Y}}\right)$ is

$$H_V^{(MT)}(x) = \frac{1 + \left[\dfrac{1 - m^2}{4}\right]x^2}{\left[1 + mx + \left(\dfrac{1 + m^2}{4}\right)x^2 + \dfrac{m}{4}x^3\right]}.$$

In this expression, $x(s)$ is determined by the initial parameters (low pass); $x^2(s) = LCs^2$. To the extent that the quadratic term in the numerator can be neglected,

$$H_V^{(MT)}(s) \xrightarrow[|x| \ll 1]{} e^{-mx} = e^{-(ms/\omega_0)}, \qquad \text{(low pass)}.$$

Thus, a value of m less than 1 shortens the characteristic delay, whereas a value greater than 1 lengthens the delay.

The presence of the term $[(1 - m^2)/4]x^2$ in the numerator places a zero in the transfer function. *This particular zero lies on the imaginary axis if m is less than 1. If m is greater than 1, the zeros are real and lie on the real axis.*

The presence of a zero on the imaginary axis is very useful if the zero is just above the poles that determine the cutoff of the filter. These then cause $|H_V(i\omega)|$ to drop to zero quite rapidly above cutoff while they cause a slightly higher amplitude than the function of an unmodified T section at frequencies above cutoff.

If m is less than 1, the zeros lie at $\pm i[4/(1 - m^2)]^{1/2}\omega_0$. To study the effect of m-deriving, the transfer function is evaluated on the imaginary axis. Let

$$x \xrightarrow[\sigma = 0]{} \frac{i\omega}{\omega_0} = i\Omega, \qquad \text{(low pass)};$$

then, writing in terms of amplitude and phase,

$$H_V^{(MT)}(i\Omega) = \rho(\Omega)e^{i\Phi(\Omega)}$$

$$= \frac{(1 - m^2)\left\{\left(\dfrac{4}{1 - m^2}\right) - \Omega^2\right\}e^{i\Phi(\Omega)}}{m\left\{\left(\dfrac{4}{m}\right)^2\left(1 - \left[\dfrac{1 + m^2}{4}\right]\Omega^2\right)^2 + \Omega^2(4 - \Omega^2)^2\right\}^{1/2}},$$

where

$$\cos \Phi(\Omega) = \rho(\Omega)\left\{\frac{1 - \left[\dfrac{1 + m^2}{4}\right]\Omega^2}{1 - \left[\dfrac{1 - m^2}{4}\right]\Omega^2}\right\}$$

and $m < 1$.

This expression was intentionally factored to favor values of m less than 1. The graph in Fig. 202 illustrates vividly the manner in which the cutoff of the section is improved by taking $m = 0.6$. A small value of m gives the lowest possible value of the zero at $2\omega_0$. A very small m, on the other hand, moves the poles too far out relative to $2\omega_0$.

When m is of the order of 0.6, the poles almost lie the same distance from the origin as the zeros (giving a sharp cutoff). These poles are quite close to the zero at

$2.5\omega_0(m = 0.6)$. The value $m = 0.6$ gives

$$\sqrt{\frac{4}{1-m^2}}\,\omega_0 = 2.5\omega_0,$$

the real pole,

$$\alpha_m = 1.96\omega_0;$$

and the complex poles,

$$\sqrt{\gamma\gamma^*} = 1.85\omega_0.$$

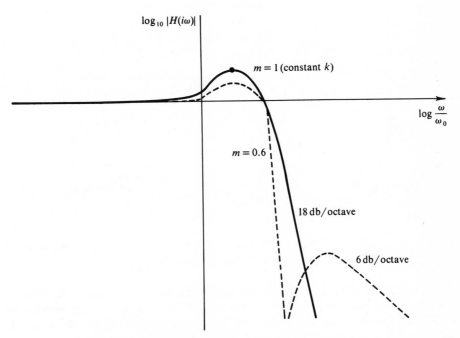

FIG. 202.   A comparison of the frequency response of a terminated, m-derived, low-pass T filter and the terminated, low-pass, elementary T filter.

A comparison of the magnitudes of the forward voltage-transfer function $|H_V(i\Omega)|$ of constant k terminated filters is shown in Fig. 202. The two curves are shown for $m = 0.6$ and $m = 1.0$ (primary T).

The values of m less than 1 give an optimum flatness and sharp cutoff in $H_V(s)$. On the other hand, the presence of the zero on the imaginary axis causes phase distortion and consequently a poor time-delay response as a function of frequency.

The frequency dependence of the time delay can be obtained quite readily from the exponential representation of $H_V(s)$. We write

$$H_V(s) = e^{-sT(s)},$$

where $T(s)$ is now a function of s. This gives a measure of the deviation of $H_V(s)$ from an ideal exponential form. Then

$$T(s) = -\frac{1}{s}\log H_V(s).$$

The complex part of $T(i\omega)$ gives the amplitude of $H_V(i\omega)$, while the real part of $T(i\omega)$ gives the time delay or phase shift $\Phi(\omega)$:

$$\Phi(\omega) = \tfrac{1}{2}\omega(T(\omega) + T^*(\omega)).$$

As a consequence, a computation of $\Phi(\omega)$ will give the delay as a function of frequency by merely multiplying by $1/\omega$. Some insight can be obtained by regarding the pole-zero diagrams of $H_V(s)$ in the three cases of $m < 1$, $m = 1$, and $1 < m$. See Fig. 203.

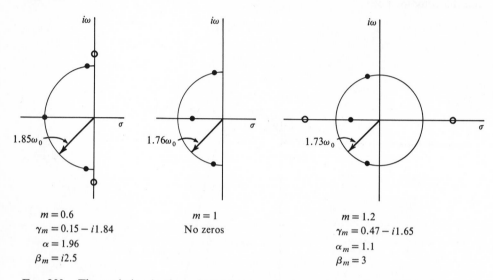

$m = 0.6$
$\gamma_m = 0.15 - i1.84$
$\alpha = 1.96$
$\beta_m = i2.5$

$m = 1$
No zeros

$m = 1.2$
$\gamma_m = 0.47 - i1.65$
$\alpha_m = 1.1$
$\beta_m = 3$

FIG. 203. The variation in the poles and zeros of a low-pass, terminated T section as the value of m is changed.

The presence of the zeros on the imaginary axis for $m = 0.6$ causes the phase to fluctuate quite rapidly at the cutoff. In the case of $1 < m$ ($m \cong 1.2$), the zeros are on the real axis and placed in such a manner that their contribution to the phase cancels. The phase is basically controlled by the first break frequency. The condition $m = +1.2$

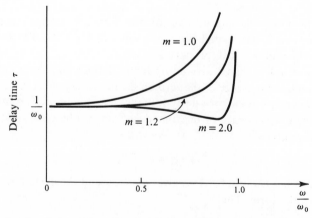

FIG. 204. A sketch of the delay characteristics of terminated, low-pass T sections for various values of m.

actually produces an optimum phase or delay response because the complex roots γ_m and γ_m^* have more damping than in the sharp cutoff case. This turns out to give better compensation in that $\Phi(\omega)$ tends to maintain a linear relation to ω over a much wider range of frequencies. See Fig. 204.

The condition $m > 1$ can be achieved only by coupling a negative inductance into the admittance branch. This can be accomplished with a transformer or by tapping into a solenoid, as shown in Fig. 205. The input impedance for the m-derived section terminated in k ohms is

$$\frac{Z_{in}^{(MT)}(s)}{k} = \frac{1 + mx + \left[\dfrac{1+m^2}{4}\right]x^2 + \dfrac{m}{4}x^3}{1 + mx + \left[\dfrac{1+m^2}{4}\right]x^2} \xrightarrow[|x| \ll 1]{} 1.$$

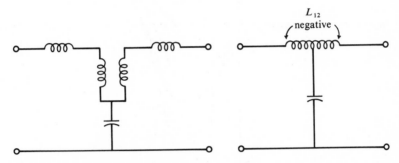

FIG. 205.   Mutual coupling to provide values of m greater than 1.

When $m = 1$, the poles are critically damped, but above the zeros at $1.75\omega_0$ and $1.3\omega_0$. The value $m = 0.6$ places the poles at $(-0.9 \pm i1.5)\omega_0$, which corresponds to a circle of radius $1.73\omega_0$. This is good design, since the complex poles and zeros tend to cancel one another except for some fluctuation due to the high-Q value of the complex zeros. See Fig. 206.

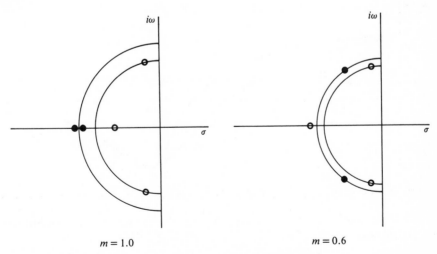

$m = 1.0$ $m = 0.6$

FIG. 206.   Variation in the poles and zeros of the input impedance of a terminated T filter as the value of m is changed.

The case of $m = +1.2$ gives poles at $(1 \pm i)\omega_0$ on a circle of radius $1.67\omega_0$. This is not as flat an H_V function as that for $m = 0.6$, since the real zero lies at $-1.1\omega_0$, giving a large increase in Z_{in} near ω_0. See Figs. 207 and 208.

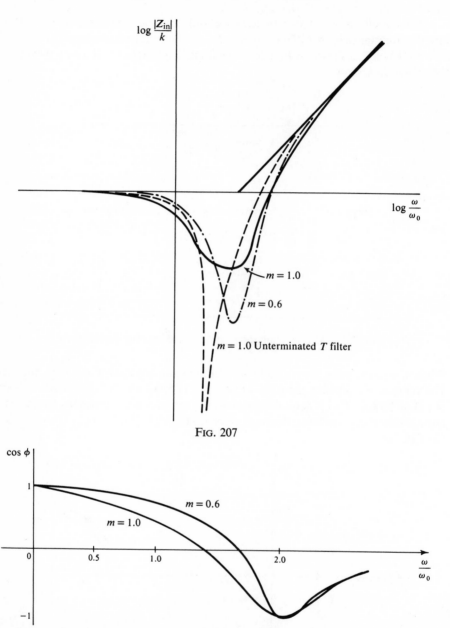

FIG. 207

FIG. 208.   Cosine of the phase response of the terminated T-filter section for two m values.

The m-derived filter with $m = 0.6$ has further distinct advantages. An ordinary T filter has an image impedance of

$$\left[\frac{L}{C}\left(1 - \frac{\omega^2}{4\omega_0^2} \right) \right]^{\frac{1}{2}} \text{ ohms.}$$

The resistive termination gives a Z_{in}^{T} which deviates somewhat from Z_0. An m-derived section terminated in $\sqrt{L/C}$ provides a Z_{in} that is a closer approximation to Z_0. Thus, a number of ordinary T sections in cascade can best be terminated in one m-derived section, which is then terminated in a pure resistance.

The combination of the two types, $m = 1$ and $m = 0.6$, is superior in that the m-derived filter offers the better impedance match and a sharp cutoff, whereas the ordinary T section provides more attenuation above cutoff.

Cascaded Sections

The system of filters in cascade provides a sharper filter characteristic than that of the individual section. Sections of the same image impedance Z_0 can be cascaded without introducing reflections at the junction. One fact that clarifies this is that the input voltage and current relations ($Z_{in}(s)$) are unaltered by any output terminal connection to the image impedance.

As mentioned previously, the last section to be terminated in a single, lumped impedance is quite important. The pure resistance termination does not give proper matching near cutoff. However the m-derived section with a resistive termination may provide a better image-impedance match at its input than does the elementary constant k section.

To illustrate a typical calculation of the response of two cascaded sections, we shall consider two elementary low-pass π sections in cascade and terminated in a resistive load.

The cascade $\mathbb{A}$ matrix for a single π section is

$$\mathbb{A} = \begin{pmatrix} \dfrac{(2 + ZY)}{2} & Z \\[2ex] \dfrac{Y(4 + ZY)}{4} & \dfrac{(2 + ZY)}{2} \end{pmatrix}.$$

When two sections are cascaded, the total $\mathbb{A}$ matrix is

$$\mathbb{A}_2(s) = \mathbb{A} \cdot \mathbb{A} = \begin{pmatrix} \dfrac{[2 + 4ZY + (ZY)^2]}{2} & Z(2 + ZY) \\[2ex] \dfrac{Y(4 + ZY)(2 + ZY)}{4} & \dfrac{[2 + 4ZY + (ZY)^2]}{2} \end{pmatrix}.$$

The forward voltage transfer and input impedance are

$$H_V^{(2,\pi)}(s) = \frac{2Z_L}{2Z(2 + x^2) + (2 + 4x^2 + x^4)Z_L}$$

and

$$Z_{in}^{(2,\pi)}(s) = \left(\frac{Z(s)}{Y(s)}\right)\frac{[4(2 + x^2) + 2(2 + 4x^2 + x^4)(Z_L/Z)]}{[(4 + x^2)(2 + x^2)Z_L + (2/Y)(2 + 4x^2 + x^4)]},$$

where

$$x^2(s) = Z(s)Y(s).$$

Again, the value of Z_L that makes $Z_{in} = Z_L$ is Z_0:

$$Z_L = Z_0 = \sqrt{\frac{Z}{Y}} \frac{1}{[1 + (ZY/4)]^{1/2}}.$$

Approximating Z_0 by setting $Z_L = \sqrt{Z/Y}$, we find

$$H_V^{(2,\pi)}(x) = \frac{1}{[1 + 2x + \frac{1}{2}(2x)^2 + x^3 + \frac{1}{2}x^4]} \xrightarrow[|x| \ll 1]{} e^{-2x}.$$

Thus, the delay in the midband region ($|x| \ll 1$), if this is a low-pass device such that $x \propto s$, is

$$\tau_d \cong \frac{2x}{s} = \frac{2}{\omega_0}.$$

As one would expect, to first-order two sections provides twice the delay of one section.

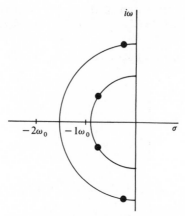

FIG. 209. The pole distribution for a cascade of two elementary, low-pass π sections. The array is terminated in k.

The poles of a single low-pass π section terminated in k ohms were located at $-(i \pm i)\omega_0$ in the s plane. The two-section filter has four poles. The reader can verify that the four poles of $H_V(s)$ are approximately at

$$-\gamma_1 = -\tfrac{1}{4}(3 - 2i)\omega_0, \qquad (\text{with } \gamma_1^*).$$

and

$$-\gamma_2 = -\tfrac{1}{4}(1 - 6i)\omega_0, \qquad (\text{with } \gamma_2^*).$$

These roots give the first cutoff at $0.9\omega_0$, with a $Q_1 = 0.6$. The second cutoff occurs at $1.52\omega_0$, with a $Q_2 = 3$. The differences in the Q values tend to provide a relatively sharp cutoff near $\sqrt{\gamma_2 \gamma_2^*}$. See Fig. 210.

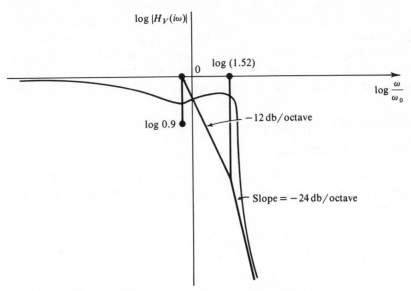

FIG. 210.   The asymptotes of the magnitude of the sinusoidal response for the voltage transfer of two low-pass π filters in cascade.

TRANSMISSION LINES

Introduction

The propagation of electromagnetic energy through a continuous medium can be approached from two different points of view. One method is to treat conductors as distributed circuit elements; the other is to use Maxwell's equations and solve the boundary-value problem.

The first method is useful when two separate conductors are utilized. In such cases, one can assign certain parameters to the problems such as inductance per unit length, capacitance per unit length, resistance per unit length, and conductance per unit length. Insofar as these parameters are constant and independent of frequency, one can derive the relationships between the voltage and the current at points along the line which are the so-called telegraphist's equations. The advantage to this approach is that it treats the line itself as a circuit element, and therefore a circuit theory for transmission lines can be developed. A disadvantage of this method is that it *requires* two separate conductors, which may not always be the case (i.e., wave guides in microwave techniques). Also, there is no indication that this approach describes only one (the transverse electromagnetic mode) of an infinite number of modes that may be excited (although in practice higher modes correspond typically to 10^{10} cps and are rarely excited).

If, instead, we start with Maxwell's equations; solutions for the propagation of electromagnetic waves bounded by a conductor or conductors can be obtained in linear homogeneous isotropic media. For hollow conductors (or wave guides), one finds that there is a lower frequency (called the *cutoff frequency* of the dominant mode) below which no energy can be propagated (this is obvious, since direct current could not be passed). When the two-conductor problem is solved, of course, the solutions include direct currents. The advantage to this approach is that one can determine the propagation characteristics of wave guides; also, one can find which modes may be excited in transmission lines if high frequencies are involved. Problems of launching signals from a cable to a wire can be analyzed in this manner. A disadvantage of this approach is that it is difficult to identify the components of solutions with circuit parameters and consequently difficult to apply the methods of ordinary circuit theory.

Circuit Theory of Transmission Lines

Telegraphist's Equations

An element of a transmission line can be represented as having distributed inductance, capacitance, and resistance per unit length, as shown in Fig. 211. The loop equations give†

$$v(x,t) - \left\{ L\frac{\partial i\,(x,t)}{\partial t} + Ri(x,t) \right\}\delta x - v(x,t) - \frac{\partial v\,(x,t)}{\partial x}\,\delta x = 0$$

and

$$i(x,t) - \left\{ C\frac{\partial v\,(x,t)}{\partial t} + Gv(x,t) \right\}\delta x - i(x,t) - \frac{\partial i\,(x,t)}{\partial x}\,\delta x = 0.$$

Therefore

$$L\frac{\partial i}{\partial t} + Ri = -\frac{\partial v}{\partial x} \qquad (1)$$

and

$$C\frac{\partial v}{\partial t} + Gv = -\frac{\partial i}{\partial x}. \qquad (2)$$

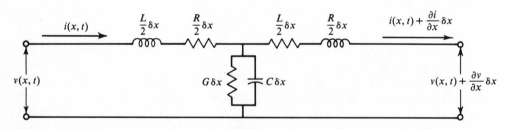

FIG. 211. An element of a long transmission line represented in terms of lumped circuit parameters.

Differentiating Eq. 1 with respect to t, and Eq. 2 with respect to x, we obtain

$$-\frac{\partial^2 i}{\partial x\,\partial t} = C\frac{\partial^2 v}{\partial t^2} + G\frac{\partial v}{\partial t} = \frac{1}{L}\frac{\partial^2 v}{\partial x^2} + \frac{R}{L}\frac{\partial i}{\partial x}.$$

---

† Throughout the discussion in this section,
  L = inductance per unit length of cable
  C = capacitance per unit length
  R = series resistance per unit length
  G = parallel conductance per unit length

Substituting Eq. 2 into the last term,

$$\frac{\partial^2 v}{\partial x^2} = LC \frac{\partial^2 v}{\partial t^2} + \{RC + LG\} \frac{\partial v}{\partial t} + RGv;$$

and the dual equation is

$$\frac{\partial^2 i}{\partial x^2} = LC \frac{\partial^2 i}{\partial t^2} + \{RC + LG\} \frac{\partial i}{\partial t} + RGi.$$

These general equations are known as the *telegraphist's equations*. Using these equations, we shall be able to discuss the transmission of energy along transmission lines. Taking the Laplace transform of equations, we have†

$$\frac{\partial^2 V(x,s)}{\partial x^2} = \{R + Ls\}\{G + Cs\}V(x,s).$$

Let us define $\gamma^2 = (R + sL)(G + sC)$. This equation then has solutions $V(x,s) = V_0(s)e^{-\gamma x} + V_0'(s)e^{\gamma x}$, where $V_0(s) = V(0,s)$.

Semiinfinite Transmission Line

If, for the moment, we consider only semiinfinite transmission lines, then $V_0'(s) \equiv 0$ [since $V(x,s)$ must be finite]. Then

$$V(x,s) = V_0(s)e^{-\gamma x},$$

where we interpret $V_0(s)$ as the Laplace transform of $v(t)$ at $x = 0$.
    Notice also that

$$L\frac{\partial i}{\partial t} + Ri = -\frac{\partial v}{\partial x}.$$

By taking the Laplace transform of this equation, we have

$$(sL + R)I(x,s) = \gamma V(0,s)e^{-\gamma x} = \gamma V(x,s).$$

Define the characteristic impedance Z_0 to be $\{V(x,s)/I(x,s)\}$, and we obtain

$$Z_0 = \sqrt{\frac{R + Ls}{G + Cs}}.$$

The two parameters γ and Z_0 are quite general so far. When a particular problem is stated, Z_0 and γ will be fixed. In order to illustrate practical transmission lines, we shall consider three important cases.
    Case 1: " *Lossless Transmission Line* "; $R = G = 0$. For this case,

$$\gamma = s\sqrt{LC} = sT \quad \text{and} \quad Z_0 = \sqrt{\frac{L}{C}},$$

where T will be identified as time per unit length. Then

$$V(x,s) = V(0,s)e^{-sTx} = V_0(s)e^{-sTx}.$$

---

† We have assumed that all voltages and currents are zero at $t = 0$. This gives no loss of generality.

The inverse transform of $V(x,s)$ gives

$$v(x,t) = v(0,t - Tx).$$

This result implies that the voltage pulse at any point x is an exact reproduction of the pulse at $x = 0$, but that it does not arrive until a time T. Hence, $T = \sqrt{LC}$ is the *delay* time per unit length. This result could also be interpreted as meaning that any disturbance of $v(t)$ at $x = 0$ travels along the transmission line with a uniform velocity. To see this, regard $V_0 = dx/dt$ when $(t - xT)$ is a constant. Then

$$V_0 = \frac{1}{T} = \frac{1}{\sqrt{LC}},$$

which is the velocity of propagation of a signal.

Case 2: "*Distortionless Line*"; $R/L = G/C$. For this case, the reader will notice that $\gamma = \{(R/Z_0) + sT\}$ and that Z_0 is still $\sqrt{L/C}$. Then

$$V(x,s) = V_0(s)e^{-(R/Z_0)x}e^{-sTx}.$$

Taking the inverse transform of $V(x, s)$,

$$v(x,t) = e^{-(R/Z_0)x}v(0,t - xT).$$

This result is similar to case 1, in that the voltage pulse is undistorted. However, the voltage pulse does suffer an attenuation of $\{R/Z_0\}$ per unit length as it travels along the transmission line.

Case 3: "*Small Loss Transmission Lines*"; $R \ll sL, G \ll sC$. Under these conditions

$$\gamma = s\sqrt{LC}\left(1 + \frac{R}{sL}\right)^{1/2}\left(1 + \frac{G}{sC}\right)^{1/2}$$

and

$$Z_0 = \sqrt{\frac{L}{C}}\sqrt{\frac{1 + (R/sL)}{1 + (G/sC)}}.$$

Expanding the square roots and keeping only terms to first order of (R/sL) or (G/sC), we find that

$$\gamma \simeq sT + \frac{R}{2Z_0} + \frac{G}{2Y_0},$$

$$Z_0 \simeq \sqrt{\frac{L}{C}}\left\{1 + \frac{1}{2s}\left(\frac{R}{L} - \frac{G}{C}\right)\right\} \rightarrow \sqrt{\frac{L}{C}}.$$

and

$$Z_0 = \frac{1}{Y_0}.$$

In a real coaxial cable, R is dominated by the resistivity of the conductor, and G is due to losses in the dielectrics. Usually one defines losses due to the conductor as $\alpha_c = R/2Z_0$; and losses due to the dielectric as $\alpha_d = G/2Y_0$.

The solution to this problem is again obtained by taking the inverse Laplace transform:

$$V(x,s) = V_0(s)e^{-(\alpha_c + \alpha_d)x}e^{-sTx}$$

and

$$v(x,t) = e^{-(\alpha_c + \alpha_d)x}v(0, t - Tx).$$

It should be pointed out that it has been assumed that R and G are independent of frequency.

Finite Transmission Lines

CHARACTERISTIC IMPEDANCE

If the transmission line is terminated with an impedance $Z(s)$, the solution is more involved than in the previous case. In the problem of the "lossless transmission line," the general solution is

$$A(s)e^{sTx} + B(s)e^{-sTx}.$$

For reasons that will become obvious later, let us define

$$A(s) = \overleftarrow{\mathbf{V}}_0(s) \quad \text{and} \quad B(s) = \overrightarrow{\mathbf{V}}_0(s),$$

where

$$\overrightarrow{\mathbf{V}}_0(s)e^{-sTx} = \overrightarrow{\mathbf{V}}_x(s)$$

and

$$\overleftarrow{\mathbf{V}}_0(s)e^{sTx} = \overleftarrow{\mathbf{V}}_x(s).$$

The general solution is

$$V(x,s) = \overrightarrow{\mathbf{V}}_x(s) + \overleftarrow{\mathbf{V}}_x(s).$$

Taking inverse Laplace transforms,

$$v(x,t) = \overrightarrow{v}(0,(t - Tx)) + \overleftarrow{v}(0, t + Tx).$$

The arrow directed to the right indicates a signal traveling to the right and vice versa for quantities directed to the left. The general solution to the wave equation for transmission lines of finite length is a pulse traveling to the right, $v_0(t - Tx)$, and a pulse traveling to the left, $v_0(t + Tx)$. In like manner, the solution for the currents is

$$I(x,s) = \overrightarrow{\mathbf{I}}_x(s) + \overleftarrow{\mathbf{I}}_x(s),$$

where

$$\overrightarrow{\mathbf{I}}_x(s) = \overrightarrow{\mathbf{I}}_0 e^{-sTx},$$

$$\overleftarrow{\mathbf{I}}_x(s) = \overleftarrow{\mathbf{I}}_0 e^{+sTx}.$$

Since $\overrightarrow{\mathbf{I}}_x$ and $\overrightarrow{\mathbf{V}}_x$ is one *set* of solutions to the wave equations, and since $\overleftarrow{\mathbf{I}}_x$ and $\overleftarrow{\mathbf{V}}_x$ is an independent set of solutions, it can be shown that

$$\frac{\overrightarrow{\mathbf{V}}_0}{\overrightarrow{\mathbf{I}}_0} = \frac{\overrightarrow{\mathbf{V}}_x}{\overrightarrow{\mathbf{I}}_x} = -\frac{\overleftarrow{\mathbf{V}}_0}{\overleftarrow{\mathbf{I}}_0} = -\frac{\overleftarrow{\mathbf{V}}_x}{\overleftarrow{\mathbf{I}}_0} = Z_0 = \sqrt{\frac{L}{C}}.$$

THE REFLECTION COEFFICIENT

Consider the termination of the cable as is shown in Fig. 212. Time-dependent voltage and current signals traveling to the right and left are indicated at the termination.

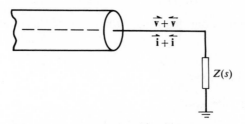

FIG. 212.   The termination of a long line.

As a boundary condition at the terminated end $(x = l)$,

$$Z(s) = \frac{\vec{V}(l,s) + \overleftarrow{V}(l,s)}{\vec{I}(l,s) + \overleftarrow{I}(l,s)}.$$

We define the voltage reflection coefficient ρ_l as

$$\rho_l = \frac{\overleftarrow{V}(l,s)}{\vec{V}(l,s)};$$

then

$$Z(s) = \frac{\vec{V}}{\vec{I}}\left(\frac{1 + \rho_l}{1 + (\overleftarrow{I}/\vec{I})}\right) = Z_0\left(\frac{1 + \rho_l}{1 - \rho_l}\right)$$

and

$$\rho_l = \frac{Z(s) - Z_0}{Z(s) + Z_0}.$$

For sinusoidal oscillations, the reflection coefficient is usually measured in terms of the voltage standing wave ratio (VSWR), or

$$VSWR = \frac{|\vec{V}| + |\overleftarrow{V}|}{|\vec{V}| - |\overleftarrow{V}|} = \left(\frac{1 + |\rho_l|}{1 - |\rho_l|}\right).$$

FINITE TRANSMISSION LINE AS A CIRCUIT ELEMENT

Consider the circuit pictured in Fig. 213(a). This is a complete circuit with a generator at the left, a termination at the right, and a length l of transmission line between them.

Writing the total voltage (Laplace) transform at $x = 0$,

$$V_0(s) = \vec{V}_0(s) + \overleftarrow{V}_0(s),$$

with

$$\vec{\mathbf{V}}_0(s) = \frac{Z_0}{Z_g + Z_0} E_g(s) + \rho_0 \overleftarrow{\mathbf{V}}_0$$

and

$$\overleftarrow{\mathbf{V}}_0(s) = \vec{\mathbf{V}}_0(s) \rho_l e^{-2Tls}.$$

Then

$$\vec{\mathbf{V}}_0(s) = \frac{Z_0 E_g}{\{Z_0 + Z_g\}} \left\{ \frac{1}{1 - \rho_0 \rho_l e^{-2Tls}} \right\}.$$

The total solution is

$$V_0(s) = \vec{\mathbf{V}}_0 + \overleftarrow{\mathbf{V}}_0,$$

or

$$V_0(s) = \frac{Z_0}{(Z_0 + Z_g)} \left\{ \frac{1 + \rho_l e^{-2Tls}}{1 - \rho_0 \rho_l e^{-2Tls}} \right\} E_g(s),$$

where

$$\rho_0 = \frac{Z_g - Z_0}{Z_g + Z_0} \quad \text{and} \quad \rho_l = \frac{Z_l - Z_0}{Z_l + Z_0}.$$

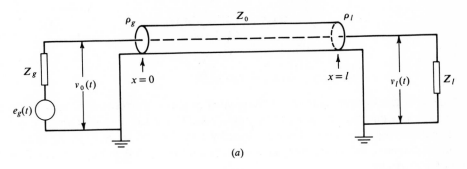

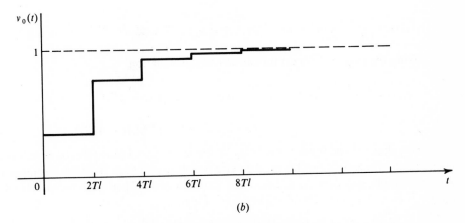

FIG. 213. (a) A schematic of a finite transmission line. (b) Input wave form when the termination is open-circuited.

Inserting the input impedance in the manner indicated,

$$V_0(s) = \left(\frac{Z_{in}}{Z_{in} + Z_g}\right)E_g(s);$$

one can demonstrate that

$$Z_{in} = Z_0\left(\frac{1 + \rho_l e^{-2Tls}}{1 - \rho_l e^{-2Tls}}\right).$$

It will be left as an exercise to show that

$$V_l(s) = \frac{Z_0}{(Z_0 + Z_g)}\left\{\frac{(1 + \rho_l)e^{-Tls}}{1 - \rho_0\rho_l e^{-2Tls}}\right\}E_g(s)$$

and

$$V_l(s) = \frac{(1 + \rho_l)e^{-Tls}}{[1 + \rho_l e^{-2Tls}]}V_0(s).$$

Several results can be concluded from these relations. First, if the load impedance is a pure resistance such that $Z = Z_0$, then $\rho_l = 0$ and

$$Z_{in} = Z_0.$$

Also,

$$V_0(s) = \left(\frac{Z_0}{Z_0 + Z_g}\right)E_g(s)$$

and

$$V_l(s) = V_0(s)e^{-sTl}.$$

That is, if the transmission line is terminated in the characteristic impedance Z_0, it behaves as a pure resistance Z_0 in the input circuit, and the output of the line is the same as the input except that it is delayed by a time Tl. Next, consider Z_g and Z_l as pure resistances, but of arbitrary magnitude, such that $\rho_0 \neq 0$ and $\rho_l \neq 0$. Then Eq. 3 can be expanded as

$$V_0(s) = \left(\frac{Z_0}{R_g + Z_0}\right)(1 + \rho_l e^{-2Tls})\{1 + \rho_0\rho_l e^{-2Tls} + \rho_0^2\rho_l^2 e^{-4Tls} + \cdots\}E_g(s).$$

Taking the inverse Laplace transforms of this equation,

$$v_0(t) = \left(\frac{Z_0}{Z_0 + R_g}\right)[e(t) + \{\rho_l(1 + \rho_0)e(t - 2Tl)U(t - 2Tl)$$

$$+ \rho_l^2\rho_0(1 + \rho_0)e(t - 4Tl)U(t - 4T_ll) + \cdots].$$

The voltage at the input is made up of the input signal plus reflections from the termination. These occur each time the pulse travels to and back from the termination. As an example, consider $R_g = 2Z_0$, $Z_l = \infty$ (open end). Then $\rho_0 = \frac{1}{3}$, $\rho_l = 1$. Let $e_g(t) = U(t)$, a step function of height 1 volt. Finally,

$$v_0(t) = \tfrac{1}{3}U(t) + \tfrac{1}{3}(1 + \tfrac{1}{3})U(t - 2Tl) + \tfrac{1}{9}(1 + \tfrac{1}{3})U(t - 4Tl) + \cdots.$$

The wave form $v_0(t)$ is shown in Fig. 213(b).

There is a large class of useful results that one can obtain by simply setting $R_g = Z_0$, $\rho_0 = 0$, and "shaping" the input pulse; then

$$V_0(s) = \tfrac{1}{2}(1 + \rho_l e^{-2Tls})E_g(s).$$

If $Z_l = Z_0$ and $\rho_l = 0$, one finds that

$$v_0(t) = \tfrac{1}{2}e_g(t).$$

On the other hand, if

$$Z_l = 0 \quad \text{and} \quad \rho_l = -1,$$

then

$$v_0(t) = \tfrac{1}{2}\{e_g(t) - e_g(t - 2Tl)\},$$

(where $e_g(t) = 0$ if $t < 0$). This result is known as *delay line clipping*. Consider, for example, $e_g(t) = U(t)$. Then

$$v_0(t) = \tfrac{1}{2}\{U(t) - U(t - 2Tl)\}.$$

This operation is useful, for example, to prevent "pile up" of pulses at the input to an amplifier.

There are many other special cases. However, let us only consider one case, which is very important at high frequencies (greater than 100 Mc) or fast rise times (greater than 4*ns*). We have been discussing transmission lines that have only two restrictions: (1) that they are lossless, and (2) that they have uniform characteristics. Our results can be related, for example, to short signal wires running parallel with a metal chassis. In order to see just how short such leads should be and at what frequencies the length becomes important, consider the case where $\omega Tl \ll 1$, so that $e^{-2sTl} \simeq 1 - 2sTl$. Then

$$Z_{in} \simeq Z_l \left\{ \frac{1 - sTl\left[\dfrac{Z_l - Z_0}{Z_l}\right]}{1 + sTl\left[\dfrac{Z_l - Z_0}{Z_l}\right]} \right\}.$$

Consider three termination conditions and the resulting input impedance:

1. If $Z_0 = Z_l$, then $Z_{in} = Z_l$.
2. If $Z_0 \gg Z_l$, then $Z_{in} \simeq Z_l + sLl$.
3. If $Z_0 \ll Z_l$, then $Z_{in} \simeq \dfrac{Z_l}{1 + [Cl]sZ_l}$,

(where $T = \sqrt{LC}$; $Z_0 = L/C$].†

For condition (1), the input impedance is a pure resistance. Condition (2) states that the input impedance behaves as if the load impedance Z_l were in series with an inductor of value Ll, where L is the inductance per unit length of the transmission line and l is the length of the transmission line. Condition (3) states that the input impedance behaves as if the load impedance were in parallel with a capacitor of value Cl. (Again, C is the capacitance per unit length.)

---

† The reader is reminded that $L =$ inductance per unit length and $C =$ capacitance per unit length.

APPENDIXES

THE SOLUTION OF CUBIC AND QUARTIC EQUATIONS

These problems of finding the roots of a cubic has been of interest since antiquity; the methods outlined here have been used for almost 300 years. Consider the general cubic

$$x^3 + bx^2 + cx + d = 0.$$

The method of Cardin can be employed by eliminating the square term. To do this, let

$$x = y - \frac{b}{3},$$

giving

$$y^3 + py + q = 0.$$

Three special cases exist, which can be solved by examination.

1. $p = 0, q \neq 0$; then the roots are $(-q)^{1/3}$.
2. $q = 0, p \neq 0$; this has roots $0, \pm\sqrt{-p}$.
3. $4p^3 + 27q^2 = 0$; giving a set of degenerate roots $-(2q/3p)$ and one root, $3q/p$.

The general equation can be solved in terms of three quantities

$$A = \left\{ -\frac{q}{2} + \sqrt{\frac{q^2}{2} + \frac{p^3}{27}} \right\}^{1/3},$$

$$B = \left\{ -\frac{q}{2} - \sqrt{\frac{q^2}{2} + \frac{p^3}{27}} \right\}^{1/3},$$

and

$$\omega = -\frac{1}{2} + i\frac{\sqrt{3}}{2}.$$

Finally, the roots are

$$y_1 = A + B,$$

$$y_2 = \omega A + \omega^2 B,$$

and

$$y_3 = \omega^2 A + \omega B.$$

The quartic is actually solved by reducing it to a cubic and then using the methods just shown. Regard the general form

$$x^4 + 2px^3 + qx^2 + rx + s = 0.$$

Rearrange this to read

$$x^4 + 2px^3 = -qx^2 - rx - s.$$

We now add a quadratic function to both sides in order to make the left-hand side a perfect square. Add

$$(p^2 + u)x^2 + pux + \frac{u^2}{4}.$$

Then our equation becomes

$$\left[x^2 + px + \frac{u}{2} \right]^2 = (p^2 + u - q)x^2 + (pu - r)x + \frac{u^2}{4} - s.$$

The right-hand side is a perfect square if the discriminant is zero, or if

$$(pu - r)^2 - 4(p^2 + u - q)\left[\frac{u^2}{4} - s \right] = 0.$$

In terms of u^n we have

$$u^3 - qu^2 + (2pr - 4s)u + (4qs - 4p^2s - r^2) = 0.$$

To solve the quartic, then, we must solve the cubic equation in u to give roots u_1, u_2, and u_3. When this is done, the quartic can be put in the form

$$\left[x^2 + px + \frac{u_j}{2} \right]^2 = (a_j x + b_j)^2.$$

Hence, two roots are obtained from

$$x^2 + px + \tfrac{1}{2}u_j = a_j x + b_j$$

and from

$$x^2 + px + \tfrac{1}{2}u_j = -a_j x - b_j.$$

The u_j has been kept general, since any one of the u_j will give all four roots.

APPENDIX B

THE ZETA TRANSFORM

Up to this point, our analysis has dealt with problems involving continuous excitation and distributed circuits. We encounter many problems that pertain to uniform and regular excitation or involve repeated networks.

The problem of a repeated network can be formally solved by means of the techniques previously developed. On the other hand, these approaches are sometimes not the most convenient.

The Zeta transform involves excitation by a regular train of delta functions; consequently, the response is a sequence rather than a function of a continuous variable. Because the sequence is a much simpler object mathematically, it can in many instances be employed for a first analysis of a system.

We manufacture the excitation function $f_{\mathscr{z}}(t)$ from a continuous function $f(t)$ by passing $f(t)$ through a switching device that produces a regular train of impulses. The amplitude variation of these impulses follows $f(t)$. See Fig. 214. Then

$$f_{\mathscr{z}}(t) = f(t)\,\Delta_T(t),$$

where

$$\Delta_T(t) = \sum_{n=-\infty}^{\infty} \delta(t - nT).$$

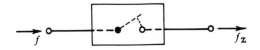

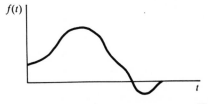
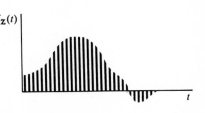

FIG. 214

If we use the one-sided transform, $f(t)$ is zero for $t < 0$ and

$$f_{\mathscr{z}}(t) = \sum_{n=0}^{\infty} f(t)\,\delta(t - nT).$$

The Laplace transform of $f_\mathscr{Z}(t)$ then appears as an exponential series expansion in s:

$$\mathscr{L}[f_\mathscr{Z}(t)] = \mathscr{L}\left[\sum_{n=0}^{\infty} f(t)\,\delta(t - nT)\right] = F_\mathscr{Z}(s) = \sum_{n=0}^{\infty} f(nT)e^{-nTs}.$$

We now define a new variable Z such that

$$Z = e^{Ts};$$

therefore,

$$F(Z) = F_\mathscr{Z}\left(s = \frac{1}{T}\log Z\right) = \sum_{n=0}^{\infty} f(nT)Z^{-n}.$$

This relation designates the form of a new transform of $f(t)$;

$$\mathscr{Z}[f_\mathscr{Z}(t)] = F_\mathscr{Z}\left(\frac{1}{T}\log Z\right) = \sum_{n=0}^{\infty} f(nT)Z^{-n}.$$

The inverse of $\mathscr{Z}[\ ]$ does *not* give $f(t)$, but only $f_\mathscr{Z}(t)$.

As an example, consider the transform

$$\frac{TZ}{[Z-1]^2}$$

Now

$$\frac{TZ}{(Z-1)^2} = \frac{T/Z}{\left[1 - \dfrac{2}{Z} + \dfrac{1}{Z^2}\right]} = T\{Z^{-1} + 2Z^{-2} + 3Z^{-3} + \cdots kZ^{-k} + \cdots\}$$

and

$$f_\mathscr{Z}(t) = \mathscr{Z}^{-1}\left[\frac{TZ}{(Z-1)^2}\right] = \sum_{n=0}^{\infty} (nT)\,\delta(t - nT).$$

The approach is analogous to that used in the development of Laplace transforms. A few specific zeta transforms are listed below.

1. The shifted impulse function:

$$\mathscr{L}[\delta(t - nT)U(t - nT)] = e^{-nTs},$$

$$\mathscr{Z}[\delta(t - nT)U(t - nT)] = Z^{-n}.$$

$$\mathscr{Z}[\delta(t)] = 1.$$

2. The exponential function:

$$\mathscr{Z}[e^{\alpha t}] = \sum_{n=0}^{\infty} e^{n\alpha T}Z^{-n} = \frac{Z}{Z - e^{-\alpha T}}.$$

3. The unit-step function:

$$\mathscr{Z}[U(t)] = \lim_{\alpha \to 0} \mathscr{Z}[e^{\alpha t}] = \frac{Z}{Z - 1}.$$

4. Sine and cosine functions:

$$\mathscr{L}[\cos \omega t] = \frac{Z(Z - \cos \omega T)}{[Z^2 - 2Z \cos \omega T + 1]},$$

$$\mathscr{L}[\sin \omega t] = \frac{z \sin \omega T}{[Z^2 - 2Z \cos \omega T + 1]}.$$

5. The ramp function:

$$\mathscr{L}[t] = \frac{TZ}{(Z-1)^2}; \qquad Z[t^m] = \sum_{n=0}^{\infty} (nT)^m Z^{-n}.$$

6. The shifted function:

$$\mathscr{L}[f(t + T)] = Z\{\mathscr{L}[f(t)] - f(0+)\},$$

$$\mathscr{L}[f(t + 2T)] = Z^2\{\mathscr{L}[f(t)] - f(0+)\} - Zf(T).$$

7. The shifting theorem:

$$\mathscr{L}[f(t - nT)U(t - nT)] = \sum_{m=0}^{\infty} f([m - n]T)U([m - n]T)Z^{-m}$$

$$= Z^{-n} \sum_{m=0}^{\infty} f([m - n]T)U([m - n]T)Z^{-(m-n)}$$

$$= Z^{-n} \sum_{k=-n}^{\infty} f(kT)U(kT)Z^{-k}$$

$$= Z^{-n} \sum_{k=0}^{\infty} f(kT)Z^{-k}$$

$$= Z^{-n}\mathscr{L}[f(t)].$$

8. Initial value theorem:

$$f(0) = \lim_{Z \to \infty} \mathscr{L}[f(t)].$$

To see this,

$$\lim_{Z \to \infty} \mathscr{L}[f(t)] = \lim_{Z \to \infty} \sum_{n=0}^{\infty} f(nT)Z^{-n} = \lim_{Z \to \infty} \{f(0) + Z^{-1}f(T) + \cdots\}.$$

If $f(0) = 0$, we can also add that

$$f(T) = \lim_{Z \to \infty} Z\mathscr{L}[f(t)].$$

9. The final value theorem:

$$\lim_{t \to \infty} f(t) = \lim_{Z \to 1} (Z - 1)\mathscr{L}[f(t)].$$

We can now apply our formalism to the solution of difference equations. Consider the problem

$$v(t) + b_1 v(t + T) + b_2 v(t + 2T) = e(t),$$

or in the special case, $t = nT$,

$$v(n) + b_1 v(n + 1) + b_2 v(n + 2) = e(n).$$

The complementary solution can be obtained from

$$v_c(n) + b_1 v_c(n + 1) + b_2 v_c(n + 2) = 0.$$

If we let

$$v_c(n) = e^{ns},$$

and

$$v_c(n + m) = e^{(n+m)s} = e^{ms}e^{ns} = Z^m e^{ns},$$

then

$$\{1 + b_1 Z + b_2 Z^2\}e^{sn} = 0.$$

This equation has roots

$$Z_1 = e^{s_1}$$

and

$$Z_2 = e^{s_2}.$$

Then

$$v_c(n) = C_1 Z_1^n + C_2 Z_2^n.$$

If the roots are degenerate, i.e., $Z_1 = Z_2$, then

$$v_c(n) = \{C_1 + C_2 n\}Z_1^n.$$

The particular solution $v_p(n)$ can now be obtained from the method of undetermined coefficients, and the complete solution is

$$v(n) = v_c(n) + v_p(n).$$

Let us return to our problem

$$v(n) + b_1 v(n + 1) + b_2 v(n + 2) = e(n);$$

if the zeta transforms are

$$\mathscr{Z}[v(n)] = V_{\mathscr{Z}}(Z)$$

and

$$\mathscr{Z}[e(n)] = E_{\mathscr{Z}}(Z),$$

then, substituting,

$$V_{\mathscr{Z}}(Z) = \frac{E_{\mathscr{Z}}(Z) + [b_2 Z^2 + b_1 Z]v(0) + b_2 Z v(1)}{\{1 + b_1 Z + b_2 Z^2\}}.$$

The formalism becomes clear when we consider a simple example. Consider a cascade of resistors as shown in Fig. 215. Taking the current node at k gives

$$-v_{k-1} + 3v_k - v_{k+1} = 0$$

or

$$-v(k) + 3v(k + 1) - v(k + 2) = 0.$$

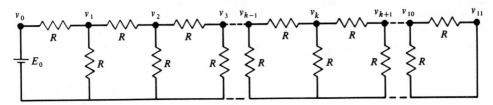

FIG. 215

In terms of the transform, this

$$-V_{\mathscr{Z}}(Z) + 3Z\{V_{\mathscr{Z}}(Z) - v(0)\} - Z^2\{V_{\mathscr{Z}}(Z) - v(0)\} + Zv(1) = 0.$$

Here, $v(0) = E_0$ and $v(1)$ will be determined from the solution:

$$V_{\mathscr{Z}}(Z) = \frac{Z(Z - 3)v(0) + Zv(1)}{[Z^2 - 3Z + 1]} = \frac{v(0)Z(Z - \frac{3}{2})}{[Z^2 - 3Z + 1]} - \frac{\{\frac{3}{2}v(0) - v(1)\}Z}{[Z^2 - 3Z + 1]}.$$

Taking the inverse,

$$v(n) = \mathscr{Z}^{-1}[V_{\mathscr{Z}}(Z)] = E_0 \cosh 0.96n - \frac{2}{\sqrt{5}}\left(\frac{3}{2}E_0 - v(1)\right) \sinh 0.96n.$$

Knowing that $v(11) = 0$, we can find $v(1)$ and obtain a general solution.

In most problems of this type, we must consider the zeta and Laplace transforms simultaneously. Consider the following cascade of RC networks. See Fig. 216. The equations for the section starting v_{k-1} are

$$-\frac{1}{R}v_{k-1} + \frac{2}{R}v_k + C\frac{dv_k}{dt} - \frac{1}{R}v_{k+1} = 0.$$

Write $k = (n + 1)$; then

$$C\frac{d}{dt}v(n + 1, t) - \frac{1}{R}\{v(n, t) - 2v(n + 1, t) + v(n + 2, t)\} = 0.$$

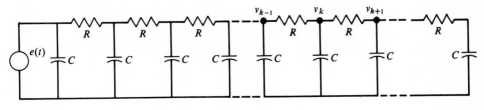

FIG. 216

Take $\mathscr{L}T$:

$$CsV(n + 1, s) - \frac{1}{R}\{V(n, s) - 2V(n + 1, s) + V(n + 2, s)\} = 0.$$

If we now take the zeta transform, with

$$\mathscr{Z}[V(n, s)] = V_{\mathscr{Z}}(Z, s),$$

we obtain

$$-\frac{1}{R} V_{\mathscr{Z}}(Z, s) + Z\left(Cs + \frac{2}{R}\right)\{V_{\mathscr{Z}}(Z, s) - V(0, s)\}$$

$$-\frac{1}{R} Z^2\{V_{\mathscr{Z}}(Z, s) - V(0, s)\} + \frac{Z}{R} V(1, s) = 0.$$

Then

$$V_{\mathscr{Z}}(Z, s) = \frac{\{Z^2 - (2 + RCs)Z\}V(0, s) + ZV(1, s)}{\{Z^2 - (2 + RCs)Z + 1\}}.$$

The solution is obtained by first finding

$$\mathscr{Z}^{-1}[V_{\mathscr{Z}}(Z, s)] = V(n, s),$$

and then by solving for

$$v(n, t) = \mathscr{L}^{-1}[V(n, s)].$$

BLOCK DIAGRAMS AND FLOW GRAPHS

BLOCK DIAGRAMS

We have noted in the section concerned with four-terminal networks that cases can be encountered that require additional attention beyond the blind application of the 2×2 matrix operators. A less dangerous procedure, but by far more cumbersome, is the two-terminal representation operators. Ultimately, this method consists of diagramming algebraic relationships in terms of graphs.

In the block diagram and flow-graph method, each element is regarded as an operator in a two-terminal box. As an example, consider our three basic, passive elements in the time and frequency representation.

Inductance

Time Domain:

$$v_L(t) = \left\{ L \frac{d}{dt} \right\} i_L(t)$$

or

$$i_L(t) = \left\{ \frac{1}{L} \int dt \right\} v_L(t).$$

Frequency Domain (initially relaxed):

$$V_L(s) = Ls I_L(s)$$

or

$$I_L(s) = \frac{1}{Ls} V_L(s).$$

Resistance

Time Domain:

$$v_R(t) = R i_R(t)$$

or

$$i_R(t) = \frac{1}{R} v_R(t) = G v_R(t).$$

Frequency Domain:

$$V_R(s) = RI_R(s)$$

or

$$I_R(s) = \frac{1}{R} V_R(s) = GV_R(s).$$

Capacitance

Time Domain (initially relaxed):

$$v_c(t) = \frac{1}{C} \int dt\; i_c(t)$$

or

$$i_c(t) = \left\{ C \frac{d}{dt} \right\} v_c(t).$$

Frequency Domain:

$$V_c(s) = \frac{1}{Cs} I_c(s)$$

or

$$I_c(s) = CsV_c(s).$$

To utilize this type of diagramming, there are several new operators to be introduced and a number of convenient rules that can be employed for the reduction of a complicated graph to a simple graph.

First we introduce the symbols for summing and for picking off a quantity without disturbing its magnitude or phase.

Summing Point Symbols

If two quantities x_1 and x_2 are brought to a summing point, the output will be the sum of the two with appropriate signs. The sum, after all, can be positive or negative. See Fig. 217.

This operation can be extended to three inputs although such a step is not particularly useful. See Fig. 218.

Because the summing symbol has four parts, at least three inputs can be introduced. More than three will require several summing operators.

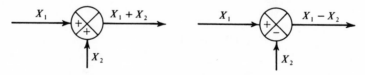

FIG. 217

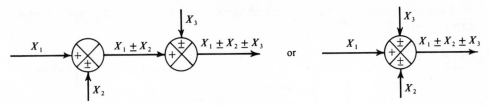

FIG. 218

Pickoff Points

In this operation, an input variable proceeds *unaltered* along several paths. Examples in nature are the pickoff voltage by a circuit with a high input impedance See Fig. 219.

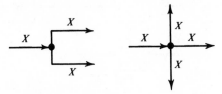

FIG. 219

As an example of this, we can regard the flow-graph diagram of a single-loop *LR* circuit. See Fig. 220.

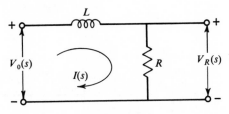

FIG. 220

In this example, the two algebraic equations relating $V_R(s)$ to $V_0(s)$ are

$$I(s) = \frac{1}{Ls} \{V_0(s) - V_R(s)\}$$

and

$$V_R(s) = RI(s).$$

The diagram of this set of equations is shown in Fig. 221, illustrating our use of the summing point and the pickoff point.

Before discussing the general set of transformations that can be used, we can reduce this simple case step by step. Two different reductions will be carried out to give the same result.

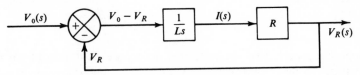

FIG. 221

First, a summing point can be moved behind a block by putting a block in each output branch. See Fig. 222.

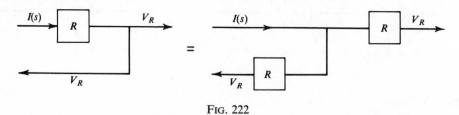

FIG. 222

We now have the step shown in Fig. 223.

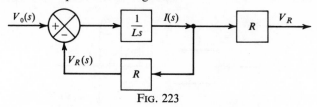

FIG. 223

Consider the general problem of the feedback loop (Fig. 224). We can obtain the general reduction from

$$Y = A(X \pm BY)$$

or

$$Y = \left(\frac{A}{1 \mp AB}\right)X.$$

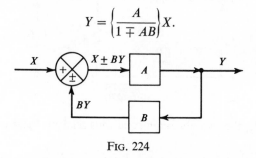

FIG. 224

Using this relation our graph reduces to the step in Fig. 225 or Fig. 226. Then

$$V_R(s) = \left(\frac{R}{Ls + R}\right)V_0(s).$$

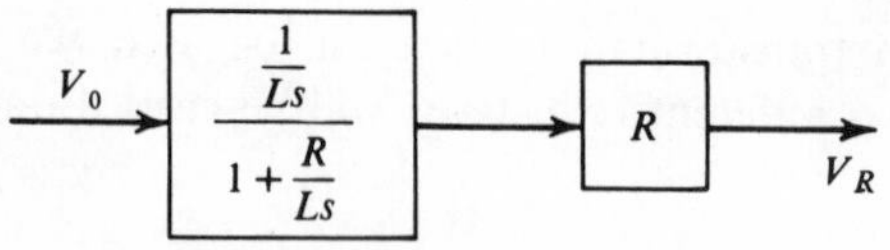

FIG. 225

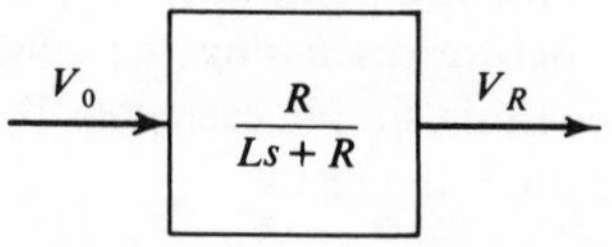

FIG. 226

A second approach also illustrates the procedure. It is possible to reduce the original network in fewer steps if the cascade of $1/LS$ and R are combined first. See Fig. 227.

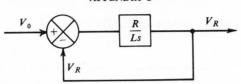

FIG. 227

This is a feedback loop, with 1 as the feedback element (i.e., $B = 1$ in our example). Then we have the case of Fig. 228.

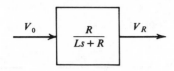

FIG. 228

With this elementary example in mind, we can list for future use the six most useful transformations employed in diagram reductions.

1. Cascade of two operators $A(s)$ and $B(s)$; Fig. 229.

FIG. 229

2. Moving a summing point ahead of a block; Fig. 230.

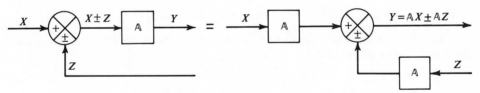

FIG. 230

3. Moving a summary point behind a block; Fig. 231.

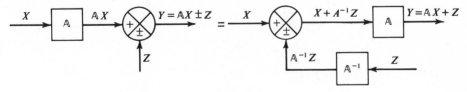

FIG. 231

4. Moving a pickoff point ahead of a block; Fig. 232.

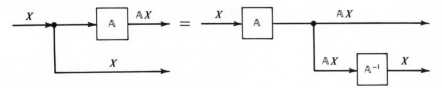

FIG. 232

5. Moving a pickoff behind a block (Fig. 233).

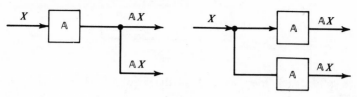

FIG. 233

6. Reduction of a feedback loop (Fig. 234).

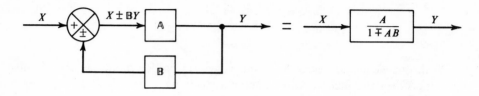

FIG. 234

Here

$$Y = A\{X \pm BY\}$$

and

$$Y = \left\{\frac{A}{1 \mp AB}\right\}X.$$

In the special case that $B = 1$ the transformation goes as $A/(1 \mp A)$.

To obtain some understanding of the use of the block diagram let us consider the circuit shown in Fig. 235.

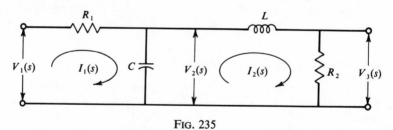

FIG. 235

The equations involved are

$$I_1 = \frac{1}{R_1}(V_1 - V_2),$$

$$V_2 = \frac{1}{Cs}(I_1 - I_2),$$

$$I_2 = \frac{1}{Ls}(V_2 - V_3),$$

and

$$V_3 = R_2 I_2.$$

These four equations result in the diagram shown in Fig. 236.

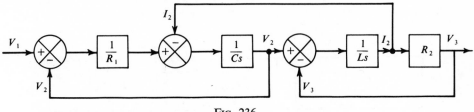

FIG. 236

The reduction will be carried out in the following manner:

1. Move the summing point on the left of the right of the operator, $\{1/R_1\}$, and exchange the order of the two adjacent summing points.
2. Shift the pickup point behind $\{R_2\}$ to the left.
3. This leaves two simple feedback loops, which can be replaced by their equivalent series operators (Fig. 237).

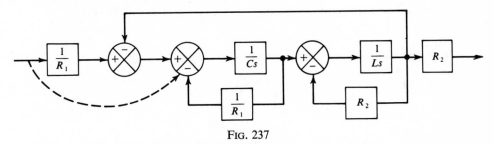

FIG. 237

4. We eliminate the cascade and then the resultant "unity" feedback loop.
5. Then we combine the cascade of three into one. (Figs. 238 and 239.) Finally

$$V_3 = \left\{ \frac{R_2}{(1 + R_1 C_1 s)(R_2 + Ls) + R_1} \right\} V_1(s).$$

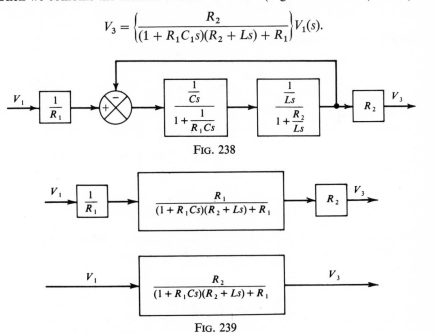

FIG. 238

FIG. 239

It is instructive to compare this method with that of the four-terminal matrices. In the cascade representation, the four-terminal matrices achieve their most reliable form. Returning to the circuit, we split it into two T sections (Fig. 240).

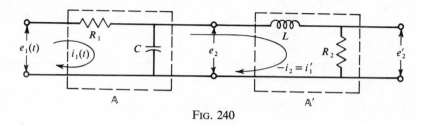

FIG. 240

Here we observe that

$$
\begin{bmatrix} E_1 \\ E_2 \end{bmatrix} = \begin{pmatrix} R_1 + \dfrac{1}{Cs} & \dfrac{1}{Cs} \\ \dfrac{1}{Cs} & \dfrac{1}{Cs} \end{pmatrix} \begin{bmatrix} I_1 \\ I_2 \end{bmatrix}; \quad \text{and} \quad \begin{bmatrix} E_1' \\ E_2' \end{bmatrix} = \begin{pmatrix} Ls + R_2 & R_2 \\ R_2 & R_2 \end{pmatrix} \begin{bmatrix} I_1' \\ I_2' \end{bmatrix}.
$$

Now converting to the $\mathbb{A}$ representation,

$$
\mathbb{A}(s) = \begin{pmatrix} 1 + R_1 Cs & R_1 \\ Cs & 1 \end{pmatrix}
$$

and

$$
\mathbb{A}'(s) = \begin{pmatrix} \dfrac{Ls}{R_2} + 1 & Ls \\ \dfrac{1}{R_2} & 1 \end{pmatrix}.
$$

The cascade combination is

$$
\mathbb{A} \cdot \mathbb{A}' = \begin{pmatrix} \left[(1 + R_1 Cs)\left(1 + \dfrac{Ls}{R_2}\right) + \dfrac{R_1}{R_2} \right] & [Ls(1 + R_1 Cs) + R_1] \\ \left[Cs\left(1 + \dfrac{Ls}{R_2}\right) + \dfrac{1}{R_2} \right] & [CLs^2 + 1] \end{pmatrix}.
$$

Now the output voltage $V_3(s)$ divided by the input voltage $V_1(s)$ is just $1/A_{11}$; therefore,

$$
V_3 = \frac{V_1(s)}{[\mathbb{A} \cdot \mathbb{A}']_{11}} = \left\{ \frac{R_2}{(1 + R_1 Cs)(R_2 + Ls) + R_1} \right\} V_1(s),
$$

which checks with the block-diagram result. This application of the matrices is perhaps the more desirable, since an additional combination with, say, a terminating network is easily computed.

We obtain

$$
V_3 = \frac{(R_2/R_1)\omega_0^2}{(s + \gamma_1)(s + \gamma_2)} V_1(s),
$$

where

$$\omega_0^2 = \frac{1}{LC},$$

$$\alpha_C = \frac{1}{2R_1C},$$

$$\alpha_L = \frac{R_2}{2L},$$

and

$$\gamma_j = +(\alpha_C + \alpha_L) \pm \sqrt{(\alpha_C + \alpha_L)^2 - [1 + (R_2/R_L)]\omega_0^2}.$$

Thus, $H_3(s) = V_3/V_1$ represents a sharp low-pass filter, the sharpness depending upon the proximity of the roots γ_1 and γ_2.

FLOW GRAPHS

This approach to network analysis will be mentioned briefly. The reader will observe at once that the flow-graph matrices are equivalent to our presentation of flat networks in terms of matrices. The major difference is that the flow-graph matrix involves branch currents and voltages, whereas the earlier discussion dealt with loop currents and loop voltages.

The nodes of the flow graph are the system variables x_j; i.e., the voltage and current transforms.

A directed branch between nodes (or variables) is an operator T_{jk} corresponding to Ls, $1/Cs$, or R, etc. The direction of T_{jk} is from x_k to x_j.

If a node has several entering branches and one output, it is a summing point.

If a node has one entering branch and several outputs it is a pickoff point.

A node can be a combined summing point and pickoff point if it has several entering branches and several outputs. The sign of a sum is provided by the branch operator leading to the node.

Consider as an example our single-loop LR circuit (Fig. 241). The algebraic relations are

$$I(s) = \frac{1}{Ls} V_1 - \frac{1}{Ls} V_R \quad \text{or} \quad x_2 = T_{21}x_1 + T_{23}x_3;$$

$$V_R(s) = RI(s) \quad \text{or} \quad x_3 = T_{32}x_2.$$

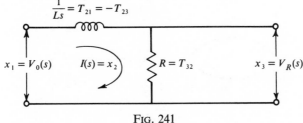

FIG. 241

In terms of the flow graph described, then we have the case of Fig. 242.

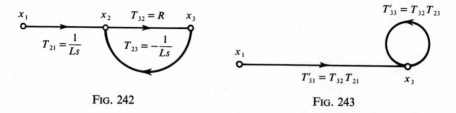

FIG. 242   FIG. 243

If we regard the algebra of this diagram and eliminate x_2 as a first step,

$$x_3 = T_{32}T_{21}x_1 + T_{32}T_{23}x_3.$$

A diagram of this equation is a two-node diagram (Fig. 243).

Finally, solving for x_3, we obtain the case of Fig. 244,

or

$$x_3 = T'_{31}\left\{\frac{1}{1 - T'_{33}}\right\}x_1 = \frac{T_{32}T_{21}}{(1 - T_{32}T_{23})}x_1,$$

giving

$$V_R(s) = \frac{\{R/Ls\}V_0(s)}{\{1 + (R/Ls)\}}.$$

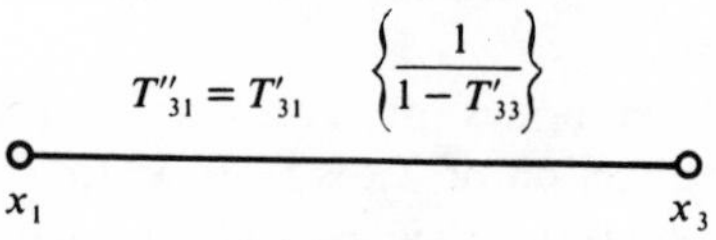

$$T''_{31} = T'_{31}\quad\left\{\frac{1}{1 - T'_{33}}\right\}$$

x_1 x_3

FIG. 244

From this simple example, we see that a few general rules should be sufficient for rapid reduction of the graphs.

1. Cascaded Operators (Fig. 245).

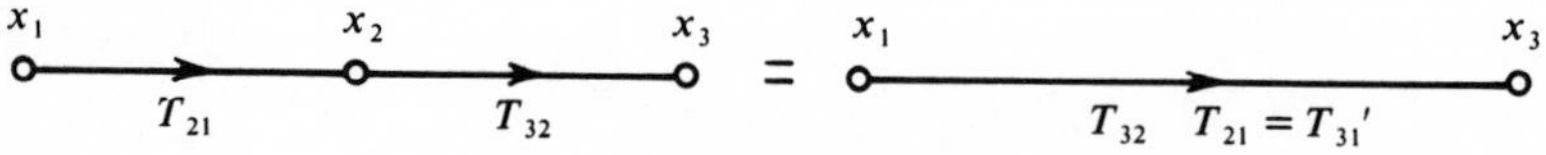

x_1 x_2 x_3 x_1 x_3

$\quad T_{21}\qquad\qquad T_{32}\qquad = \qquad\qquad T_{32}\quad T_{21} = T'_{31}$

FIG. 245

2. Superposed Operators (notice that the directions are the same). See Fig. 246.

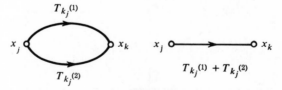

FIG. 246

3. Elimination of a node. There are several equivalent situations and we shall describe more than one.

(a) Elimination of a pickoff node (Fig. 247).

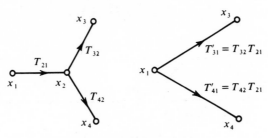

FIG. 247

(b) Elimination of a summing point (Fig. 248).

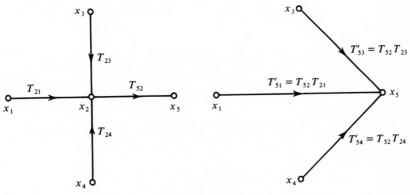

FIG. 248

(c) Elimination of a summing point and a pickoff point (Fig. 249).

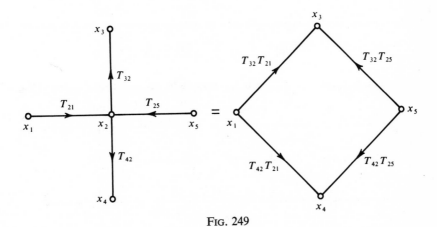

FIG. 249

4. Reduction of a feedback loop (Fig. 250), giving

$$x_3 = \{T_{32}T_{21}\}x_1 + \{T_{32}T_{23}\}x_3$$

or

$$x_3 = \frac{T_{32}T_{21}}{[1 - T_{32}T_{23}]}x_1.$$

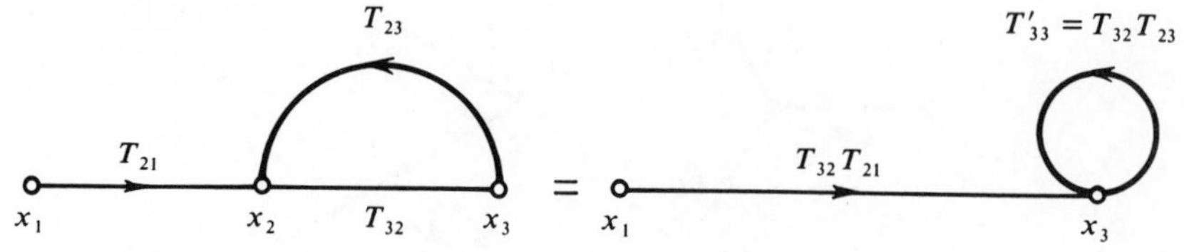

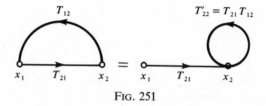

$$x_2 = T_{21}x_1 + T_{23}x_3 \text{ and } x_3 = T_{32}x_2;$$

FIG. 250

If we allow $T_{21} = +1$, we see the case in Fig. 251.

FIG. 251

Finally, from our algebra, we see that a branch T_{21} in cascade with a circle T_{22} is as shown in Fig. 252,

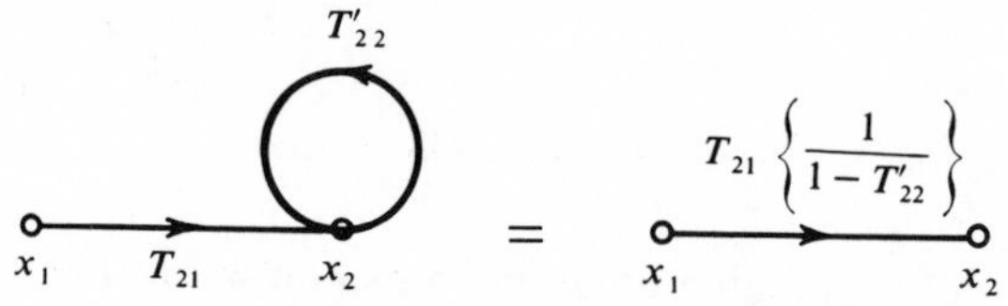

FIG. 252

or

$$x_2 = \frac{T_{21}}{[1 - T'_{22}]}x_1 = \frac{T_{21}}{[1 - T_{21}T_{12}]}x_1.$$

We are in a position to apply these techniques to our two-loop problem (Fig. 253).

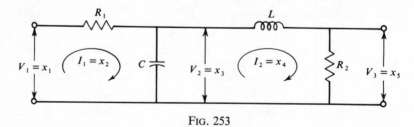

FIG. 253

Referring to the original set of algebraic equations used in the block-diagram analysis, we obtain the equivalent flow graph (Fig. 254).

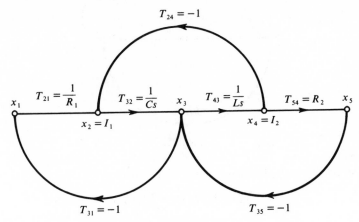

FIG. 254

We first eliminate the pickoff point at x_4 (Fig. 255).

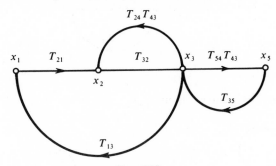

FIG. 255

The straight branch connecting x_1 and x_3 can be combined with the intermediate feedback loop (Fig. 256).

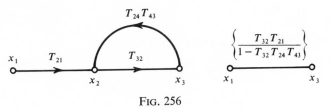

FIG. 256

Define Fig. 257.

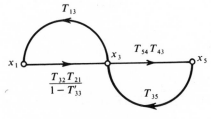

FIG. 257

The node at x_3 can now be eliminated to give Fig. 258.

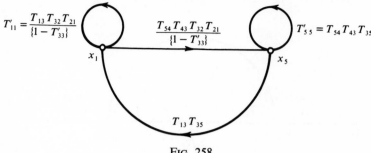

$$T'_{11} = \frac{T_{13} T_{32} T_{21}}{\{1 - T'_{33}\}}$$

$$\frac{T_{54} T_{43} T_{32} T_{21}}{\{1 - T'_{33}\}}$$

$$T'_{55} = T_{54} T_{43} T_{35}$$

$$T_{13} T_{35}$$

Fig. 258

Eliminating the loop at x_1, we get Fig. 259, where

$$T_{13} T_{32} T_{21} = (1 - T'_{33}) T'_{11}.$$

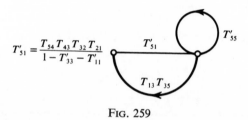

$$T'_{51} = \frac{T_{54} T_{43} T_{32} T_{21}}{1 - T'_{33} - T'_{11}}$$

$$T'_{51}$$

$$T'_{55}$$

$$T_{13} T_{35}$$

Fig. 259

Now we reduce the feedback loop $T_{13} T_{35}$, giving Fig. 260 or Fig. 261.

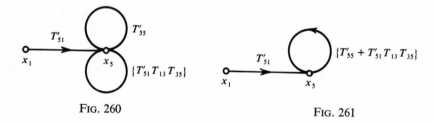

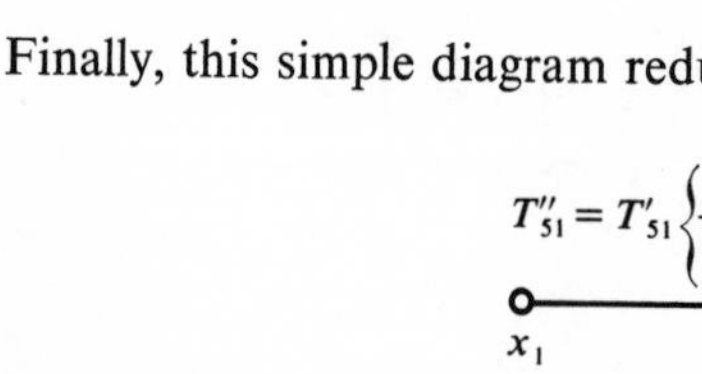

$$T'_{51}$$

$$T'_{55}$$

$$\{T'_{51} T_{13} T_{35}\}$$

$$T'_{51}$$

$$\{T'_{55} + T'_{51} T_{13} T_{35}\}$$

Fig. 260

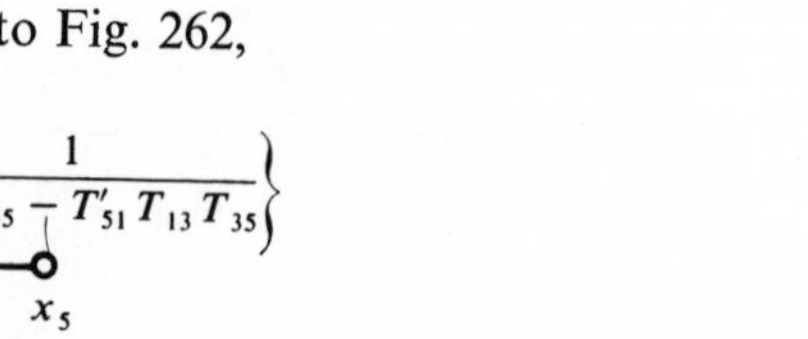

Fig. 261

Finally, this simple diagram reduces to Fig. 262,

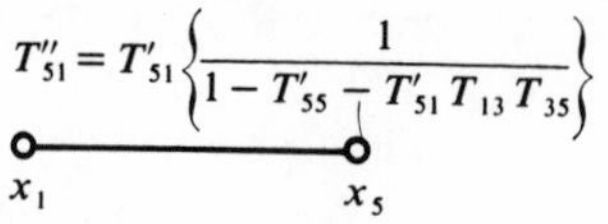

$$T''_{51} = T'_{51} \left\{ \frac{1}{1 - T'_{55} - T'_{51} T_{13} T_{35}} \right\}$$

Fig. 262

where $x_5 = T''_{51} x_1$,

and

$$T''_{51} = \frac{T_{54} T_{43} T_{32} T_{21}}{[1 - T'_{33} - T'_{11} - (1 - T'_{11}) T_{54} T_{43} T_{35}]} = \frac{G_1 R_2 \omega_0^2}{[S^2 + 2(\alpha_C + \alpha_L) S + (1 + G_1 R_2) \omega_0^2]}.$$

This is the same result that was obtained by other methods.

PROBLEMS

PROBLEMS

PROBLEMS FOR CHAPTER 1

PROBLEM 1-1

a. The electrostatic energy stored in a system of N stationary point charges q_j is

$$U = \tfrac{1}{2} \sum_{j=1}^{N} q_j V_j,$$

where V_j is the potential at the location q_j set up by all charges *except* q_j. Show that the energy stored in a charge distribution $\rho(\mathbf{r})$ is

$$U = \tfrac{1}{2} \iiint_{\text{all space}} \mathbf{D} \cdot \boldsymbol{\mathscr{E}} \, d\mathbf{r};$$

Here, $d\mathbf{r}$ = volume element.

b. In the case of a condenser of capacitance C, demonstrate that the energy stored is

$$U = \frac{1}{2} CV^2 = \frac{1}{2} \frac{Q^2}{C}.$$

c. Show that

$$\frac{1}{2} \iiint_{\substack{\text{volume} \\ \text{of } C}} \frac{\partial}{\partial t} (\mathbf{D} \cdot \boldsymbol{\mathscr{E}}) \, d\mathbf{r} = \frac{IQ}{C},$$

PROBLEM 1-2

The energy stored in a current loop I_j is $I_j \phi_j$, where ϕ_j is the magnetic flux linking the current I_j:

$$\phi_j = \sum_{\text{all } k} \phi_{jk} = \sum_{\text{all } k} L_{jk} I_k.$$

Here, L_{jk} is a geometric factor relating the flux at the jth loop to the current I_k. The total energy stored in N loops is

$$\tfrac{1}{2} \sum_{m=1}^{N} I_m \phi_m,$$

289

where

$$\phi_m = \sum_k \phi_{mk}.$$

If

$$U = \tfrac{1}{2} \iiint_{\text{all space}} \mathbf{B} \cdot \mathbf{H} \, d\mathbf{r} = \tfrac{1}{2} \sum_{m=1}^{N} I_m \phi_m,$$

show that

$$\frac{1}{2} \iiint \frac{\partial}{\partial t} (\mathbf{B} \cdot \mathbf{H}) \, d\mathbf{r} = \sum_{l=1}^{N} \sum_{k=1}^{N} I_l L_{lk} \frac{dI_k}{dt}.$$

PROBLEM 1-3

a. Show that the capacitance of the special geometries noted below has the form shown. C for a parallel-plate condenser $= \varepsilon \varepsilon_0 A/d$, where $A =$ the face area and d is the plate separation. C per unit length for a coaxial cable $= 2\pi\varepsilon\varepsilon_0/\log(b/a)]$, where b is the radius of the outer cylinder and a is the radius of the inner cylinder.

b. Show that the self-inductance of a toroidal coil having a rectangular cross section is

$$L = \frac{\mu\mu_0 N^2 h}{2\pi} \log\left\{\frac{2R + W}{2R - W}\right\},$$

where $N =$ total number of turns
$R =$ mean radius of the toroid
$W =$ width of rectangular cross section in the direction of R
$h =$ height of the rectangular cross section

c. Show that the inductance per unit length of a coaxial cable is $[\mu\mu_0/2\pi)\log(b/a)$. Again, b/a is the ratio of the outer radius to the radius of the inner conductor.

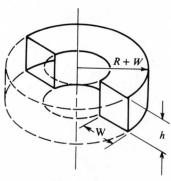

FIG. P1-3

d. Show that the capacitance per unit length and inductance per unit length for a long straight wire of radius R and a distance d above a grounded conducting plane, where $d/R \gg 1$, are respectively

$$C \simeq \frac{2\pi\varepsilon_0}{\log(2d/R)}$$

and

$$L \simeq \frac{\mu_0}{2\pi} \log\left(\frac{2d}{R}\right).$$

PROBLEM 1-4

Two electric circuits are coupled by a mutual inductance L_{12} as shown in Fig. P1-4. The primary circuit is excited by a sinusoidal voltage generator $e_1(t)$, where

$$e_1(t) = E_1 \sin \omega_0 t.$$

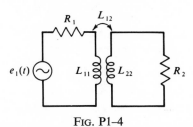

FIG. P1–4

Write down the loop equations for the currents and voltages. Using standard techniques, uncouple the equations and solve for the two currents, subject to the initial conditions that

$$i_1(0+) = 0,$$

and

$$i_2(0+) = 0.$$

The coils are coupled in such a manner that L_{12} is positive.

PROBLEM 1-5

Solve the following problems, using Kirchhoff's laws:

a. See Fig. P1-5(a). Find the branch current $\mathscr{I}_{12}$.

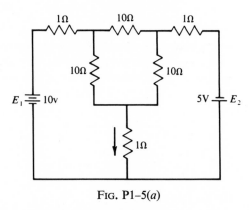

FIG. P1–5(a)

b. The principle of superposition states that the current in any branch is a linear superposition of the currents (with appropriate signs) supplied by each voltage source.

To prove this, find $\mathcal{J}_{12}$ in Problem (a) by first shorting out $E_2 = 5$ volts and computing the contribution of E_1. Then short E_1, leaving E_2 in the problem, and compute the contribution of E_2. The algebraic sum should be $\mathcal{J}_{12}$.

c. Find the current delivered by the battery in the circuit shown in Fig. P1-5(c). Also compute the current in the 4-ohm resistor.

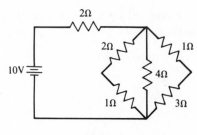

FIG. P1–5(c)

d. A cubical array of 1-ohm resistors is shown in the accompanying diagram. Two sets of opposite corners are connected by 1-ohm resistors. Compute the total resistance between points a and b in Fig. P1-5(d).

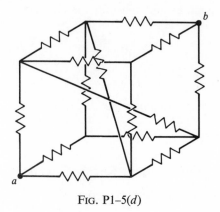

FIG. P1–5(d)

e. An ideal constant-current generator $i_s(t)$ is assumed to have an infinite impedance. Such a generator is placed in parallel with a voltage generator having an internal resistance R_G and a load resistance R_L. Compute the voltage across the load.

f. The switch is closed at $t = 0$; compute the voltage across R as a function of time, Fig. P1-5(f).

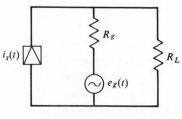

FIG. P1–5(f)

g. The switch S is opened at $t = 0$. Compute the voltage across R as a function of time, Fig. P1-5(g). Assume steady state before $t = 0$.

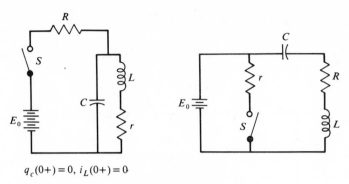

$$q_c(0+) = 0, \; i_L(0+) = 0$$

Fig. P1–5(g)

h. S_1 is opened and S_2 is closed at $t = 0$, Fig. P1-5(h). At $t = 0-$, all passive elements are initially relaxed, i.e., $q_c(0-) = 0$ and $i_L(0-) = 0$.

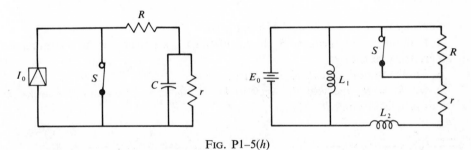

Fig. P1–5(h)

PROBLEM 1-6

The total average radiated power from a short electric-dipole antenna is

$$\frac{4\pi^2 I_0^2}{3C} \left(\frac{d}{\lambda}\right)^2,$$

where I_0 is the amplitude of the current and d is the length of the antenna. A magnetic dipole radiates an average power, given by

$$\frac{2\pi^2}{3C} \frac{I_0^2}{2} \left(\frac{d}{\lambda}\right)^4,$$

where d is the circumference of the loop.

Treat the radiated power as a resistive loss and compute the electric dipole and magnetic dipole radiation resistance for a circuit 2 cm in diameter and with an effective linear length of 2 cm for currents of the following frequencies:

60 cps	10 Mc
400 cps	100 Mc
10 kc	1000 Mc = 1 gigacycle/sec
100 kc	10^4 Mc = 10 gigacycles
1 Mc	

PROBLEM 1-7

Consider the network shown in Fig. P1-7.
a. Find v' and v.
b. Remove the T section between a, a', and bb', and find v'.
Compare with (a).

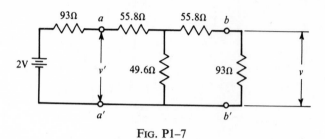

FIG. P1–7

PROBLEM 1-8

Consider the T and π networks in Fig. P1-8.
a. Find the input impedance R_{in} by calculating v/i, when each circuit is terminated by an arbitrary resistor R_0.
b. Find v' in both cases and calculate $\alpha = v'/v$.
c. Set $R_{in} = R_0$ and find R_1, R_2, and R_a, R_b, in terms of α_0 and R. Check the previous problem to find R_{in} and α_0.

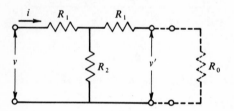 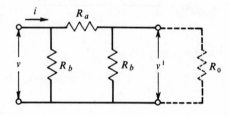

FIG. P1–8

PROBLEMS FOR
CHAPTER 2

PROBLEM 2-1

There are many ways of simulating a delta function. In order to obtain a crude model for the derivative of a $\Delta(t)$, we employ a function

$$f(t) = 0, \qquad \frac{T}{2} < |t|;$$

$$f(t) = +1, \qquad -\frac{T}{2} < t < \partial;$$

$$f(t) = -1, \qquad 0 < t < \frac{T}{2}.$$

a. Integrate this function and obtain the resultant $\Delta(t)$; plot this.

b. Integrate a second time and obtain (also plot) the corresponding approximate step function.

c. In the *RLC* network shown in Fig. P2-1(c) obtain the response $i(t)R = v_R(t)$ if the circuit is excited by $f(t), \int_0^t f(t') \, dt'$, and $\int_0^t dt' \int_0^{t'} f(t'') \, dt''$.

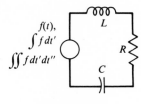

FIG. P2–1(c)

PROBLEM 2-2

We shall demonstrate in this problem that if the input pulse of a circuit is much shorter than the time decay constant T (i.e., $RC = T$ in Fig. P2-2(a)), then the *shape* of the output wave form is independent of the width of the input pulse.

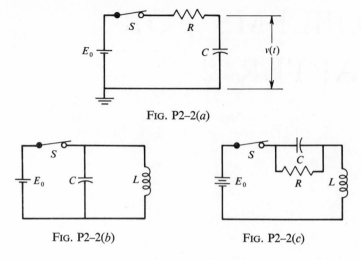

FIG. P2–2(a)

FIG. P2–2(b)   FIG. P2–2(c)

a. Let RC in Fig. P2-2(a) be 100 sec and $E = 10^{-2}$ volts. Suppose switch S is closed at $t = 0$ and opened at $t_0 = 1000$ sec. Find $v(t)$.

b. Repeat (a) for $E = 10^{-1}$ volt and $t_0 = 100$ sec.

c. Repeat (a) for $E = 1$ volt and $t_0 = 10$ sec.

d. Repeat (a) for $E = 10$ volt and $t_0 = 1$ sec.

e. Repeat for circuits in Fig. P2-36 where $T = 1/\sqrt{LC} = 100$ sec, etc.

PROBLEM 2-3

The equations of motion of a simple pendulum are given by

$$\frac{d^2\Theta}{dt^2} + \frac{g}{l}\,\Theta = \frac{F(t)}{ml}$$

where Θ is the angle between the pendulum and the vertical, g is the acceleration due to the gravitational field of the earth, l is the length of the pendulum, m is the mass of the bob, and F is the external force applied to the bob and perpendicular to the string, Fig. P2-3.

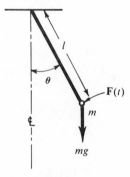

FIG. P2–3

Consider the pendulum initially at rest and let $\mathbf{F}(t)$ be caused by a single sharp blow with a hammer. If the duration of the blow is short compared to the period of the pendulum, the force can be considered as a delta function. Let $F(t)/ml = k\,\delta(t)$ (where k is a measure of the strength of the blow) and $\omega^2 = (g/l)$. Find the response, $\Theta(t)$, of the pendulum to the blow of the hammer.

PROBLEM 2-4

The ideal step excitation can be handled readily by switching a battery into a circuit. To obtain the response of an LR circuit to a delta-function excitation, we shall solve the first quadrature in terms of a step excitation.

Consider the LR circuit excited by $E_0\delta(t)$ shown in Fig. P2-4(a).

If $i(0+)$ and $q'(0+)$ are zero in both circuits, show that the solution $v(t)$ can be obtained by solving the step excited-$R'C'$ circuit [Fig. P2-4(b)]. What is the relation among L, R, R', and C'?

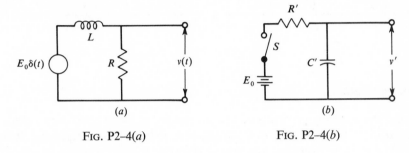

(a)   (b)

FIG. P2–4(a)   FIG. P2–4(b)

PROBLEM 2-5

Repeat Problem 2-4, replacing the ideal voltage source and opened series switch with an ideal current generator and closed parallel switch.

PROBLEM 2-6

Show that $\Phi(t)$ is a linear operator if it is represented by

$$\Phi(t) = \frac{d^3}{dt^3} + a_2 \frac{d^2}{dt^2} + a_1 \frac{d}{dt} + a_0,$$

where the a_j are independent of t.

PROBLEM 2-7

Find Green's functions (source functions in the time domain) $h(t)$ for the following passive operators, i.e., $H^{-1}(t)\,h(t) = \delta(t)$. See Fig. P2-7 (a), (b), and (c).

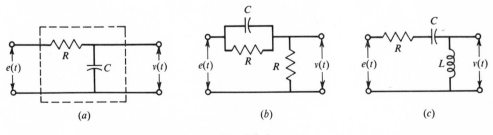

(a)   (b)   (c)

FIG. P2–7

PROBLEM 2-8

Obtain the characteristic frequencies or eigenfrequencies of the voltage transfer functions ($H^{-1}(t)$) for the circuits shown in Fig. P2-8 (a), (b), and (c):

$$H^{-1}(t)v(t) = e(t).$$

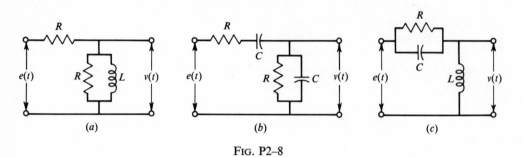

FIG. P2–8

PROBLEM 2-9

Solve the one-loop problems below, subject to the initial conditions stated.

a. At $t = 0$, the switch is closed; $i_L(0+) = 0$, and $q_c(0+) = CE_0/2$; Fig. P2-9(a).

b. At $t = 0$, the switch is closed. Find $v(t)$; Fig. P2-9(b).

c. See Fig. P2-9(c). I_0 is an ideal current generator providing a constant d-c current. The shorting switch is opened at $t = 0$. If $q_c(0+) = 0$, find $v(t)$.

d. See Fig. P2-9(c). At $t < 0$, the switch S is open, and the circuit is in steady-state operation. I_0 is a constant. The switch is closed at $t = 0$; find $v(t)$.

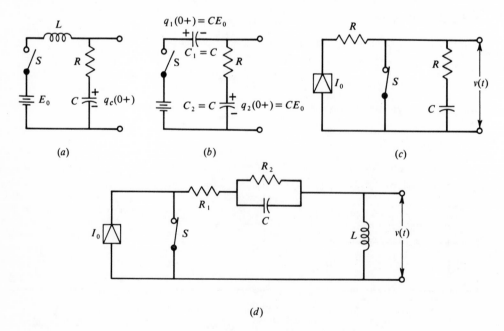

(a)   (b)   (c)

(d)

FIG. P2–9

PROBLEM 2-10

Solve the following circuit problems, subject to the initial conditions stated.

a. The switch is closed at $t = 0$. Initially, the current through L is zero while $q_c(0+)$ is CE_0. Find $v(t)$; Fig. P2-10(a).

b. See Fig. P2-10(b). The switch is closed at $t < 0$ and the circuit is conducting in steady state. At $t = 0$, the switch is opened. Find $v(t)$.

c. See Fig. P2-10(c). At $t = 0$, the switch is opened. Initially, all passive elements are relaxed, i.e., $q_c(-0+) = 0$, and $i_L(0+) = 0$.

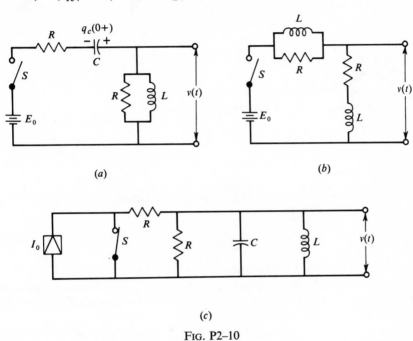

(a)

(b)

(c)

Fig. P2–10

PROBLEM 2-11

Regard the three 3×3 matrices shown and perform the operations indicated.

$$A = \begin{pmatrix} 1 & 1 & 1 \\ 1 & 2 & 3 \\ 1 & 4 & 9 \end{pmatrix}; \quad B = \begin{pmatrix} 2 & 5 & 3 \\ 3 & 1 & 2 \\ 1 & 2 & 1 \end{pmatrix};$$

$$C = \begin{pmatrix} -1 & 1 & -1 \\ -3 & 2 & -1 \\ -3 & 1 & 0 \end{pmatrix}.$$

a. Compute the sums $A + B$, $B + C$, $A + B + C$.
b. Compute the transpose of each matrix.
c. Compute the inverse of each matrix.
d. Compute the magnitude of each matrix.
e. Compute the products $A \cdot B$, $B \cdot C$, and $A \cdot B \cdot C$.
f. Compute the magnitude of $A \cdot B \cdot C$ and compare it with the product of the magnitudes $|A| \, |B| \, |C|$.

PROBLEM 2-12

Use the orthogonal transformation (special case of a unitary transformation),

$$\mathbb{S} = \begin{pmatrix} \dfrac{1}{\sqrt{2}} & \dfrac{1}{\sqrt{2}} & 0 \\[2ex] -\dfrac{1}{2\sqrt{2}} & \dfrac{1}{2\sqrt{2}} & \dfrac{\sqrt{3}}{2} \\[2ex] \dfrac{\sqrt{3}}{2\sqrt{2}} & -\dfrac{\sqrt{3}}{2\sqrt{2}} & \dfrac{1}{2} \end{pmatrix}$$

and perform the following operations:
  a. Show that $|\mathbb{S}| = 1$.
  b. Compute $\mathbb{S}^{-1}$ and show that $\mathbb{S}^{-1} = \tilde{\mathbb{S}}$.
  c. Using the matrix $\mathbb{A}$, of Problem 2-11, compute

$$\mathbb{S} \cdot \mathbb{A} \cdot \tilde{\mathbb{S}}.$$

PROBLEM 2-13

Write in matrix form the two simultaneous equations given below.

$$x - 3y = \alpha,$$

$$2x + y = \beta.$$

  a. Solve the simultaneous equations graphically for $\alpha = -3$ and $\beta = 8$.
  b. Solve the simultaneous equations by algebraic means for a general α and β.
  c. Find det $\mathbb{A}$, trace $\mathbb{A}$, and $\mathbb{A}^{-1}$ (where $\mathbb{A}$ is the matrix of the coefficients).
  d. Compute $\mathbb{A}^{-1} \cdot \mathbb{A}$ and $\mathbb{A} \cdot \mathbb{A}^{-1}$.
  e. Solve the matrix equation for $\mathbf{r} = \mathbb{A} \cdot \boldsymbol{\rho}$. Compare your answer with (b); $\mathbf{r}$ is the vector $\begin{bmatrix} x \\ y \end{bmatrix}$, and $\boldsymbol{\rho}$ is the vector $\begin{bmatrix} \alpha \\ \beta \end{bmatrix}$.

PROBLEM 2-14

Consider the complex matrix $\mathbb{H} = \begin{pmatrix} 7 & 4(1 - i) \\ 4(1 + i) & 5 \end{pmatrix}$

  a. Prove that this matrix is Hermitean conjugate.
  b. Find the magnitude of this matrix.
  c. The matrix eigenvalue problem involves finding the vectors $\mathbf{r}_i$ and the scalar eigenvalues λ_j that satisfy the relation

$$\mathbb{H} \cdot \mathbf{r}_i = \lambda_i \mathbf{r}_i.$$

If this problem is written out in its corresponding algebraic form, one can demonstrate that the magnitude

$$|\mathbb{H} - \lambda \mathbb{I}| = 0$$

(i.e., must be zero) if the components of $\mathbf{r}$ are to be nontrivial (i.e., not zero). Set the determinant equal to zero and show that the roots of the resulting polynomial are 3 and 1. Use these roots one at a time to find the corresponding $\mathbf{r}_i$. Because the diagonal-izing transformation $\mathbb{S}^{-1}$ satisfies the same equation as $\mathbf{r}_i$, construct $\mathbb{S}^{-1}$ from the components of the two vectors and show that

$$\mathbb{H}' = \mathbb{S} \cdot \mathbb{H} \cdot \mathbb{S}^{-1} = \begin{pmatrix} 1 & 0 \\ 0 & 3 \end{pmatrix}.$$

Here, $\mathbb{S}^{-1}$ is actually the transformation matrix that takes the diagonal form $\mathbb{H}'$ to the original form $\mathbb{H}$.

PROBLEM 2-15

a. Prove that the trace of a matrix is invariant under a unitary transformation. In other words, if $\mathbb{U}$ is a unitary operator and the trace of $\mathbb{A}$ is the sum of the diagonal elements,

$$\text{Tr } \mathbb{A} = \sum_{\text{all } j} A_{jj},$$

show that $\text{Tr } \mathbb{A} = \text{Tr}\{\mathbb{U}^{-1} \cdot \mathbb{A} \cdot \mathbb{U}\}$

b. Prove that the magnitude of $\mathbb{A}$ is invariant under a unitary transformation.

c. Relate these statements concerning invariance to all the coefficients of the polynomial $\prod_{\text{all } k} (x - \lambda_k)$, where the λ_k are the eigenvalues of $\mathbb{A}$.

PROBLEM 2-16

Compute the matrix products:

a. $\mathbb{A} \cdot \mathbb{A}$ with $\mathbb{A} = \begin{pmatrix} 1 + ZY & Z \\ Y & 1 \end{pmatrix}.$

b. $\mathbb{A} \cdot \mathbb{A} \cdot \mathbb{A}$ from the matrix shown in (a).

c. $\mathbb{B} \cdot \mathbb{B}$ with $\mathbb{B} = \dfrac{1}{(1 - ZY)} \begin{pmatrix} (1 + ZY) & 2Z \\ 2Y & (1 + ZY) \end{pmatrix}.$

d. $\mathbb{B} \cdot \mathbb{B} \cdot \mathbb{B}$.

PROBLEM 2-17

Determine the Fourier series of each of the five wave forms shown in Fig. P2-17.

a. Square wave; Fig. 2-17(a):

$$e(t) = -E_0 ; \qquad \frac{-\pi}{\omega} \leqslant t \leqslant 0$$

$$e(t) = +E_0 ; \qquad 0 \leqslant t \leqslant \frac{\pi}{\omega}.$$

Ans:

$$E(t) = \frac{4E_0}{\pi} \sum_{n=1}^{\infty} \frac{\sin n\omega t}{n},$$

where $n = 1, 3, 5, \ldots$ (only odd integers).

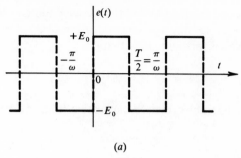

(a)

FIG. P2–17(a)

b. Rectangular wave; Fig. P2-17(b):

$$e(t) = 0, \qquad -\frac{\pi}{\omega} < t < -\frac{\tau}{2};$$

$$e(t) = E_0, \qquad -\frac{\tau}{2} < t < +\frac{\tau}{2};$$

$$e(t) = 0, \qquad \frac{\tau}{2} < t < \frac{\pi}{\omega}.$$

Ans.:

$$E(t) = E_0 \frac{\tau}{T} + \frac{E_0}{\pi} \sum_{n=1}^{\infty} \frac{1}{n} \sin\left(\frac{n\omega\tau}{2}\right) \cos n\omega t.$$

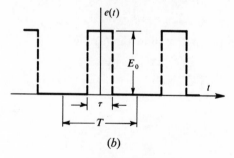

(b)

FIG. P2–17(b)

c. Full sine wave rectification; Fig. P2-17(c):

$$e(t) = E_0 \sin \omega t, \qquad 0 \leqslant t \leqslant \frac{\pi}{\omega};$$

$$e(t) = -E_0 \sin \omega t, \qquad \frac{\pi}{\omega} \leqslant t \leqslant \frac{2\pi}{\omega}.$$

Ans.:

$$e(t) = \frac{2E_0}{\pi} - \frac{4E_0}{\pi} \sum_{n=1}^{\infty} \frac{\cos 2n\omega t}{(4n^2 - 1)}.$$

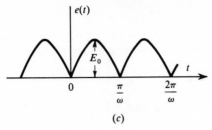

(c)

FIG. P2–17(c)

d. Half-wave rectification; Fig. P2-17(d):

$$e(t) = 0, \qquad -\frac{\pi}{\omega} \leqslant t \leqslant 0 ;$$

$$e(t) = E_0 \sin \omega t, \qquad 0 \leqslant t \leqslant \frac{\pi}{\omega}.$$

Ans.:

$$e(t) = \frac{E_0}{\pi} + \frac{E_0}{2} \sin \omega t - \frac{2E_0}{\pi} \sum_{n=1}^{\infty} \frac{\cos 2n\omega t}{(4n^2 - 1)}.$$

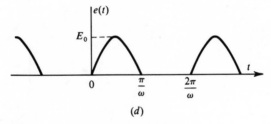

(d)

FIG. P2–17(d)

e. Sawtooth; Fig. P2-17(2e):

$$e(t) = \frac{2t}{T} E_0, \qquad -\frac{T}{2} < t < \frac{T}{2}.$$

Ans.:

$$e(t) = \frac{2\pi E_0}{\omega^2} \sum_{n=1}^{\infty} (-1)^{n+1} \frac{\sin n\omega t}{n}.$$

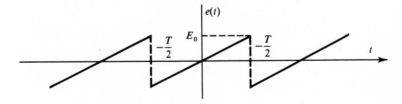

(e)

FIG. P2–17(e)

PROBLEM 2-18

Find the Fourier integral of the following functions, Figs. P2-18 (a), (b), (c), and (d):

a. $f(t) = 1, \qquad -\dfrac{T}{2} < t < \dfrac{T}{2} ;$

$\qquad = 0, \qquad \dfrac{T}{2} < |t|.$

b. $f(t) = e^{-t^2/2\sigma^2}.$

c. $f(t) = \sin \omega_0 t, \qquad 0 \leqslant t \leqslant \dfrac{\pi}{\omega_0} ;$

$\qquad = 0, \qquad t \leqslant 0 \quad \text{and} \quad \dfrac{\pi}{\omega_0} < t.$

d. $f(t) = 0, \qquad t < 0$

$\qquad = e^{-t/\tau}, \qquad 0 < t.$

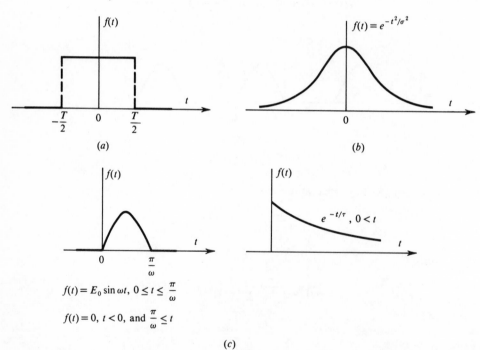

(a)

(b)

$f(t) = E_0 \sin \omega t, \; 0 \leq t \leq \dfrac{\pi}{\omega}$

$f(t) = 0, \; t < 0, \; \text{and} \; \dfrac{\pi}{\omega} \leq t$

(c)

Fig. P2–18

PROBLEM 2-19

The time domain representation of an amplitude-modulated wave can be written as

$$e(t) = m(t)e^{i\omega_0 t}$$

a. If $\mathscr{F}[m(t)] = M(\omega)$, show that $\mathscr{F}[e(t)] = M(\omega - \omega_0)$.

b. Find $\mathscr{F}[e(t)]$ when

$$m(t) = E_0 \sin \omega_M t$$

and when

$$m(t) = \sum_{n=-\infty}^{\infty} \left\{ \frac{\sin(n\pi/2)}{n\pi} \right\} e^{in(\omega_M t - (\pi/2))}.$$

PROBLEM 2-20

The time domain representation of a frequency and (or) phase-modulated wave is

$$e(t) = E_0 e^{i\omega_0 t} e^{i\rho(t) \sin \omega_M t}$$

Using the expansion

$$e^{i\rho \sin \omega_M t} = \sum_{-\infty}^{\infty} J_n(\rho) e^{in\omega_M t},$$

$(J_n(\rho))$ is the cylindrical Bessel function of order n). Find the Fourier transform in the three cases: first, when ω_M is constant and $\rho(t)$ varies in time; second, when $\omega_M \rho(t)$ is constant but ω_M varies in time; and third, when ρ is constant but ω_M varies in time (this is phase modulation).

a. First let ω_M be constant, and

$$\rho(t) = 2U(-t) + 5U(t).$$

In other words, the modulating frequency is stepped at $t = 0$ from $2\omega_M$ to $5\omega_M$.

b. Second, let $\omega_M \rho = \omega_D$ be constant, but

$$\omega_M = \frac{\omega_D}{\rho_0} \left\{ \frac{2}{5} U(-t) + U(t) \right\}.$$

c. Third, $\rho_0 = \text{constant} = 1$, and

$$\omega_M = \omega_0 \{ U(-t) + 2U(t) \};$$

i.e., the frequency is doubled at $t = 0$.

PROBLEM 2-21

Voltmeters can be constructed to respond to various parameters of a periodic wave form. A peak reading meter is set to record the maximum amplitude of the rectified wave. An average reading meter reads the average value of the rectified wave, while an rms meter reads the square root of the sum of the squares of the Fourier components.

a. Compute the response of each of the three meters to a pure sine wave of amplitude E_0.

b. Compute the response of each of the three meters to the periodic gate:

$$g(t) = 0, \qquad -\pi < \omega_0 t < 0;$$

$$g(t) = E_0, \qquad 0 < \omega_0 t < \pi; \text{ etc.}$$

c. An averaging meter is calibrated to record the rms value of a sine wave instead of the average value. What will be the reading on this meter when the wave form of the periodic gate of part (b) is inserted?

PROBLEM 2-22

Find the inverse Laplace transform of $U(t)$ formally by integrating over the appropriate contour:

$$\mathscr{L}^{-1}\left[\frac{1}{s}\right] = \frac{1}{2\pi i}\int_{\sigma-i\infty}^{\sigma+i\infty} \frac{1}{s} e^{st}\, ds.$$

PROBLEM 2-23

Find by contour integration the Laplace transform of the following functions:

a. $U(t)$.

b. e^{-at}.

c. $\sin \omega t$.

d. $\cos \omega t$.

e. $\sinh \beta t$.

f. $\cosh \beta t$.

g. t^n.

h. $\dfrac{e^{-at} - e^{-\beta t}}{(\alpha - \beta)}$.

i. $e^{-at} \sin(\omega t + \phi)$.

PROBLEM 2-24

Find by integration the Laplace transform of the following operator functions:

a. $\dfrac{d}{dt} f(t)$.

b. $\dfrac{d^n}{dt^n} f(t)$.

c. $\displaystyle\int^t f(x)\, dx$.

d. $e^{-at} f(t)$.

e. $U(t - \tau) f(t - \tau)$.

f. $\displaystyle\int^t f_1(x) f_2(t - x)\, dx$.

g. $f(t + T) = f(t)$, for all $t > 0$ (periodic).

PROBLEM 2-25

Find the Laplace transform of the following wave forms (use the figures of Problem 2-17 except for the condition that the wave forms are zero for $t < 0$):

a. Half rectified sine wave.
b. Full rectified sine wave.
c. Sawtooth.
d. Square wave.
e. Periodic gate.
f. Symmetric square wave.

Find the Laplace transform of the following functions:

g. Step function:

$$U(t) = 0, \qquad 0 < t;$$
$$U(t) = 1, \qquad t \geqslant 0.$$

$Ans.: \dfrac{1}{s}$.

h. Gate function:

$$g_T(t) = U(t) - U(t - T).$$

Ans.: $\dfrac{1}{s}\{1 - e^{-sT}\}.$

i. Ramp function:

$$R_T = \frac{t}{T}g_T(t).$$

Ans.: $\left\{\dfrac{1 - (1 + Ts)e^{-sT}}{Ts^2}\right\}$

j. Pulse of combined exponentials:

$$f(t) = 0, \qquad t < 0;$$
$$f(t) = E_0 e^{-\alpha t}(1 - e^{-\beta t}); \qquad 0 \leqslant t.$$

Ans.: $E_0\left\{\dfrac{1}{s + \alpha} - \dfrac{1}{s + \alpha + \beta}\right\}.$

k. Single sine pulse:

$$f(t) = \sin \omega t, \qquad 0 \leqslant t \leqslant \frac{\pi}{\omega};$$

$$f(t) = 0, \qquad t < 0 \quad \text{and} \quad \frac{\pi}{\omega} \leqslant t.$$

Ans.: $\dfrac{\omega}{s^2 + \omega^2}(1 + e^{-\pi s/\omega}).$

l. Single sine squared pulse:

$$f(t) = 0, \qquad t \leqslant 0 \quad \text{and} \quad \frac{\pi}{\omega} \leqslant t;$$

$$f(t) = \sin^2 \omega t, \qquad 0 \leqslant t \leqslant \frac{\pi}{\omega}.$$

Ans.: $\left(\dfrac{2\omega^2}{s^2 + 4\omega^2}\right)\left(\dfrac{1 - e^{-\pi s/\omega}}{s}\right).$

PROBLEM 2-26

Illustrate the integration theorem and the differentiation theorem by finding the Laplace transform of

$$f(t) = t^2 + a$$

in the following three ways:

a. Directly as $\qquad \mathscr{L}[t^2 + a].$

b. Find $\qquad \mathscr{L}\left[\dfrac{d}{dt}\left(\dfrac{1}{3}t^3 + at\right)\right] = s\mathscr{L}\left[\dfrac{t^3}{3} + at\right].$

c. Find $\qquad \mathscr{L}\left[\displaystyle\int_0^t (2t')\,dt'\right] = \dfrac{1}{s}\mathscr{L}[2t] + \dfrac{1}{s}f^{-1}(0+).$

PROBLEM 2-27

Illustrate the convolution theorem by considering $f(t) = 1 + t$ and $g(t) = t^2$. Find

$$\mathscr{L}\left[\int_0^t f(t - t')g(t')\,dt'\right]$$

by direct integration. Then show that this agrees with the answer obtained by calculating

$$\mathscr{L}\left[\int_0^t f(t')g(t - t')\,dt'\right],$$

and

$$\mathscr{L}[f(t)] \cdot \mathscr{L}[g(t)].$$

PROBLEM 2-28

The voltage response of a linear circuit to a step function is $e^{-\beta t}$. Using the convolution integral, find the response of the circuit to a ramp:

$$\frac{t}{T}\{U(t) - U(t - T)\}.$$

PROBLEM 2-29

The voltage response of a linear circuit to a δ function is observed experimentally to be $\sin \omega t$. Find the response to a gate function:

$$E_0\{U(t) - U(t - T)\}.$$

PROBLEM 2-30

A voltage response of a passive linear circuit to a δ function is observed experimentally to be an exponential $e^{-\alpha t}$. Find the voltage response of the circuit to the ramp function:

$$\frac{t}{T}\{U(t) - U(t - T)\}.$$

PROBLEM 2-31

Find the inverse transform $f(t)$ of the functions $F(s)$ given below, using Heaviside's expansion theorem.

a. $F(s) = \dfrac{s^2 - 4s + 3}{s^3 + 7s^2 + 10s}$.

b. $F(s) = \dfrac{1}{s^3 + (2\alpha + 1)s^2 + (\alpha^2 + 2\alpha\beta + \beta^2)s + \alpha^2 + \beta^2}$.

c. $F(s) = \dfrac{1}{s^3 + s^2 - s - 1}$.

(See Appendix A.)

PROBLEM 2-32

a. Consider the simple high-pass function $s/(s + \omega_0)$ and the simple low-pass function $\omega_0/(s + \omega_0)$ as transfer functions $H(s)$. Find $v(0)$ and $v(\infty)$, where $v(t) = \mathcal{L}^{-1}[H(s)(Es)]$ for

(1) $e(t) = \delta(t)$;
(2) $e(t) = U(t)$;
(3) $e(t) = t$.

b. Repeat (a) for the three transforms occurring in Problem 2-31.

PROBLEM 2-33

Find the roots of the following equations (see Appendix A):
a. $18x^3 - 33x^2 - 5x + 6 = 0$.
b. $x^3 - 2x^2 - 6x - 8 = 0$.
c. $x^4 + 2x^3 - 14x^2 - 32x - 32 = 0$.
d. $x^4 + 4x^3 + 6x^2 + 4x + 5 = 0$.

PROBLEM 2-34

One cycle of a sinusoidal current is applied to a GL parallel network as shown in Fig. P2-34. At $t = 0$, the switch is closed. It is opened long enough for one cycle to be transmitted to the network. Compute the voltage at the output as a function of time. The period is $2\pi/\omega_0$.

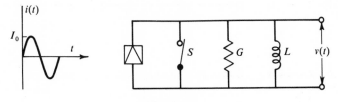

FIG. P2–34

PROBLEM 2-35

A voltage pulse $e(t) = E_0 e^{-\alpha t}(1 - e^{-\alpha t})U(t)$ (where $\alpha = 10^6$ rad/sec) is applied to the terminals of the networks shown in Fig. P2-35. In each case, compute the response $v(t)$.

a. Use Fig. P2-35(a).

b. Same as (a) except that $R = 10$ ohms and $C = 10^{-3}$ μf. Compare both outputs with the true integral of $e(t)$. Plot these.

c. See Fig. P2-35(c). Again $R = 100$ ohms and $C = 1$ μf.

d. Same as (c) except that $R = 10$ ohms and $C = 10^{-3}$ μf. Compare both outputs with the true derivative of $e(t)$. Plot these.

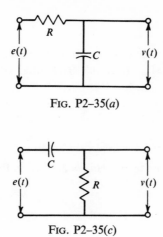

FIG. P2–35(a)

FIG. P2–35(c)

PROBLEM 2-36

Compute the voltage-transfer functions for each of the circuits shown (transfer to an open circuit) in Figs. P2-36(a) through (f).

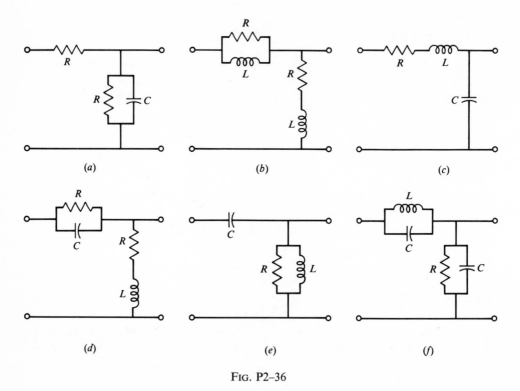

FIG. P2–36

PROBLEM 2-37

Compute the current transfer to a short circuit in each of the circuits of Figs. P2-37(a) through (f).

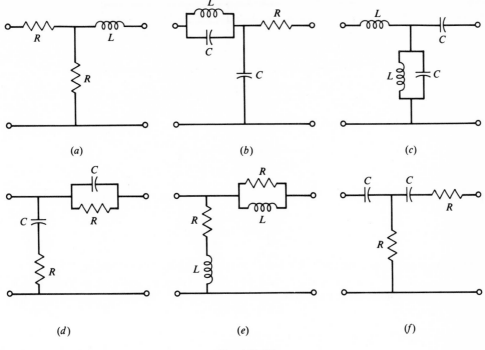

(a)   (b)   (c)

(d)   (e)   (f)

FIG. P2–37

PROBLEM 2-37A

Consider the circuit of Fig. P2-37A.

a. Calculate the input impedance Z.

b. For what values of L and R_1 in terms of R_2 and C will the impedance be a pure resistance for all frequencies?

c. Find the value of Z_{in}.

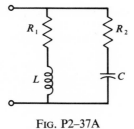

FIG. P2–37A

PROBLEM 2-37B

Consider the circuit in Fig. P2-37B.

a. Show that the current-transfer ratio $H_I(s) = I_R(s)/I_g(s)$, where

$$H(s) = \frac{(\omega_0/Q)s}{\{s^2 + (\omega_0/Q)s + \omega_0^2\}}$$

where $Q = RC\omega_0$ and $\omega_0 = 1/\sqrt{LC}$.

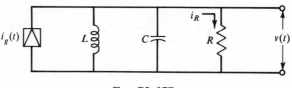

FIG. P2–37B

b. Show that $H_I(s)$ can be written as

$$H_I(s) = \frac{(\gamma_+ + \gamma_-)s}{(s + \gamma_+)(s + \gamma_-)}$$

where

$$\gamma_\pm = \frac{\omega_0}{2Q} \{1 \pm \sqrt{1 - 4Q^2}\}$$

What value(s) of Q give underdamping? critical damping? overdamping?

c. Calculate $H(i\omega)$ and show that whether γ_+ and γ_- are real or complex, it can be written in the following forms:

(1) $H(i\omega) = \dfrac{(\gamma_+ + \gamma_-)\omega}{\{i(\omega^2 - \gamma_+\gamma_-) + \omega(\gamma_+ + \gamma_-)\}} .$

(2) $H(i\omega) = \dfrac{(\omega_0/Q)\omega}{\{i(\omega^2 - \omega_0^2) + \omega_0(\omega/Q)\}} .$

(3) $H(i\omega) = \dfrac{1}{\{1 + iQ((\omega/\omega_0) - (\omega_0/\omega))\}} .$

(4) $H(i\omega) = \cos \phi e^{-i\phi}, \quad \text{with} \quad \tan \phi = Q\left(\dfrac{\omega}{\omega_0} - \dfrac{\omega_0}{\omega}\right).$

d. Show that $|H(i\omega)|$ is a maximum for $\omega = \omega_0$ and that $\|H(i\omega)\|$ is equal to $1/\sqrt{2}$ for

$$\omega_\pm = \frac{\omega_0}{2Q} \{\sqrt{4Q^2 + 1} \pm 1\}.$$

e. Show that

$$\frac{\omega_0}{\omega_+ - \omega_-} = Q.$$

PROBLEM 2-37C

Consider the LRC circuit in Problem 2-37B such that $(\omega_+ - \omega_-) = 2$ percent of ω_0. Find and plot the response of the circuit to the following excitations:

a. $i_g(t) = I_0\omega_0 \, \delta(t)$.

b. $i_g(t) = I_0 U(t)$.

c. $i_g(t) = I_0\{U(t) - U(t - T)\}$; (discuss $\omega_0 T = n\pi$).

PROBLEM 2-38

Do Problem 1-4, by Laplace transform techniques; Fig. P2-38:

$$e_1(t) = E_1 \sin \omega_0 t$$

with $i_1(0+) = 0$ and $i_2(0+) = 0$.

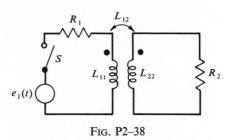

FIG. P2–38

PROBLEM 2-39

A square voltage gate of width T and amplitude E_0 is applied to each of the circuits of Problem 2-36. Compute the response.

PROBLEM 2-40

The response of a system to a step excitation of amplitude E_0 is

$$v(t) = E_0 e^{-at} \sin at \, U(t).$$

What is the response to this system to a half sine wave of half-period equal to π/a? See Fig. P2-40.

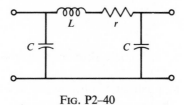

FIG. P2–40

PROBLEM 2-41

If the response of Problem 2-40 is taken from the circuit shown in Fig. P2-43, find the relation among a and R, L, and C.

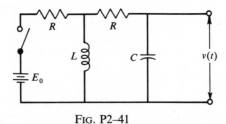

FIG. P2–41

PROBLEM 2-42

Consider the equation $V(s) = H(s)E(s)$, where $H(s) = \omega_0/(s + \omega_0)$. Calculate the time delay τ of a pulse for this circuit by the first centroid method described in the text; then calculate the time delay by approximating $H(s)$ by an exponential. Check these answers by direct calculation of

$$\tau = \frac{\displaystyle\int_0^\infty t e_{\text{in}}\, dt}{\displaystyle\int_0^\infty e_{\text{in}}\, dt} - \frac{\displaystyle\int_0^\infty t v_{\text{out}}\, dt}{\displaystyle\int_0^\infty v_{\text{out}}\, dt}.$$

PROBLEM 2-43

Consider a single section of a low-pass, voltage-excited, phase shift network; Fig. P2-43(a). Compute the time delay for a gate of width T when
  a. $T = 10RC$;
  b. $T = RC$;
  c. $T = RC/10$.
  d. Compare the attenuation and delay characteristics of the circuit in Fig. P2-43(a) and the LC low-pass device in Fig. P2-43(d), where $\sqrt{LC} = RC$.

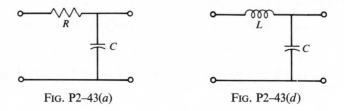

FIG. P2–43(a)   FIG. P2–43(d)

PROBLEM 2-44

Calculate the time delay and phase shift for two low-pass sections in cascade, shown in Fig. P2-44.
  a. Consider the delay to a gate of width T where $RC \ll T$.
  b. Calculate and graph the phase shift and attenuation as a function of frequency from $1/100RC$ to $100/RC$. Obtain at least ten points on the graph.

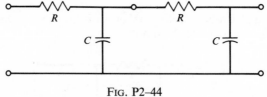

FIG. P2–44

PROBLEM 2-45

  a. The optimum variation of phase with frequency is a linear one. For the low-pass pi section shown in Fig. 3-14a, compute the *deviation* of the phase response from linearity, from zero to $10\omega_0$, where $\omega_0 = 1/\sqrt{LC}$. Graph your results, using at least ten points.

b. Obtain the phase-response curve for the four Q values $\frac{1}{4}$, $\frac{1}{2}$, $1/\sqrt{2}$, and $\sqrt{10}$.

PROBLEM 2-46

Consider the time delay of a gate of width T passing through a low-pass circuit having a voltage transfer

$$H_V(s) = \frac{\omega_0^2}{\{s^2 + 2as + \omega_0^2\}}.$$

Assume that $T > 1/\omega_0$. Compare the time-delay calculation by the first centroid method with the calculation using the rms delay for the four Q values of $Q = \frac{1}{4}$, $\frac{1}{2}$, $1/\sqrt{2}$, $\sqrt{10}$.

PROBLEM 2-47

The response to a step excitation has a rise time that is determined by the time taken by the response to change from 0.1 to 0.9 of the value at large t.

a. Compare the rise times of a response to a step excitation that is applied to the transfer

$$\frac{\omega_0^2}{(s^2 + 2as + \omega_0^2)}$$

for Q values of $\frac{1}{4}$, $\frac{1}{2}$, $1/\sqrt{2}$, and $\sqrt{10}$.

b. Determine the ratio of the overshoot to the value at large t in the case $Q = \sqrt{10}$.

PROBLEM 2-48

Compute the rise time of the response to a step excitation that is applied to a transfer

$$H_V = \frac{\omega_0^3}{s^3 + 5.5s^2 + 10s + 6}.$$

PROBLEMS FOR CHAPTER 3

PROBLEM 3-1

Construct the duals of the circuits shown in Figs. P3-1(a) and (b).

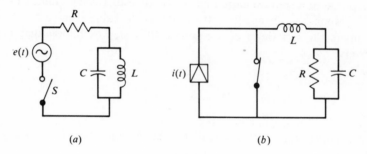

(a)   (b)

FIG. P3–1

PROBLEM 3-2

a. In the Wheatstone bridge circuit shown in Fig. P3-2 replace the circuit exterior to the branch *ab* by its Thévenin equivalent.

b. If $E_0 = 10$ volts, $r = 10$ ohms, $R_1 = R_2 = R_3 = 1k$, and $R_4 = 1001$ ohms, find the current through $R_L = 10$ ohms.

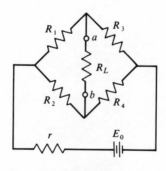

FIG. P3–2

PROBLEM 3-3

Compute the Thévenin equivalent circuit for the simple networks shown in Figs. P3-3(a) and (b).

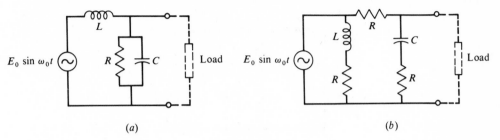

(a)   (b)

FIG. P3–3

PROBLEM 3-4

Construct the Norton equivalents for the circuits of Problem 3-3.

PROBLEM 3-5

a. Compute the Thévenin equivalent circuit for the network shown in Fig. P3-5.

b. Compute the Norton equivalent circuit for the mesh shown in Fig. P3-5.

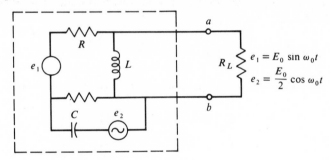

$$e_1 = E_0 \sin \omega_0 t$$

$$e_2 = \frac{E_0}{2} \cos \omega_0 t$$

FIG. P3–5

PROBLEM 3-6

Construct the Thévenin equivalent for the circuit diagrammed in Fig. P3-6.

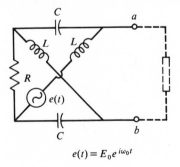

$$e(t) = E_0 e^{i\omega_0 t}$$

FIG. P3–6

PROBLEM 3-7

In the nonflat twin-T resistive network shown in Fig. P3-7, find the current in the load branch designated if all the resistors are 1 ohm. Solve this problem with Kirchhoff's laws.

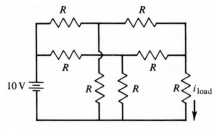

FIG. P3–7

PROBLEM 3-8

The circuit in Problem 7 can be reduced to the parallel-parallel combination of two T networks terminated in a load resistor. Solve this problem by matrix methods.

PROBLEM 3-9

a. Find the voltage-transfer function of the network shown in Fig. P3-9. Use a Y combination and then employ a cascade multiplication.

b. What is the image impedance of this network? Does it correspond to a set of real passive elements?

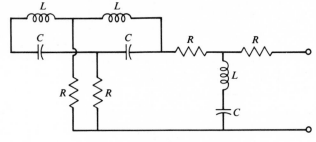

FIG. P3–9

PROBLEM 3-10

Obtain the voltage and current transfers for the circuit shown in Fig. P3-10 by using matrix techniques.

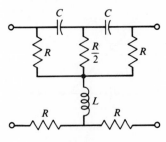

FIG. P3–10

PROBLEM 3-11

Design a bandpass T section in the form shown in Fig. P3-11. What is the resonant frequency? What is the amplitude and phase of the response to a sinusoid at the center frequency?

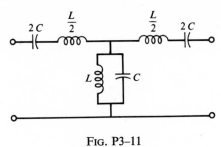

FIG. P3–11

PROBLEM 3-12

Find the hybrid H matrix of the four-terminal network shown in Fig. P3-12.

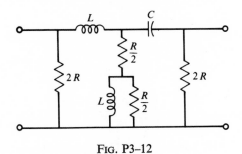

FIG. P3–12

PROBLEM 3-13

    a. Find $\mathbb{A}$ and $\mathbb{H}$ matrices for the T and Γ networks.
    b. Find the $\mathbb{A}$ and $\mathbb{H}$ matrices for the symmetric T and symmetric π networks.

PROBLEM 3-14

Compute the open-circuit impedance, short-circuit impedance, and input impedance when terminated in Z_0 for the networks shown in Figs. P3-14(a) through (d).

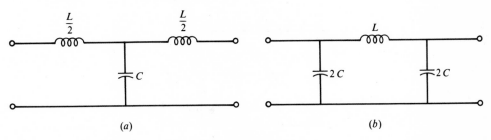

FIG. P3–14

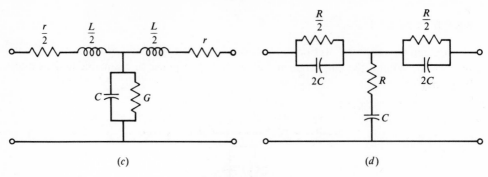

FIG. P3–14 (Con't.)

PROBLEM 3-15

Compare the input impedances of the circuit in Fig. P3-15 when it is terminated in the following loads:

a. $Z_L = Ls$.

b. $Z_L = \dfrac{1}{Cs}$.

c. $Z_L = \sqrt{\dfrac{L}{C}}$,

d. $Z_L = \dfrac{1 + L\ s^2}{Cs}$.

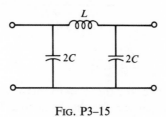

FIG. P3–15

PROBLEM 3-16

The antisymmetric lattice shown in Fig. P3-16 is terminated in a resistance equal to $\sqrt{L/C}$. Find its response to a gate of width $T = \sqrt{LC}$.

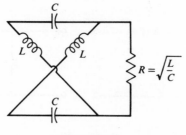

FIG. P3–16

PROBLEM 3-17

A low-pass T filter is cascaded with a low-pass lattice, which in turn is terminated in a resistive load $\sqrt{L/C}$. Find the input impedance as a function of frequency as shown in Fig. P3-17.

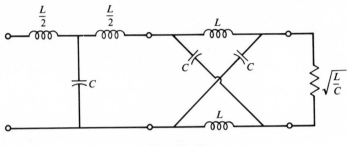

FIG. P3–17

PROBLEM 3-18

A linearized transistor is shown in Fig. P3-18 as an ideal current generator shunted by a conductance g_C. The generator is excited by the input current i_1 to give a current output βi_1, where $\beta \gg 1$. In terms of the resistive elements shown, compute the hybrid $\mathbb{H}$ matrix for this device.

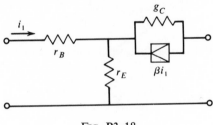

FIG. P3–18

PROBLEMS FOR CHAPTER 4

PROBLEM 4-1

Find and sketch the output of a high-pass RC network with (Fig. P4-1)

$$H_V(s) = \frac{s}{s + \omega_0},$$

with each of the five pulses in Problem 2-25, where

$$T = \frac{1}{\alpha} = \frac{1}{5\beta} = \frac{\pi}{\omega}$$

for $\omega_0 T = 0.1$, 1.0, 10.0. Compare with the true derivative of the wave forms.

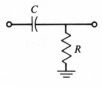

FIG. P4–1

PROBLEM 4-2

Under what circumstances does the circuit in Fig. P4-2 give approximately the second derivative of the input pulse?

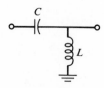

FIG. P4–2

PROBLEM 4-3

Repeat Problem 4-1 for the integrating circuit (Fig. P4-3) where

$$H_V(s) = \frac{\omega_0}{s + \omega_0}.$$

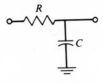

FIG. P4–3

PROBLEM 4-4

Consider the T pad in Fig. P4-4. Define

$$Z^2 = Z_1(Z_1 + 2Z_2),$$

$$\alpha = \frac{Z_1 + Z_2}{Z_2} + \frac{Z_1(Z_1 + 2Z_2)}{Z_2 Z_0},$$

$$\alpha_0 = \frac{Z_0 + Z_1 + Z_2}{Z_2},$$

$$\lambda = \frac{Z_1 + Z_2}{Z_2}.$$

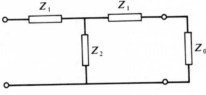

FIG. P4–4

a. Show that the input impedance is given by

$$Z_{\text{in}} = Z_0 \frac{\alpha}{\alpha_0}.$$

b. Show that α is the voltage attenuation factor equal to $E_{\text{out}}/E_{\text{in}}$ for arbitrary Z_1, Z_2, Z_0.

c. For $Z_{\text{in}} = Z_0$, show that $\alpha = \alpha_0$, and $Z = Z_0 = Z_2\sqrt{\lambda^2 - 1}$, and $\alpha_0 = \lambda + \sqrt{\lambda^2 - 1}$. Hence, if Z_1/Z_2 is independent of s, the process of attenuation does not distort the pulse.

d. Rearranging (c), show that for $Z_{\text{in}} = Z_0$,

$$Z_1 = Z_0\left(\frac{\alpha_0 - 1}{\alpha_0 + 1}\right), \qquad Z_2 = Z_0 \frac{2\alpha_0}{\alpha_0^2 - 1}.$$

e. As an exercise to examine the effects of small mismatch between Z_{in} and Z_0, show that for $(Z_{in} \sim Z_0)$,

$$\left[\frac{\delta\alpha}{\alpha}\right]_{\alpha=\alpha_0} \simeq -\left(\frac{\alpha_0^2 - 1}{2\alpha_0^2}\right)\left[\frac{\delta Z_0}{Z_0}\right],$$

and

$$\left[\frac{\delta Z_{in}}{Z_{in}}\right]_{Zin=Z_0} \simeq \frac{1}{\alpha_0^2}\left[\frac{\delta Z_0}{Z_0}\right].$$

f. RG-63 coaxial cable has a characteristic impedance of $Z_0 = 93$ ohms. Find Z_1 and Z_2 for a 4:1 attenuator terminated in the characteristic impedance. Check your answer with Problem 1-7.

PROBLEM 4-5

If the pi-filter in Fig. P4-5 is terminated in its characteristic impedance Z_0, then

$$Z_{in} = Z_0$$

Let

$$\lambda = \frac{Z_1 + Z_2}{Z_2}.$$

Show that

$$Z_{in} = \frac{Z_1}{\sqrt{\lambda^2 - 1}} = Z_0$$

and

$$Z_1 = \left(\frac{\alpha_0^2 - 1}{2\alpha}\right)Z_0, \qquad Z_2 = \left(\frac{\alpha_0 + 1}{\alpha_0 - 1}\right)Z_0.$$

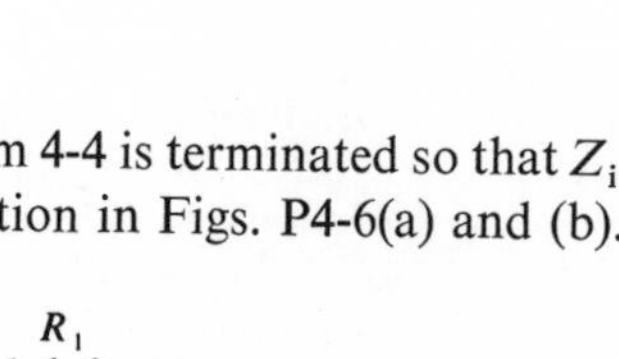

FIG. P4–5

PROBLEM 4-6

If the T filter of Problem 4-4 is terminated so that $Z_{in} = Z_0$, find Z_0 for the following distortionless configuration in Figs. P4-6(a) and (b).

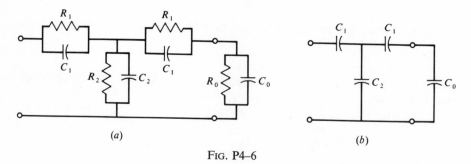

(a)

(b)

FIG. P4–6

PROBLEM 4-7

Repeat Problem 4-6 for the pi filter of Problem 4-5.

PROBLEM 4-8

The bridges mentioned below are employed to measure unknown capacitances and inductances in terms of known parameters. In each case the unknown quantities are indicated and the particular calculation required is specified.

a. Graph the null response of a Wien bridge as a function of frequency. Calculate its response to a gate of width $T = 1/\omega_{RC} = RC$.

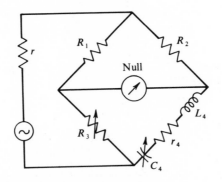

Resonance Bridge

FIG. P4–8(b)

b. The resonance bridge may be employed to measure an unknown inductance in terms of a known capacitance C_4 and variable resistance R_4. Derive the relations for L_4 and r_4 in terms of the other parameters; Fig. P4-8(b). Find L_4, r_4 in terms of R_1, R_2, R_3, and C_3.

c. The Hay bridge shown in Fig. P4-8(c) is set to find L_4 and r_4. Express the unknowns in terms of the other parameters.

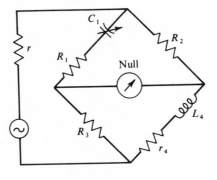

Hay Bridge

FIG. P4–8(c)

d. Obtain the impedance Z_4 in the Maxwell bridge in terms of Z_1, Z_2, and Z_3 Fig. P4-8(d).

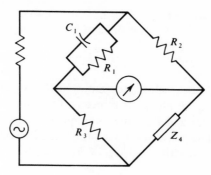

Maxwell Bridge

FIG. P4–8(d)

e. Find the expression for L_4 and r_4 in terms of the parameters shown in Fig. P4-8(e) for the Owen bridge.

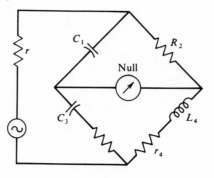

Owen Bridge

FIG. P4–8(e)

f. Find the value of the unknowns C_4 and r_4 in terms of C_1, R_1, C_3, and R_2. This diagram is a form of the Schering bridge; Fig. P4-8(f).

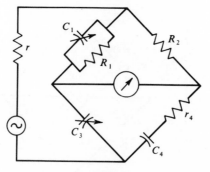

Schering Bridge

FIG. P4–8(f)

g. Discuss and compare the properties of the five bridges.

PROBLEM 4-9

Show that Figs. 160a and 160b are equivalent circuits for the ideal transformer for $k \neq 1$. What is the physical significance of the small inductor $(1 - k^2)L_{11}$?

PROBLEM 4-10

If the secondary of a transformer is center-tapped, find an equivalent circuit.

PROBLEM 4-11

Find the voltage output across an ideal transformer with $k \neq 1$ for the following excitations:
a. δ function from a voltage source and a current source.
b. Step function from a voltage source and a current source.
c. Gate function from a voltage source and a current source, of width T such that

$$\frac{1}{a'_{22}} \ll T \ll \frac{1}{a_{22}}.$$

PROBLEM 4-12

Consider a pulse-inverting transformer inserted in a coaxial cable circuit such that the voltage generator impedance $R_g = Z_0$ and the load impedance $R_L = Z_0$.
a. What would be the ratio of $L_{11}/L_{22} = (N_1/N_2)^2$ to give a maximum voltage output?
b. With the conditions found in (a), sketch the output voltage of a gate function with width T, such that

(1) $T \simeq \dfrac{(1 - k^2)}{a_{22}} \ll \dfrac{1}{a_{22}}$,

(2) $\dfrac{(1 - k^2)}{a_{22}} \ll T \ll \dfrac{1}{a_{22}}$,

(3) $T \simeq \dfrac{1}{a_{22}}$,

(4) $T \gg \dfrac{1}{a_{22}}$.

PROBLEM 4-13

Consider the circuit shown in Fig. P4-13. Given that

$$k^2 = \frac{L_{12}^2}{L_{11}L_{22}}, \qquad \omega_j^2 = \frac{1}{L_{jj}C_j}, \qquad Q_j = \frac{\omega_j L_{jj}}{R_j}.$$

a. Show that the forward voltage transfer is given by

$$H_V(s) = \frac{-(L_{21}/L_{11})\omega_2^2 s^2}{[s^2 + (\omega_1/Q_1)s + \omega_1^2][s^2 + (\omega_2/Q_2) + \omega_2^2] - k^2 s^4}.$$

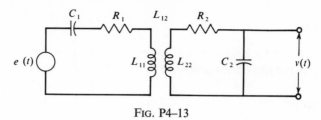

FIG. P4–13

b. Show that the roots are

$$s_\pm \simeq -\frac{\omega_0}{2Q_0(1-k)} \pm i\frac{\omega_0}{(1-k)};$$

for the following experimental data:

$$L_1 = L_2 = 150 \text{ mh},$$

$$C_1 = C_2 = 0.01 \ \mu\text{f},$$

and

$$R_1 = R_2 = 1330 \ \Omega.$$

Plot $|H(i\omega)|$ for the following values of L_{12}: 24, 74, -51, -101, mh.

c. In part (a), let $L_1 = L_2 = 150$ mh; $C_1 = 0.01 \ \mu\text{f}$, $C_2 = 0.005 \ \mu\text{f}$. Plot $|H(i\omega)|$ for $L_{12} = 24$, 49, 99 mh.

PROBLEM 4-14

In Problem 4-13(b), let $R_1 = R_2 = 0$ and show that

$$s_\pm = i\sqrt{\frac{\omega_1\omega_2}{1-k^2}}\sqrt{\frac{1}{2}\left(\frac{\omega_1}{\omega_2}+\frac{\omega_2}{\omega_1}\right) \pm \frac{1}{2}\sqrt{\left(\frac{\omega_1}{\omega_2}-\frac{\omega_2}{\omega_1}\right)^2 + 4k^2}}.$$

PROBLEM 4-15

Design a single T low-pass filter for maximal flatness. The cutoff frequency should be 1 Mc. The natural resistance of the inductances is 1 ohm. Terminate in Z_0, Fig. P4-15. If simple L and C units will not satisfy the requirement, create a Z and Y combination that will.

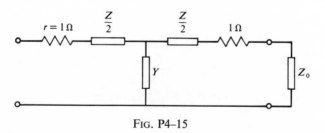

FIG. P4–15

PROBLEM 4-16

Two LC low-pass π sections are cascaded and terminated in $\sqrt{L/C}$. Design the ZY components of the π to produce a maximally flat response.

PROBLEM 4-17

a. Design a bandpass T filter that is maximally flat. Use a series resonant section for Z and a tank circuit for the Y sections. See Fig. P4-17.

b. Find the center frequency and the width at the half-power points.

c. Graph the asymptotes of the sinusoidal response in a log-log plot.

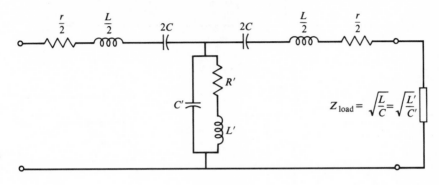

$$Z_{load} = \sqrt{\frac{L}{C}} = \sqrt{\frac{L'}{C'}}$$

Fig. P4–17

PROBLEM 4-18

a. Calculate the phase response as a function of frequency for two elementary low-pass π filters in cascade when terminated in $k = \sqrt{L/C}$.

b. Plot the phase as a function frequency up to ten times the cutoff frequency.

PROBLEM 4-19

a. m-derive the following low-pass π section; Fig. P4-19.

b. Compute the frequency and phase response for $m = 0.7$.

c. Same as (b) except set $m = 1.2$.

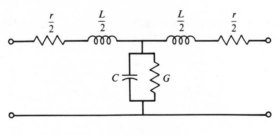

Fig. P4–19

PROBLEM 4-20

Two filter sections are connected in a parallel-parallel configuration. One is a low-pass T; the second is a bandpass T. Design values of L, C, L', C' to give as flat a response as possible. This is called *split banding*, and since the two filters load one another, design a load to optimize the response. See Fig. P4-20.

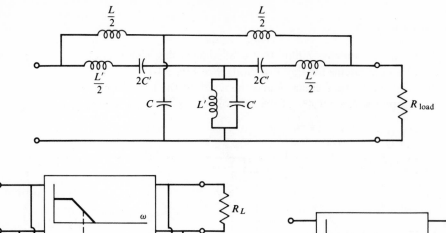

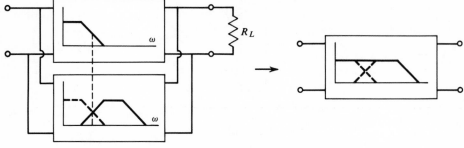

FIG. P4–20

PROBLEM 4-21

For the low-pass T filter, let $x = s/\omega_0$; then

$$H_T(x) = \frac{1}{1 + x + \frac{1}{2}x^2 + x\frac{1}{4}^3} \simeq e^{-x}$$

Compute:

$$\varepsilon(x) = \frac{e^{-x} - H(x)}{e^{-x}}$$

for $x = \frac{1}{2}$, $x = 1$, $x = \sqrt{2}$, $x = 2$, and $x = 3$.

PROBLEM 4-22

In Fig. P4-22 let the 50-ohm coaxial cable be of such a length that it takes a voltage pulse 50 nanosec to go from one end to the other. Find $v_0(t)$ if $e_g(t)$ is a step function of 1-volt amplitude for

a. $R_L = 0$,   d. $R_L = 100\Omega$,
b. $R_L = 25\Omega$,   e. $R_L = \infty$.
c. $R_L = 50\Omega$,

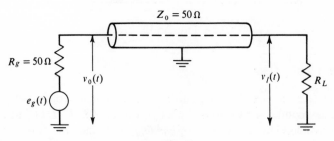

FIG. P4–22

PROBLEM 4-23

a. Repeat Problem 4-22 but find $v_l(t)$ for each of the cases.

b. Repeat Problem 4-22 but find $v_0(t)$ when $R_g = 25$ and 100 ohms.

PROBLEM 4-24

Find $v_a(t)$ and $v_b(t)$ in Fig. P4-24, where at $t = 0$ S is closed and

$$R_g = 50\Omega, \qquad T_2 = 30 \text{ nanosec,}$$
$$Z_0 = 50\Omega, \qquad T_3 = 5 \text{ nanosec,}$$
$$T_1 = 20 \text{ nanosec,} \qquad R_L = 100\Omega.$$

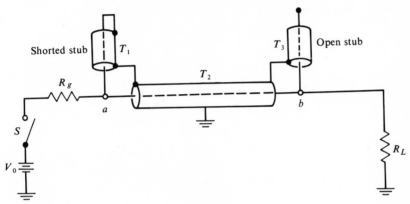

FIG. P4–24

PROBLEM 4-25

If $e_g(t) = E_g U(t)$ in Fig. P4-22, and if R_L is replaced by the elements listed below, find the characteristic time constant and sketch $v_0(t)$ for each case:

a. $R \neq Z_0$.

b. Capacitor C.

c. Inductor L.

d. Capacitor C and resistor R and in parallel.

e. Inductor L and resistor R in series.

PROBLEM 4-26

Find $v_0(t)$ in Fig. P4-22 for $R_L = 0$, 50 ohms, ∞ , for

a. $e_g(t) = E_g t/T\{U(t) \cdot U(t - \tau)\}$,

b. $e_g(t) = E_g t/T\{U(t) - U(t - \tau)\}$,

where T is the time for a pulse to travel from one end to the other of the cable, and $\tau \ll T$.

PROBLEM 4-27

The inductance per unit length and the capacitance per unit length of an infinite coaxial transmission line was found in Problem 1-3.

a. Calculate the characteristic impedance Z_0.

b. If polyethylene is used as a dielectric (dielectric constant equal 2.3), find the characteristic impedance in ohms of a coaxial cable in which the radius of the outer cylinder is five times the radius of the inner cylinder.

c. Find b/a of a 50 ohm cable with polyethylene as a dielectric.

PROBLEM 4-28

A pulse generator is pictured in Fig. P4-28. At $t = 0$, the switch S is closed. Find $v(t)$ for

a. $Z_L = R_L = Z_0$.

b. $Z_L = R_L \| C$.

c. $Z_L = R_L$ in series with L.

(Assume $R = \infty$ for the pulse calculation. It is simply a d-c path for the cable to charge up again after S is opened.)

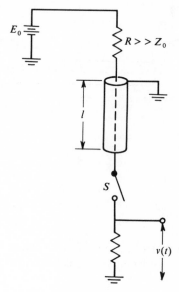

FIG. P4–28

PROBLEM 4-29

In Problem 1-1, the capacitance per unit length and inductance per unit length of a single strand of wire a distance d above an infinite plane were found.

a. Calculate the characteristic impedance of such a "strip line" transmission line.

b. If a transistor circuit is to be terminated at 100 ohms, how far from the chassis (i.e., "infinite plane") should a lead wire 1.5×10^{-2} in. radius be placed to minimize distortions?

c. Would it be feasible to try to match a 500-ohm terminating resistor as suggested in part (b)?

d. A lead 2 in. long is to be used in a circuit that must respond well up to a frequency of 100 Mc is $\frac{1}{2}$ in. above the chassis. If the wire leads to a current generator of 25-ohm input impedance, does the lead behave predominantly as an inductor or capacitor? Find the value? If instead, it is terminated in a 2K resistor, does it behave predominantly as an inductor or capacitor? What is the value? Is the lead negligible in either case? How long should it be in each case? (Take same radius as above.)

INDEX

INDEX